Energy Conversion

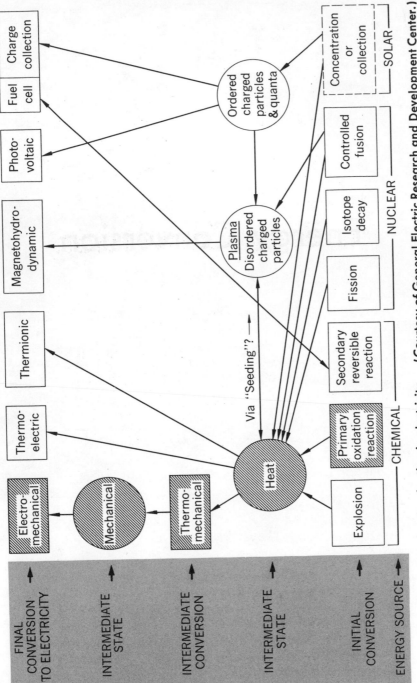

Fig. 1-1. Energy conversion terminating in electricity. (Courtesy of General Electric Research and Development Center.)

ENERGY CONVERSION

Electromechanical, Direct, Nuclear

EDWARD M. WALSH

Virginia Polytechnic Institute

THE RONALD PRESS COMPANY • NEW YORK

Library of Congress Catalog Card Number: 67–21682

PRINTED IN THE UNITED STATES OF AMERICA

Name of Library:	W. R. Banks

Lot No: CRM

Write or type title, volume, months, page nos., year, call nos, imprint in the exact order to be stamped on the spine.

Energy Conversion
TK145
W25

22

Bindery Use Only			
	6	3	
Trim	Pica	Cover	No.

To Stephanie

and My Parents

Preface

During the past decade significant advances have been made in the field of energy conversion. As a result of the availability of a high-temperature heat source, and the requirements of a power system for use in space, the direct conversion of thermal into electrical energy has become one of the most rapidly developing areas in the field of energy conversion. Thermoelectric, photoelectric, and fuel cell power supplies have already proved effective in space, while other systems, such as the magnetohydrodynamic, electrogasdynamic, and thermionic, are under development for land-based or space-bound energy conversion.

The nuclear reactor has become universally accepted as a nuclear-to-thermal energy converter, and now plays an important role in power utility planning, while for lengthy manned space missions the only practical energy source appears to be nuclear. Consequently, a basic knowledge of the principles of nuclear-to-thermal energy conversion is important to those involved in the design and operation of future land-based power stations, and would certainly be of benefit to those concerned with the development of future space vehicles.

In the author's judgment, an undergraduate course in energy conversion should not merely introduce more complicated mathematics, more involved field theory, and more abstract concepts in the analysis of electromechanical energy conversion, but should give proper consideration to the new material in the field, and thus kindle the imagination of the space-age student. Accordingly, in this book, pointless idealistic abstraction is avoided, and emphasis is directed to the study of these important new developments.

The text is divided into three parts, and, since each part is complete in itself, any desirable order of study may be employed. Electromechanical energy conversion is discussed in Part I because this topic at present dominates the study of the field. However, if it is thought better to handle the course in the logical sequence of conversion, the order of parts can be reversed, so as to begin with Part III on the conversion from nuclear to thermal energy. The material in Part II, which deals with direct converters, is rather diverse, and so it is possible to study the five chapters in any desired order.

v

Because of the flexibility introduced by the nature of the material in Part II, the text is suitable for either a two-semester or a three-quarter course sequence. Since in most cases it is considered desirable to place major emphasis on electromechanical energy conversion, a complete semester may be devoted to Part I and Appendix G, and the material in Parts II and III covered in the other semester, or, in the case of a three-quarter sequence, most or all of two quarters may be devoted to Part I, and suitable material selected for study from Parts II and III during the third quarter.

EDWARD M. WALSH

Blacksburg, Virginia
August, 1967

Contents

II DIRECT THERMAL-ELECTRICAL CONVERSION

III   NUCLEAR-THERMAL CONVERSION

APPENDIX

Introduction

Man today, as in prehistoric times, strives to release energy and to utilize it. The difference between this age of well-being and that of the cave dweller can only be attributed to our superior knowledge in the field of energy conversion. Prehistoric man, who built a fire to cook a meal or heat his dwelling, gave little thought, if any, to the fact that he was in the process of converting chemical energy into thermal energy. Yet his ability in initiating the chemical-thermal energy conversion process, controlling it, and utilizing it governed greatly the extent of his well-being. So also today, in order to relieve his toil and increase his comfort, man strives to improve current energy conversion techniques and find ways in which to utilize new energy sources.

Since the development of the steam engine and, subsequently, that of the electric generator, the study of energy conversion has been devoted almost exclusively to improving the means used in converting chemical to thermal energy, thermal to mechanical energy, and finally mechanical to electrical energy. However, as seen in Fig. I-1, there are many other ways in which electrical energy may be produced besides the conventional approach associated with the boiler, turbine, and generator.

Although the conversion of mechanical to electrical energy certainly plays a most important part in the field of energy conversion, the so-called *direct converters*, which convert thermal energy into electrical energy directly, have many advantages and will be utilized to a greater extent in the future. The development of the nuclear reactor, which converts nuclear energy into thermal energy, has caused revolutionary changes in the conventional field of energy conversion, and is certainly the cause of interest in many of the unconventional direct and indirect methods of producing electricity. Although all of the theoretically possible energy conversion techniques illustrated in Fig. I-1 are not considered in this text, all those which are generally accepted and are likely to be accepted in the near future are dealt with.

3

Electromechanical Conversion

system of Fig. 1–3.   Prior to saturation the flux increases in an approximately linear manner as the applied mmf is increased, and a linear approximation to the magnetization curve is usually acceptable.   Such an approximation is shown in Fig. 1–5.

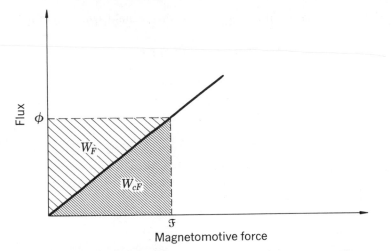

Magnetomotive force

Fig. 1–5.   Linear approximation of the magnetization curve for a system operating below the saturation level.

Assuming the system in Fig. 1–3 is clamped, so that no mechanical movement of the components is possible, none of the energy supplied from the electrical source can be converted into mechanical energy.   Therefore (if copper losses may be neglected), all of the energy supplied from the source must be stored in the form of magnetic field energy.   Then, for an incremental input of source energy ΔW_s, the increase in field energy is

$$\Delta W_F = \Delta W_s \tag{1-10}$$

Therefore if the energy supplied from the electrical source is determined, this is equal to the energy stored in the magnetic field.

Consider a voltage e applied to the coil so that a current i flows for an increment of time Δt.   Then the increment of energy supplied by the source is

$$\Delta W_s = ei\,\Delta t \tag{1-11}$$

But, at all times,

$$e = N\frac{d\phi}{dt}$$

Therefore, in differential terms,

$$dW_s = N\frac{d\phi}{dt}\,i\,dt = Ni\,d\phi$$

But
$$\mathcal{F} = Ni \qquad dW_s = dW_F$$
Therefore
$$dW_F = \mathcal{F} \, d\phi \qquad (1\text{--}12)$$

By integration, the total energy stored in the field when the flux is ϕ is

$$W_F = \int_0^\phi \mathcal{F}(\phi) \, d\phi \qquad (1\text{--}13)$$

Equation 1–13 is represented graphically by the area above the magnetization curve as shown in Fig. 1–4b.

Although the area under the magnetization curve has no physical significance, it will be found convenient to consider it in the subsequent theoretical work. For this reason it is assigned a name and called *coenergy*, and represented by the symbol W_{cF}. The area between the magnetization curve and the mmf axis is obtained by integration and so the coenergy of the field is

$$W_{cF} = \int_0^{\mathcal{F}} \phi(\mathcal{F}) \, d\mathcal{F} \qquad (1\text{--}14)$$

where the applied mmf is $\mathcal{F}$.

When the magnetization curve is assumed to be linear, the areas above and below the curve are equal, or in other words, the coenergy of the field is equal to the energy stored in the field, so that

$$W_{cF} = W_F \qquad (1\text{--}15)$$

In summary, then:

1. Coenergy is given by the area between the magnetization curve and the mmf axis.
2. Coenergy has no physical significance.
3. Coenergy is a convenient mathematical expression.
4. Coenergy equals energy, when the magnetization curve is linear.

The energy stored in the magnetic field may be expressed in a number of useful forms when the linear approximation is used.

Directly from the geometry of Fig. 1–5,

$$W_F = \int_0^\phi \mathcal{F}(\phi) \, d\phi$$
$$= \tfrac{1}{2}\mathcal{F}\phi \qquad (1\text{--}16)$$

and since $\mathcal{F} = \phi \mathcal{R}$

$$W_F = \tfrac{1}{2}\phi^2 \mathcal{R} \qquad (1\text{--}17)$$

and since $\phi = \mathcal{F}\mathcal{P}$

$$W_F = \tfrac{1}{2}\mathcal{F}^2 \mathcal{P} \qquad (1\text{--}18)$$

and since $\mathfrak{F} = Ni$

$$W_F = \tfrac{1}{2}Ni\phi \tag{1-19}$$

and since $L = N\phi/i$

$$W_F = \tfrac{1}{2}Li^2 \tag{1-20}$$

Up to this point, movement of the system components has not been permitted and so no mechanical work has been, or could be, done. Now it is assumed that the movable element is permitted to move by an incremental amount Δx, so that mechanical work of magnitude $\Delta W_m = f\,\Delta x$ is done.

There are two specific conditions under which this mechanical work can be done. In the first case it can be assumed that the flux is maintained constant. (In the case of Fig. 1–3 it can be supposed that, as the plunger is permitted to move the distance Δx, the current to the coil is varied by an amount which will maintain the flux constant.) In such a case the magnetization curves before and after the displacement would be as shown in Fig. 1–6a.

Since mechanical energy is now expended, the energy supplied from the source must be equal to the energy stored in the field plus the mechanical work done, or

$$\Delta W_s = \Delta W_F + \Delta W_m \tag{1-21}$$

However, in this case, since the flux remains constant and $\Delta W_s = \mathfrak{F}\,\Delta\phi$, $\Delta W_s = 0$, and so

$$\Delta W_m = -\Delta W_F \tag{1-22}$$

From Eq. 1–8,

$$f\,\Delta x = -\Delta W_F$$

or, in differential form,

$$\boxed{f = -\left.\frac{dW_F}{dx}\right|_{\phi=\text{const.}}} \tag{1-23}$$

This is an important relationship since it permits the evaluation of the force on a component once the energy stored in the field is known. Since $\Delta W_m = -\Delta W_F$, the mechanical work done is accomplished at the expense of the energy stored in the magnetic field. Graphically then, from Fig. 1–6a, the mechanical work done is equal to the area enclosed by the magnetization curves and the constant flux line. Using Eqs. 1–16 and 1–17 in Eq. 1–23,

$$f = -\frac{1}{2}\,\phi\,\left.\frac{d\mathfrak{F}}{dx}\right|_{\phi=\text{const.}} \tag{1-24}$$

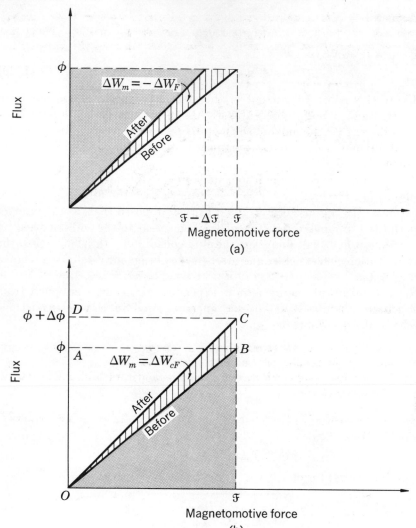

Fig. 1–6. Magnetization curves for (a) displacement at constant flux and (b) displacement at constant mmf.

and

$$f = -\frac{1}{2}\, \phi^2 \left.\frac{d\mathcal{R}}{dx}\right|_{\phi\,=\,\text{const.}} \tag{1–25}$$

Equation 1–25 is particularly useful in practice since it is frequently possible to evaluate the reluctance of the magnetic circuit in terms of the displacement x.

Example 1–2. The system shown in Fig. 1–7 consists of a cylindrical plunger, of radius $R = 2$ cm, free to move axially in a cylindrical solenoid. If the flux density is maintained constant at 0.15 weber/m² in the axial air gap and the

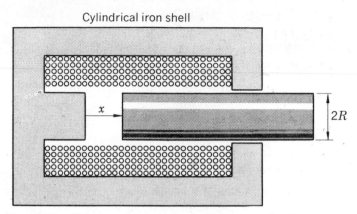

Cylindrical iron shell

Fig. 1–7. Cross-section of simple electromechanical system.

radial air gap is negligible, find, assuming linearity, negligible reluctance of the iron flux path, and no leakage or fringing,

(a) The force on the plunger for a gap $x = 0.5$ cm.
(b) The force on the plunger for a gap $x = 0.25$ cm.
(c) The mechanical work done when the plunger moves from a gap of $x = 0.5$ cm to 0.25 cm.

(a) The reluctance of the axial air gap, and consequently that of the magnetic flux path, is given by

$$\mathcal{R} = \frac{x}{\mu_0 \pi R^2}$$

From Eq. 1–25,

$$f = -\frac{1}{2} \phi^2 \frac{d\mathcal{R}}{dx} \bigg|_{\phi = \text{const.}}$$

$$= -\frac{\phi^2}{2\mu_0 \pi R^2} \bigg|_{\phi = \text{const.}}$$

$$= -\frac{(\pi R^2)^2 B^2}{2\mu_0 \pi R^2} \bigg|_{\phi = \text{const.}}$$

$$= -\frac{\pi R^2 B^2}{2\mu_0} \bigg|_{\phi = \text{const.}}$$

$$= -\frac{\pi \times 2^2 \times 10^{-4} \times 0.15^2}{2 \times 4 \times \pi \times 10^{-7}}$$

$$= -11.2 \text{ newtons}$$

The negative sign means that the force on the plunger is in the direction of decreasing x.

(b) When the air gap is reduced to $x = 0.25$ cm,

$$f = -11.2 \text{ newtons}$$

since the expression derived for f is independent of x, and B is maintained constant.

(c) The mechanical work done is equal to the difference in energy stored in the field before and after movement, and so, from Eqs. 1–17 and 1–22,

$$W_m = -\Delta W_F = \frac{\phi^2(0.5 - 0.25) \times 10^{-2}}{2\mu_0 \pi R^2} = \frac{\pi B^2 R^2 (0.25) \times 10^{-2}}{2\mu_0}$$

$$= \frac{\pi(0.15)^2 \times 4 \times 10^{-4} \times 0.25 \times 10^{-2}}{2 \times 4 \times \pi \times 10^{-7}}$$

$$= 2.81 \times 10^{-2} \text{ joule}$$

In this particular case, since the force on the plunger is independent of x,

$$W_m = f \Delta x$$

$$= 11.2 \times (0.5 - 0.25) \times 10^{-2}$$

$$= 2.81 \times 10^{-2} \text{ joule}$$

which verifies the previous solution.

It is also possible to keep the mmf constant during an incremental displacement.   In the case of the system in Fig. 1–3, the mmf remains constant if the current through the solenoid is maintained constant during the displacement.   Figure 1–6b shows the magnetization curves before and after displacement.   As before, an expression is sought for the mechanical energy involved so that the force may be determined by differentiation.   Again the basic energy equation is

$$\Delta W_s = \Delta W_m + \Delta W_F \qquad (1\text{–}26)$$

However, in this case the energy supplied from the source is no longer equal to zero, since

$$\Delta W_s = \int_\phi^{\phi+\Delta\phi} \mathcal{F}(\phi) \, d\phi \qquad (1\text{–}27)$$

Then from Eqs. 1–26 and 1–27 and Fig. 1–6b,

$$\Delta W_m = \int_\phi^{\phi+\Delta\phi} \mathcal{F}(\phi) \, d\phi - \left(\int_0^{\phi+\Delta\phi} \mathcal{F}(\phi) \, d\phi - \int_0^\phi \mathcal{F}(\phi) \, d\phi \right) \qquad (1\text{–}28)$$

or

$$f \Delta x = ABCDA - (OCDO - OBAO)$$

$$= ABCDA + OBAO - OCDO$$

$$= OBCDO - OCDO$$

$$= OBCO$$

$$= \Delta W_{cF}$$

Therefore,

$$f = \frac{dW_{cF}}{dx}\Big|_{\mathfrak{F}\,=\,\text{const.}}$$ (1-29)

Equation 1–29 expresses the fact that the rate of change of coenergy for a displacement in the x direction at constant mmf is the force in that direction.

It is recalled that, when a linear magnetization curve is assumed, the coenergy and energy of the field are equal, so that in such a case Eq. 1–29 becomes

$$f = \frac{dW_F}{dx}\Big|_{\mathfrak{F}\,=\,\text{const.}}$$ (1-30)

Equations 1–16, 1–18, and 1–20 may be substituted in Eq. 1–30 for W_f, giving

$$f = \frac{1}{2}\,\mathfrak{F}\,\frac{d\phi}{dx}\Big|_{\mathfrak{F}\,=\,\text{const.}}$$ (1-31)

$$f = \frac{1}{2}\,\mathfrak{F}^2\,\frac{d\mathcal{P}}{dx}\Big|_{\mathfrak{F}\,=\,\text{const.}}$$ (1-32)

$$f = \frac{1}{2}\,i^2\,\frac{dL}{dx}\Big|_{\mathfrak{F}\,=\,\text{const.}}$$ (1-33)

Since the energy supplied by the source is seen to equal twice the mechanical output (for in Fig. 1–6 area $ABCDA$ is equal to twice area $OBCO$), excess energy must be supplied to the field. In other words, for a displacement at constant mmf, half of the energy supplied by the source is used as mechanical output, while the other half is stored in the field. This is often termed the *"fifty-fifty rule."*

Example 1–3. If the solenoid in Fig. 1–7 has 200 turns, what constant current must be supplied to produce a force of -11.2 newtons on the plunger when the gap is 0.5 cm? If the gap is decreased to 0.3 cm, find

(a) The energy supplied by the source.
(b) The mechanical output.
(c) The additional energy stored in the field.

Equation 1–32 may be used in the form

$$f = \frac{1}{2}\,N^2 i^2\,\frac{d\mathcal{P}}{dx}\Big|_{i\,=\,\text{const.}}$$

where $\mathcal{P} = \dfrac{\mu_0 \pi R^2}{x}$

$\dfrac{d\mathcal{P}}{dx} = -\dfrac{\mu_0 \pi R^2}{x^2}$

so that

$$f = -\frac{\pi}{2}\mu_0 \left(\frac{NiR}{x}\right)^2$$

$$i^2 = -\frac{2f}{\pi\mu_0}\left(\frac{x}{NR}\right)^2 = \frac{2 \times 11.2}{\pi \times 4 \times \pi \times 10^{-7}}\left(\frac{0.5 \times 10^{-2}}{200 \times 2 \times 10^{-2}}\right)^2$$

$$i = 8.85$$

$$i = 2.98 \text{ amp}$$

(a) Since the energy supplied by the source is given by $\mathcal{F}\,\Delta\phi$, the change in flux must be found:

$$\phi = \frac{\mathcal{F}}{\mathcal{R}} = Ni\left(\frac{\mu_0\pi R^2}{x}\right)$$

Therefore, for $x = 0.5$ cm,

$$\phi_1 = \frac{200 \times 2.98 \times 4\pi \times 10^{-7} \times \pi \times 4 \times 10^{-4}}{0.5 \times 10^{-2}}$$

$$= 1.89 \times 10^{-4} \text{ weber}$$

and for $x = 0.3$ cm,

$$\phi_2 = 3.15 \times 10^{-4} \text{ weber}$$

The energy supplied by the source is therefore

$$\begin{aligned} W_s &= Ni\,\Delta\phi \\ &= 200 \times 2.98 \times (3.15 - 1.89) \times 10^{-4} \\ &= 0.075 \text{ joule} \end{aligned}$$

(b) Applying the "fifty-fifty rule," the mechanical output is

$$W_m = 0.5W_s = 0.0375 \text{ joule}$$

(c) The additional energy stored in the field is

$$W_f = 0.0375 \text{ joule}$$

In many electromechanical devices, rotation rather than translation is involved. In such cases it is of interest to find the torque, rather than the force. Since

$$\text{torque} = (\text{force})(\text{radius arm})$$

and

$$\text{angle of rotation} = \frac{\text{circumferential translation}}{\text{radius arm}} \qquad (1\text{-}34)$$

or

$$T = fR \qquad \theta = x/R \qquad (1\text{-}35)$$

Equation 1–23 and Eq. 1–29 become

$$T = -\frac{dW_F}{d\theta}\bigg|_{\phi\,=\,\text{const.}} \tag{1–36}$$

$$T = \frac{dW_{cF}}{d\theta}\bigg|_{\mathfrak{F}\,=\,\text{const.}} \tag{1–37}$$

Equations 1–24, 1–25, 1–31, 1–32, and 1–33 may also be expressed in terms of torque and angle of rotation, as follows:

$$T = -\frac{1}{2}\,\phi\,\frac{d\mathfrak{F}}{d\theta}\bigg|_{\phi\,=\,\text{const.}} \tag{1–38}$$

$$T = -\frac{1}{2}\,\phi^2\,\frac{d\mathfrak{R}}{d\theta}\bigg|_{\phi\,=\,\text{const.}} \tag{1–39}$$

$$T = \frac{1}{2}\,\mathfrak{F}\,\frac{d\phi}{d\theta}\bigg|_{\mathfrak{F}\,=\,\text{const.}} \tag{1–40}$$

$$T = \frac{1}{2}\,\mathfrak{F}^2\,\frac{d\mathcal{P}}{d\theta}\bigg|_{\mathfrak{F}\,=\,\text{const.}} \tag{1–41}$$

$$T = \frac{1}{2}\,i^2\,\frac{dL}{d\theta}\bigg|_{\mathfrak{F}\,=\,\text{const.}} \tag{1–42}$$

Figure 1–8a shows a schematic diagram of a reluctance motor, which is the simplest of all a-c motors. It consists of a stator, wound with an N-turn coil and excited from a single-phase source, and of a rotor consisting of a magnetic material which causes the permeance of the air gap to vary from a maximum permeance $\mathcal{P}_d$, called the *direct-axis permeance*, when $\theta = 0$, to a minimum $\mathcal{P}_q$, the *quadrature-axis permeance*, when $\theta = \pi/2$.

Equation 1–41 may be used to analyze the system and show that under a certain condition an average torque is produced. This is the criterion which must be established when analyzing any system to determine if motor operation is possible.

It is assumed that the permeance of the air gap varies sinusoidally, as shown in Fig. 1–8b, between the upper and lower limits $\mathcal{P}_d$ and $\mathcal{P}_q$, respectively, so that for an angle of rotation θ the permeance is

$$\mathcal{P} = \tfrac{1}{2}(\mathcal{P}_d + \mathcal{P}_q) + \tfrac{1}{2}(\mathcal{P}_d - \mathcal{P}_q)\cos 2\theta \tag{1–43}$$

and so

$$\frac{d\mathcal{P}}{d\theta} = -(\mathcal{P}_d - \mathcal{P}_q)\sin 2\theta \tag{1–44}$$

If the coil is excited by a sinusoidally varying current

$$i = I \cos \omega_0 t \tag{1–45}$$

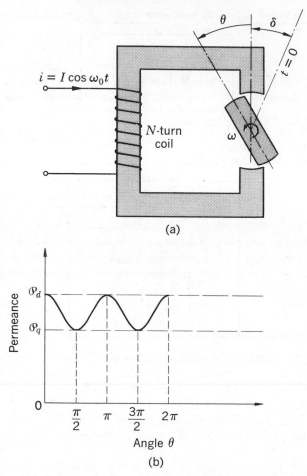

(a)

(b)

Fig. 1–8. (a) Schematic diagram of a reluctance motor. (b) Variation of air-gap permeance with angle of rotor rotation.

and if at time $t = 0$ the rotor is in a position $\theta = -\delta$, the instantaneous torque is obtained by substituting Eqs. 1–44 and 1–45 in Eq. 1–41:

$$T = -\tfrac{1}{2}N^2I^2 \cos^2 \omega_0 t \, (\mathcal{P}_d - \mathcal{P}_q) \sin 2\theta \qquad (1\text{–}46)$$

If the rotor is rotating at a speed ω, then $\theta = \omega t - \delta$, so that

$$
\begin{aligned}
T &= -\tfrac{1}{4}N^2I^2(\mathcal{P}_d - \mathcal{P}_q)(1 + \cos 2\omega_0 t)[\sin 2(\omega t - \delta)] \\
&= -\tfrac{1}{4}N^2I^2(\mathcal{P}_d - \mathcal{P}_q)[\sin 2(\omega t - \delta) + \cos 2\omega_0 t \sin 2(\omega t - \delta)] \\
&= -\tfrac{1}{4}N^2I^2(\mathcal{P}_d - \mathcal{P}_q)\{\sin 2(\omega t - \delta) + \tfrac{1}{2}\sin [2(\omega + \omega_0)t - 2\delta] \\
&\qquad\qquad\qquad\qquad\qquad + \tfrac{1}{2}\sin [2(\omega - \omega_0)t - 2\delta]\}
\end{aligned}
$$

Since the average value of time-dependent sinusoidal terms is zero, the average torque is zero except when

$$\omega = \omega_0$$

that is to say, when the rotor makes half a revolution during one cycle of the supply current. When $\omega = \omega_0$, the instantaneous torque is

$$T = -\tfrac{1}{4}N^2I^2(\mathcal{P}_d - \mathcal{P}_q)[\sin 2(\omega_0 t - \delta)$$
$$+ \tfrac{1}{2}\sin (4\omega_0 t - 2\delta) + \tfrac{1}{2}\sin (-2\delta)] \quad (1\text{–}47)$$

and so the average torque is

$$\boxed{T_{\mathbf{av}} = \tfrac{1}{8}N^2I^2(\mathcal{P}_d - \mathcal{P}_q)\sin 2\delta} \quad\quad (1\text{–}48)$$

Therefore an average torque is produced, provided $\omega = \omega_0$ and $\delta \neq 0$. The reluctance motor is said to be a *synchronous machine* since it can only operate at one speed, which is dependent on the frequency of the electrical supply. Since $\omega = \omega_0$, the synchronous speed in revolutions per minute is

$$\mathfrak{N}_0 = \frac{\omega_0}{2\pi} \times 60 \text{ rpm}$$

where ω_0 is in radians per second, or

$$\mathfrak{N}_0 = 60f \text{ rpm} \quad\quad (1\text{–}49)$$

where f is the supply frequency in cycles per second.

The reluctance motor is not capable of starting, and so the rotor must be brought up to synchronous speed by some other means. Obviously, this is a severe limitation to such a motor; but in certain cases its simplicity and the fact that it runs at only a constant speed may outweigh the problem of starting it. For example, the simple electric clock motor may be started manually by rotating it above synchronous speed, and letting it lock into synchronism as it slows down. Clock motors may be made self-starting by the provision of auxiliary windings.

1–3. FORCE AND TORQUE IN MULTIPLY EXCITED SYSTEMS

Many systems have more than one electrical input. Consider the simple and common case of two coils, with self-inductances L_1 and L_2, excited from two external sources. It is assumed that there is a mutual inductance M between the two coils. In the case of the translatory system of Fig. 1–9a, the objective is to determine an expression for the force between the two members, and in the case of the rotary system to determine an expression for the torque on the member which is free to rotate.

If the energy stored in the field is evaluated, then Eq. 1–30 may be

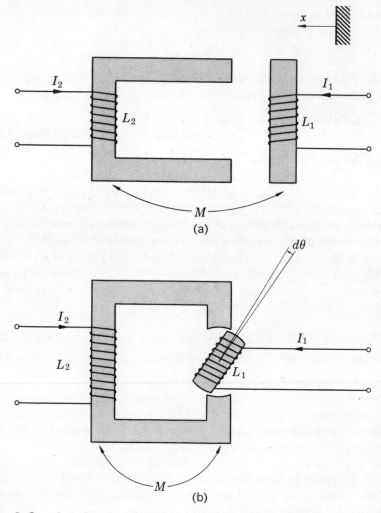

Fig. 1–9. (a) Dually excited translatory system. (b) Dually excited rotary system.

used to find the required force. For two mutually coupled coils, the total field energy under linear conditions is

$$W_F = \tfrac{1}{2}I_1^2L_1 + \tfrac{1}{2}I_2^2L_2 + I_1I_2M \qquad (1\text{--}50)$$

and so, when the energy and coenergy are equal and the number of coil turns is constant,

$$f = \frac{dW_F}{dx}\bigg|_{I_1I_2 = \text{const.}}$$

Therefore,

$$f = \frac{1}{2} I_1{}^2 \frac{dL_1}{dx} + \frac{1}{2} I_2{}^2 \frac{dL_2}{dx} + I_1 I_2 \frac{dM}{dx} \tag{1-51}$$

where I_1 and I_2 are assumed independent of the displacement. Similarly, the expression for torque is

$$T = \frac{1}{2} I_1{}^2 \frac{dL_1}{d\theta} + \frac{1}{2} I_2{}^2 \frac{dL_2}{d\theta} + I_1 I_2 \frac{dM}{d\theta} \tag{1-52}$$

Equations 1–51 and 1–52 may be simply extended to account for more than two sources.

Example 1–4. Two coils are mounted so that one may rotate within the other. The self-inductances of coils 1 and 2 are 1.0 and 1.5 mh, respectively, and the mutual inductance is $M = 0.98 \cos \theta$ mh, where θ is the angle between the coils. If the coil currents are $i_1 = I_1 \sin \omega t$ and $i_2 = I_2 \sin (\omega t - \alpha)$, find

(a) The instantaneous torque.
(b) The time-average torque.
(c) The time-average torque if $I_1 = 5$ amp, $I_2 = 4$ amp, $\theta = 45°$, and the current phase difference $\alpha = 15°$.

(a) Since the self-inductances are independent of θ in this case, the last term in Eq. 1–52 gives the instantaneous torque:

$$T = -0.98 I_1 I_2 \sin \omega t \sin (\omega t - \alpha) \sin \theta$$

or

$$T = -0.98 I_1 I_2 [\cos \alpha - \cos (2\omega t - \alpha)] \sin \theta$$

(b) Since the time-average value of the cosine term is zero over a cycle,

$$T_{\text{av}} = -0.98 I_1 I_2 \cos \alpha \sin \theta$$

(c) For the specified numerical values,

$$T_{\text{av}} = -0.98 \times 5 \times 4 \times \cos 15° \times \sin 45°$$
$$= -13.4 \text{ newton-m}$$

The negative sign indicates that the direction of the average torque is such that θ, the angle between the coils, tends to decrease.

1–4. MECHANICAL FORCE AND TORQUE FROM ELECTROSTATIC FIELD THEORY

In a manner analogous to that of Art. 1–2, expressions may be developed for force and torque in systems which employ electric rather than magnetic fields. Considering the capacitor of Fig. 1–10a as the basic system, and assuming a linear charging curve as in Fig. 1–10b, the energy stored in the

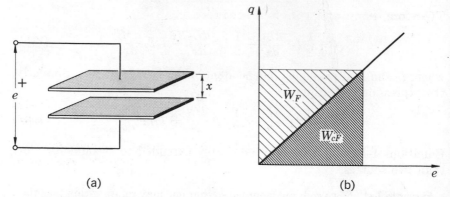

Fig. 1–10. (a) Basic electric field system. (b) Charging curve.

electric field is

$$W_F = \tfrac{1}{2}qe \tag{1–53}$$

where q is the charge on the capacitor and e is the voltage applied across it. Since the capacitance $C = q/e$, Eq. 1–53 becomes

$$W_F = \tfrac{1}{2}Ce^2 \tag{1–54}$$

The expressions for force are analogous to Eqs. 1–23 and 1–30 when the charging curve is assumed linear and the coenergy equals the energy:

$$f = -\frac{dW_F}{dx}\bigg|_{q=\text{const.}} \tag{1–55}$$

$$f = \frac{dW_F}{dx}\bigg|_{e=\text{const.}} \tag{1–56}$$

Substituting Eq. 1–54 in Eq. 1–56 gives the useful relationship

$$f = \frac{1}{2}\,e^2\,\frac{dC}{dx}\bigg|_{e=\text{const.}} \tag{1–57}$$

Under the conditions specified in Eq. 1–55 the charge is maintained constant, that is to say, the capacitor is isolated from the electric source and one of its plates is given a virtual displacement dx. Mechanical work $f\,dx$ is done at the expense of the field energy and no energy is supplied by, or given to, the source. However, under the conditions of Eqs. 1–56 and 1–57, the capacitor is maintained in contact with the source at an interelectrode potential e. When the plates are given a virtual displacement dx and mechanical work $f\,dx$ is done, this energy is supplied by the source; the source also supplies additional energy $f\,dx$, which is stored in the field. Here, as previously, the "fifty-fifty rule" applies.

We may summarize with four equations.

1. When q is constant,

$$\Delta W_s = 0 \qquad (1\text{–}58)$$

$$\Delta W_m = -\Delta W_F \qquad (1\text{–}59)$$

2. When e is constant,

$$\Delta W_s = \Delta W_F + \Delta W_M \qquad (1\text{–}60)$$

$$\Delta W_m = \Delta W_F \qquad (1\text{–}61)$$

An electrostatic synchronous motor, analogous to the reluctance motor discussed in Art. 1–2, is shown in Fig. 1–11. It is a rotary capacitor in

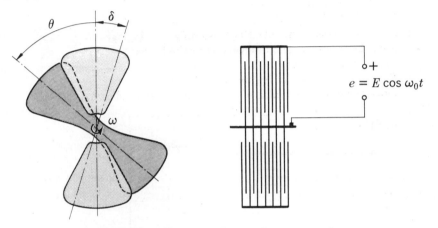

Fig. 1–11. Electrostatic synchronous motor.

which the interelectrode capacitance varies between a maximum C_d and a minimum C_q, and can be represented as a function of θ by

$$C = \tfrac{1}{2}(C_d + C_q) + \tfrac{1}{2}(C_d - C_q)\cos 2\theta \qquad (1\text{–}62)$$

If the interelectrode potential applied is $e = E \cos \omega_0 t$ and $t = 0$ when the rotor is in the position $\theta = -\delta$, then, from Eq. 1–57, an average torque

$$\boxed{T_{av} = \tfrac{1}{8}E^2(C_d - C_q)\sin 2\delta} \qquad (1\text{–}63)$$

is produced, provided the rotor runs at the synchronous speed $\mathfrak{N}_0 = 60f$ rpm, which is governed by the frequency of the supply. As in the case of the reluctance motor, the electrostatic motor is basically not self-starting and must be brought up to synchronous speed by some auxiliary means. Except for special applications, the electrostatic motor has the additional disadvantage that high interelectrode potentials, or large electrode areas, are required if a significant torque is to be generated. This observation applies to electric field devices in general, and as a result almost all motors, generators, and transducers rely on the magnetic field as the coupling medium.

PROBLEMS

1-1. The solenoid shown in Fig. P1-1 consists of a 500-turn coil wound on a uniform core of cross-sectional area 4×10^{-4} m. The length of the air gap is 0.5×10^{-2} m. Assuming the reluctance of the core is negligible, and $\mu_0 = 4\pi \times 10^{-7}$ weber/amp-turn-m in the air gap, and $I = 10$ amp:

   a. Find the magnetomotive force present.
   b. Find the reluctance of the magnetic circuit.
   c. Find the total magnetic flux, which circulates.
   d. Find the magnetic flux density, assuming no fringing.
   e. Find the magnetic field intensity H in the air gap.
   f. Find the flux linkages.
   g. Find the permeance of the magnetic circuit.
   h. Draw the electrical analog of the magnetic circuit shown.

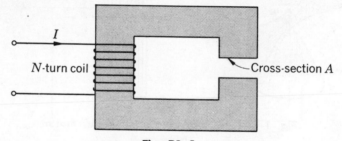

Fig. P1-1.

1-2. A solenoid with the dimensions shown in Fig. P1-2 is wound with an N-turn coil. The plunger has a constant lateral spacing of c from the core.

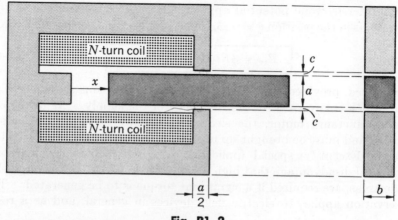

Fig. P1-2.

Assuming that the reluctance of the iron is negligible:

a. Determine an expression for the reluctance of the magnetic path as a function of the plunger position x.
b. If the flux density is maintained constant at B weber/m², determine the energy stored in the field as a function of x.
c. If the flux density is maintained constant at B weber/m², determine the force on the plunger as a function of x.

Dimensions in centimeters

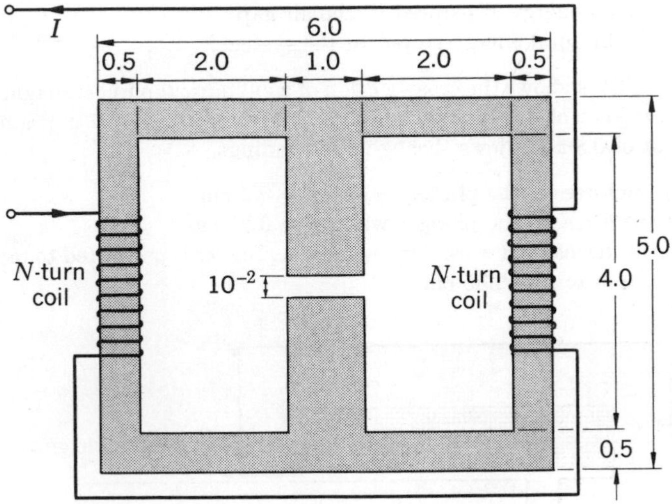

(a)

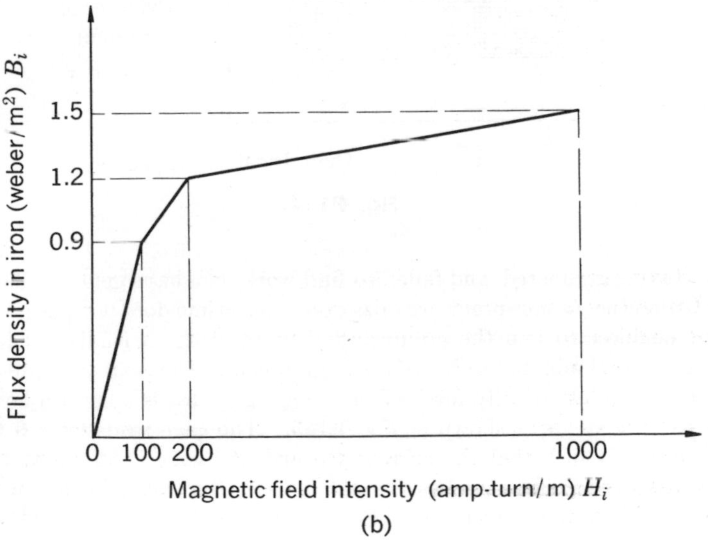

(b)

Fig. P1–3.

1-3. Figure P1–3a shows the cross-section of an iron core of constant depth 0.5 cm. The core carries an N-turn coil on each of the outer limbs. These coils are connected in series and a constant current I flows through them. Since the flux density is high, a single linear approximation for the magnetization curve is unacceptable. Figure P1–3b shows a three-unit piece-wise linear approximation for the magnetization curve. If the magnetic field intensity H_i, within the iron, is constant at 1000 amp-turn/m and $N = 250$ turns:

    a. Find the magnetic flux density in the air gap.
    b. What is the coil current I?
    c. What is the energy W_0 stored in the air gap?
    d. What is the total energy stored in the system?

1-4. Figure P1–4 shows the cross-section of a cylindrical plunger magnet. The coil has inductance of 0.6 henry when the plunger is at $x = 0.7$ cm, and a constant current of 0.8 amp flows through the windings.

    a. Find the force on the plunger when $x = 0.7$ cm.
    b. Find the force on the plunger when $x = 0.35$ cm.
    c. Find the mechanical work done when the plunger is permitted to move from $x = 0.7$ cm to $x = 0.35$ cm.

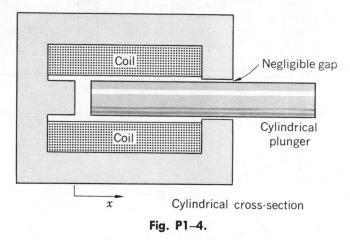

Fig. P1–4.

1-5. Having graduated, and failed to find work, you have gone to Chicago and joined Crime Inc. (a non-profit organization . . . crime does not pay). You are the first engineer to join the group and your services are badly needed. The "boss" is to be eliminated as he drives from home. The plan is as follows.

A gun is to be electrically fired when the gas gage reads a certain level. The circuit you propose is as shown in Fig. P1–5. The gage reads from 0 to 20 gal and its design is such that the current through the gage is 50 ma at FULL and 500 ma at EMPTY. Therefore, as the gas is used, the current through the gage increases. When the current reaches a certain value the solenoid is pulled inwards and actuates the trigger of an appropriately positioned weapon. A force of 1 newton is required to move the trigger and this is supplied via the 1:5 lever arm. The dimensions of the cylindrical solenoid are shown.

If the tank was full of gas when the "boss" left home, how many miles will he have traveled when there is a nasty bang? His car does 12 miles/gal. Assume a linear relationship between gage current and fuel in the tank. The tank holds 20 gal when full.

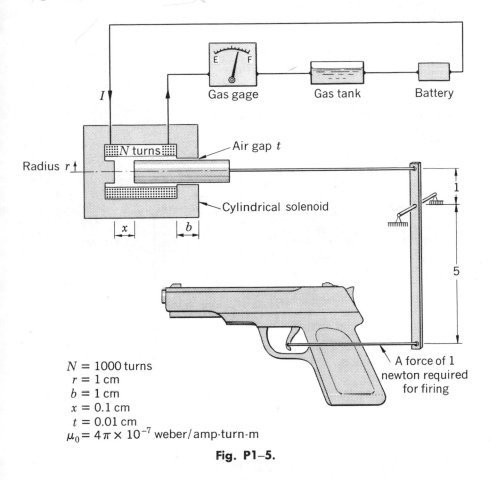

$N = 1000$ turns
$r = 1$ cm
$b = 1$ cm
$x = 0.1$ cm
$t = 0.01$ cm
$\mu_0 = 4\pi \times 10^{-7}$ weber/amp-turn-m

Fig. P1–5.

1–6. The electromagnetic braking system shown in Fig. P1–6 is used to stop the rotation of a flywheel. Pressure is applied to the friction pad by an electromagnet through a lever arm which increases the thrust by a 5:1 ratio. If the air gap in the electromagnet has a cross-sectional area of 4 cm² and a length of 0.25 cm when the friction pad contacts the drum, and the solenoid has a 1000-turn winding, what values satisfy the questions in the following page?

a. Find an expression for the force produced on the plunger when a d-c current I flows through the winding.
b. What current is required to produce on the friction pad a pressure force of 200 newtons?
c. What is the reluctance of the air gap when braking?
d. What is the inductance of the coil when braking?
e. What is the energy stored in the field when braking?
f. What is the air-gap flux when braking?
g. If the kinetic coefficient of friction between the flywheel and the friction pad is 0.6, the radius of the flywheel 1 m, and the stored energy in the flywheel is 5000 joules, how many revolutions does the flywheel make under constant braking pressure before coming to rest?

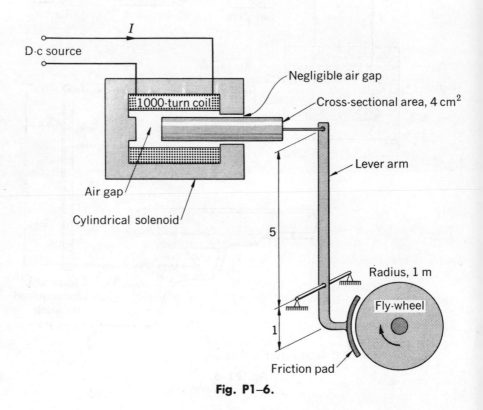

Fig. P1–6.

1–7. The plunger in the cylindrical iron-clad solenoid shown in Fig. P1–7 is supported so that it can move freely in the vertical direction. The air gap between the shell and the plunger can be assumed to be uniform and 0.01 in. long. Neglect leakage and fringing in the air gaps. The exciting coil has 1000 turns and carries a current with a constant value of 3.0 amp.

a. Neglecting the mmf in the iron, find the flux density in weber/m² between the working faces of the center core and plunger for a gap g of 0.2 in. (1 m = 39.37 in.).

b. Compute the energy stored in the magnetic field, in joules.

c. Calculate the coil inductance in henrys.

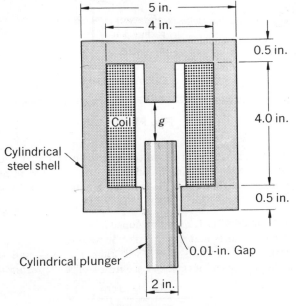

Fig. P1–7.

1-8. Two coils are free to rotate relative to each other; the mutual inductance between them is given by $M = 0.5 \cos \theta$ henry, where θ is the angular displacement between the coils. If the coils have self-inductances of $L_1 = 0.7$ henry and $L_2 = 0.6$ henry:

a. Find the torque between the coils when $\theta = 70°$ and the coil currents are i_1 and i_2, respectively.

b. If coil 2 is short-circuited when $\theta = 70°$ and a current $i_1 = 15 \sin \omega t$ passes through coil 1, find the average torque between the coils.

1-9. The mutual inductance between the rotor and stator windings of the device shown in Fig. P1–9 is given by $M_{sr} \cos \theta$. In this case $M_{sr} = 1$ henry. The windings are 2-pole and the rotor current is constant at 1 amp.

a. What is the torque in newton-m required at the shaft to lift a mass of 1 kg from the ground?

b. What is the minimum d-c stator current which must be supplied in order to just lift the mass off the ground, if $\theta = 45°$ when the mass is about to rise?

c. How much higher will the mass be lifted if the stator current is increased by 15 percent?

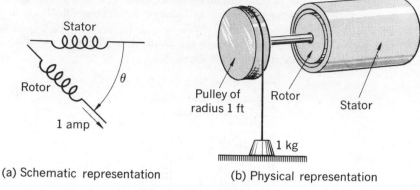

Stator

Rotor

θ

1 amp

Pulley of radius 1 ft

Rotor

Stator

1 kg

(a) Schematic representation   (b) Physical representation

Fig. P1–9.

1–10. A reluctance motor with geometry as shown in Fig. P1–10 has a maximum output of 1 hp when rotating at 3600 rpm. Consider, in addition to the usual assumptions, that the reluctance of the air gap varies sinusoidally as the rotor rotates.

a. What is the maximum torque developed?
b. Find the quadrature- and direct-axis reluctance.
c. If the maximum torque is developed when $\theta = 45°$, find the number of turns in the stator coil if it draws a current of 4 amp from the source.

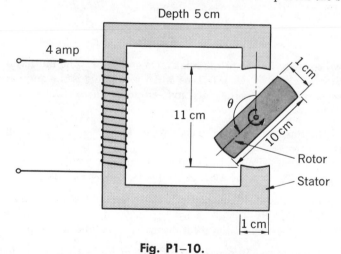

Depth 5 cm

4 amp

11 cm

θ

1 cm

10 cm

Rotor

Stator

1 cm

Fig. P1–10.

1–11. An electrostatic motor is to be designed to operate at a fixed speed of 3600 rpm and to develop a maximum power of 0.5 hp. If the rotor is to consist of 5000 plane vanes interleaved between 5000 plane stator vanes, with an air gap of 5×10^{-4} m between individual vanes:

a. Find the total difference in capacitance required between the direct and quadrature values.

b. If the quadrature capacitance is 15 percent of the direct capacitance, find the effective area of each vane on the stator if it is shaped like those in Fig. 1–11.

Assume that a maximum potential gradient of 1.2×10^6 volts/m may be tolerated in the air gaps between rotor and stator vanes.

2

Direct-Current Electromechanical Conversion

Electromechanical devices may be divided into two groups: direct current, and alternating current. In this chapter the important devices of the first group will be considered. Each group may also be subdivided into power devices and control devices. However, it will be seen that, due to their inherent characteristics, the d-c group is better suited to control applications, whereas the a-c group is better suited to large-scale energy conversion under essentially steady-state conditions. With this in mind, it appears that a detailed analysis of the d-c devices under both steady-state and transient conditions is called for, whereas, for the a-c devices, performance as a function of load is important.

2–1. BASIC D-C GENERATORS AND MOTORS

The d-c generator is an electromechanical device which converts mechanical energy into direct-current electrical energy. The energy conversion process depends on the fact that a voltage is generated in a conductor which is moved across a magnetic field. Consider the case of the N-turn coil of Fig. 2–1a placed in a magnetic field. If the coil is rotated at an angular speed ω so that the flux ϕ linking the coil varies as a function of time t, then, according to Faraday's law, the generated voltage is

$$e_g = N \frac{d\phi}{dt} \tag{2–1}$$

In the mathematically simple case of $\phi = \phi_r \cos \omega t$, Eq. 2–1 becomes

$$e_g = -N\phi_r\omega \sin \omega t \tag{2–2}$$

and an alternating voltage is generated which varies sinusoidally with time. In practice, the waveform of the generated voltage may be more

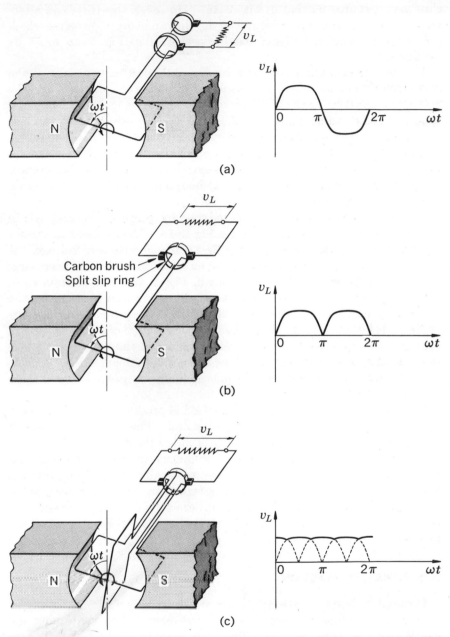

Fig. 2–1. (a) A-c generator with output through slip rings. (b) Mechanically rectified generator with a two-segment commutator. (c) Basis of the d-c generator with two coils and a four-segment commutator.

closely represented by that in Fig. 2–1a. However, this is still an alternating voltage. Since it is desired to develop an energy converter which generates a constant voltage, the basic system in Fig. 2–1a must be modified.

The first modification is shown in Fig. 2–1b. The two ends of the N-turn coil are connected to two insulated segments of a *slip ring*, and the voltage is picked up by two carbon *brushes* which press against the rotating slip ring. The arrangement acts like a mechanical switch which reverses the terminal connections each half-cycle. By suitably positioning the brushes, the switching takes place whenever the output voltage tends to change sign, and an output voltage like that shown in Fig. 2–1b is obtained. The voltage no longer changes sign, although it still fluctuates between zero and a peak value.

The voltage fluctuation may be reduced by putting a second coil in a plane normal to the first, as shown in Fig. 2–1c. This coil now generates a peak voltage at the time when the first coil generates zero voltage. A slip ring with four insulated segments, or *commutator*, is now necessary. An output voltage waveform like that in Fig. 2–1c is then obtained, in which the voltage fluctuation may be made as small as required by the addition of more coils. The two coils in Fig. 2–1c are not shown interconnected; however, when there are many coils, as there are in practice, they are so connected that their voltages add and the output voltage is the sum of the voltages generated in the individual coil sides. In this way, effective use is made of all the coils and large output voltages may be generated.

In most d-c machines, the magnetic field is produced by passing a d-c current through coils wound around iron poles. These poles are mounted on an iron yoke. This fixed assembly is called the *stator*.

The coils and the commutator assembly, which rotate within the stator, together constitute the *rotor*. The coils are usually imbedded in slots cut into the periphery of a cylindrical iron structure, which is *laminated*, or built up from thin sheets of steel, in order to reduce eddy current loss. The assembly of conductors in which the voltage is generated is called the *armature*.

2–2. ARMATURE REACTION

Figure 2–2 shows cross-sections of a two-pole d-c machine. The rotor consists of a cylindrical assembly with peripheral slots containing the distributed armature winding. The main magnetic field flux ϕ_m is produced by the north and south poles, which are usually excited by means of a d-c current passed through the field windings.

The generated current, flowing through the armature as shown, itself

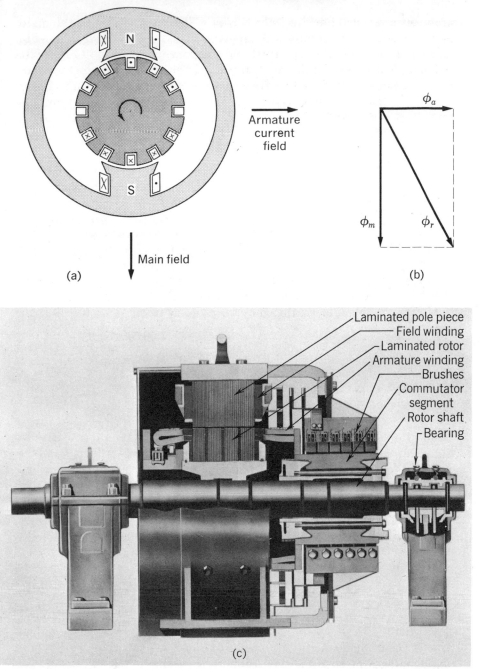

Fig. 2–2. (a) Simplified radial cross-section through a 2-pole d-c generator. (b) Magnetic flux diagram. (c) Axial cross-sectional view of d-c generator. (Courtesy of Westinghouse Electric Corporation.)

produces a magnetic field ϕ_a which is in a direction normal to the main field. Therefore the resultant magnetic field ϕ_r is produced by the main field component and the armature field component, as shown in Fig. 2–2b.

Figure 2–3 shows the flux distribution in the air gap due to the main field and the field produced by the armature current. It is seen that, for $0 \leq \theta \leq \pi/2$ and $\pi \leq \theta \leq 3\pi/2$, both fields are in the same direction, but for $\pi/2 \leq \theta \leq \pi$ and $3\pi/2 \leq \theta \leq 2\pi$, both fields are opposing. As a

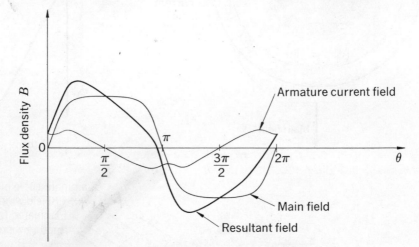

Fig. 2–3. Flux density distribution in air gap due to the main field and the field produced by the armature current.

result the net flux density distribution is as shown. \In practice, saturation effects limit the increase in flux density when the two fields reinforce so that there is actually a net decrease in total flux. This effect is called *armature reaction* and becomes more important as the load is increased./ \It is important to recognize that the magnitude of ϕ_a is dependent on the load current, while ϕ_m is constant if the field excitation is constant. \As a result, both the magnitude and direction of the resultant magnetic flux varies with the load current, and so the correct position of the brushes on the commutator also varies with the load.

2–3. INTERPOLES

' Originally, brushes were mounted about the commutator so that their position could be manually adjusted as the load was varied. The obvious disadvantages of such an arrangement were eliminated by the use of interpoles. These are small poles, as shown in Fig. 2–4a, which produce a magnetic field equal and opposite to ϕ_a. The load current itself is

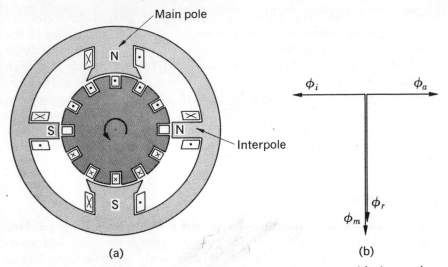

Fig. 2–4. (a) Cross-section of a 2-pole generator with interpoles. (b) Magnetic flux diagram.

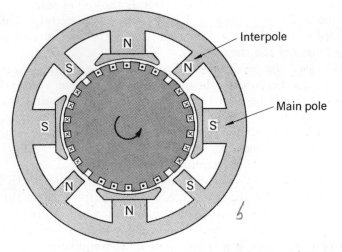

Fig. 2–5. Four-pole d-c generator with interpoles.

passed through the interpole windings so that their field ϕ_i varies with the load current. By using the correct number of interpole turns, it is therefore possible to provide a field which is at all times equal and opposite to that of the armature winding. The resultant field has then the same direction as the main field and the correct position for the brushes on the commutator remains independent of the load.

Frequently, d-c machines have more than two main poles. They may have four, six, eight, etc., poles placed alternately around the stator; an even number of poles must always be used. However, the choice of the number is governed by the speed of the rotor and the terminal voltage required. A large number of poles are used for low speeds and high voltages. The simplified cross-section of a four-pole machine with inter-poles is shown in Fig. 2–5. The direction of current flow in the rotor conductors is shown outward under the north poles and inward under the south poles. The individual conductors are so connected that their potentials reinforce and are fed to the exterior through the commutator and brushes.

2–4. EXCITATION

It has already been mentioned that the main field of a d-c machine is produced by passing a d-c exciting current through the main field winding, but the source of the supply was not discussed. However, the way in which the machine is excited determines its operating characteristics; hence d-c machines are classified by the way in which they are excited.

The most obvious means of excitation is the use of some separate d-c source; the machine is then said to be *separately excited*. This case is represented schematically in Fig. 2–6a, where the field current I_f is regulated by means of the rheostat R_f.

In most cases, the requirement of a separate d-c source is inconvenient. However, since d-c power is being generated, it seems appropriate that some of this should be used to excite the field. There are two ways in which the field winding may be connected. In the first case the field winding is placed in parallel with the load, across the output terminals, as in Fig. 2–6b, and the generator is said to be *shunt-excited*. A field rheostat R_f controls the amount of current diverted to the field.

The field winding may of course also be placed in series with the load, as in Fig. 2–6c, so that all, or most, of the load current passes through the field. The generator is then said to be *series-excited*. In this case only a small number of turns are needed to produce the required flux, since the field current is so much greater than in the equivalent shunt-excited machine.

Since, as will be shown, the characteristics of the shunt and series machines are very different, it is often convenient to use both shunt and series windings to generate the flux and achieve desired characteristics. In such a case the excitation is said to be *compound;* the circuit for such a machine is shown in Fig. 2–6d. This is a *short-shunt* machine, since the shunt winding is placed next to the armature at aa'. It could also be connected at bb', in which case it would be called a *long-shunt* machine.

An apparent objection to the use of other than separately excited

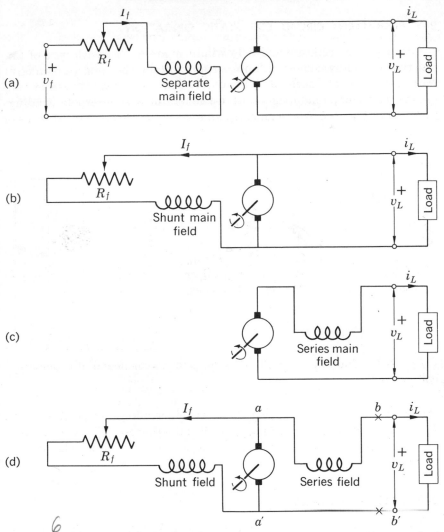

Fig. 2–6. (a) Separately excited d-c generator. (b) Shunt-excited d-c generator. (c) Series-excited d-c generator. (d) Compound short-shunt-excited d-c generator.

machines arises in that no current is available to excite the field windings until a voltage has been generated and yet apparently none can be generated until the field has been excited. But a small amount of residual flux is present and, although no current flows initially through the field winding, the small voltage generated by the rotation of the armature through the residual flux is usually sufficient to cause a current to flow; then the voltage quickly builds up.

2–5. EQUIVALENT CIRCUIT FOR STATIC OPERATION

Although the armature and field windings are wound with wire of low resistivity, usually copper, it is important to take the total resistance of these windings into account. The equivalent circuit under static conditions for a compound long-shunt d-c generator with interpole windings is shown in Fig. 2–7, where r_a, r_f, r_i, and r_s are the effective resistances of

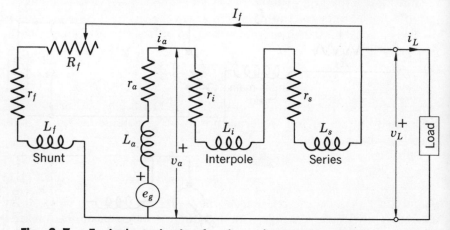

Fig. 2–7. Equivalent circuit of a long-shunt compound d-c generator with interpoles.

the armature, shunt, interpole, and series field windings, respectively, and L_a, L_f, L_i, and L_s are the respective self-inductances. The voltage generated in the armature winding as it rotates in the magnetic field is represented by a voltage source e_g.

2–6. VOLTAGE EQUATION

The voltage generated by the armature as it rotates in the magnetic field is proportional to the speed of rotation ω_m and to the effective flux per pole ϕ_p, so that

$$e_g = k\omega_m\phi_p \tag{2-3}$$

where k is a constant and is given by

$$k = \frac{PZ}{2\pi a} \tag{2-3a}$$

where P is the number of poles, Z is the number of conductors in the armature winding, and a is the number of parallel current paths through the winding. The definition of a "single conductor" is a length of insulated conducting material stretched between opposite ends of a rotor, and there-fore if a coil has N turns, it will contain $2N$ conductors. The number of parallel current paths through a winding is a property of the way in which the armature is wound and so the latter is specified for a given machine.

2-7. STATIC CHARACTERISTICS OF THE D-C GENERATOR

The most important characteristic of a generator is its external charac-teristic. This indicates the manner in which the terminal voltage v_L varies as the load current increases from no load to full load. Use is made of the *generator equation,*

$$v_a = e_g - i_a r_a \qquad (2\text{--}4)$$

which expresses the armature voltage at the brushes, v_a, in terms of the generated voltage e_g and the armature resistive voltage drop $i_a r_a$ under steady-state conditions.

Substituting Eq. 2–3 in Eq. 2–4 gives

$$v_a = k\omega_m \phi_p - i_a r_a \qquad (2\text{--}5)$$

Equation 2–5 gives the relationship between the armature voltage and current, thus providing a means for determining the generator characteris-tics for the variously excited systems of Fig. 2–6.

2-8. SEPARATELY EXCITED D-C GENERATORS

For the separately excited generator of Fig. 2–6a, $v_L = v_a$ and $i_L = i_a$, so that Eq. 2–5 becomes

$$v_L = k\omega_m \phi_p - i_L r_a \qquad (2\text{--}6)$$

Equation 2–6 indicates that, for constant speed and flux, the terminal voltage decreases linearly by an amount $i_L r_a$ with increasing load current, as shown by curve a in Fig. 2–8. Since in most cases r_a is small, the change in output voltage between no load and full load is only a few percent of the no-load voltage.

It should be noted that the assumption of constant speed and flux is made. The constant-speed assumption may be justified in the case of a governed mechanical driving source; but the flux per pole decreases, due to armature reaction and saturation. As a result, the $k\omega_m \phi_p$ term decreases as the load is increased so that in fact the external characteristic drops off at a greater rate, as shown by curve b of Fig. 2–8.

The output voltage, and consequently the output power, of a separately excited d-c generator may be easily adjusted by variation of the excitation current. This is of significant advantage since in general the power

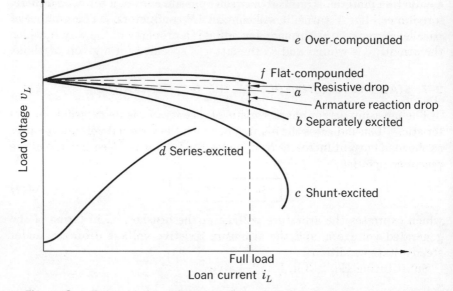

Fig. 2-8. External d-c generator characteristics: (a) separately excited with ϕ_p constant; (b) separately excited with armature reaction; (c) shunt-excited; (d) series-excited; (e) overcompounded; (f) flat-compounded.

required to excite the field is only a small percentage of the full-load generator power and so the separately excited generator may be considered a high-gain power amplifier and a useful component of a control system. For this reason its dynamic characteristics are considered under Art. 2–16.

2-9. SELF-EXCITED D-C GENERATORS

The generator equation for the shunt-excited machine of Fig. 2–9 is

$$v_L = k\omega_m\phi_p - i_a r_a$$

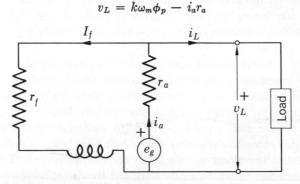

Fig. 2-9. Equivalent circuit of a d-c shunt generator.

Again the variation of the load voltage v_L as a function of the load current is required. In this case, however, the flux ϕ_p is being produced by the exciting current I_f, which is given by

$$I_f = \frac{v_L}{r_f} \tag{2-7}$$

and so is dependent on the output voltage v_L. It is apparent, therefore, that when v_L decreases as the machine is loaded, ϕ_p also decreases, and so the effects are cumulative. As a result, the load voltage of a shunt generator drops off considerably between no load and full load. This is shown by curve c of Fig. 2-8.

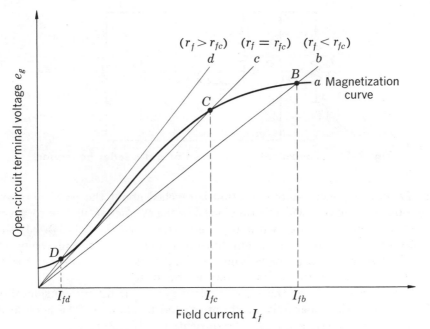

Fig. 2-10. Magnetization curve and field resistance curves.

Although it was mentioned that the flux ϕ_p is produced by the field current I_f, the relationship between the two is non-linear, due to residual magnetism and saturation, and therefore the relationship between e_g and I_f is also non-linear, as shown by curve a in Fig. 2-10. This is called a *magnetization curve* and is similar to part of a *B-H* curve. In practice it is easy to obtain the curve, since, when the machine is unloaded, $v_L = e_g$, and a series of terminal voltage readings may be taken, with the generator driven at a constant speed, while the field current (supplied from a separate d-c source) is varied.

If the resistance of the field circuit of a shunt-excited generator is greater than a certain critical value r_{fc}, then the machine cannot be self-exciting. The magnetization curve permits the determination of this critical value. Under no-load starting conditions, $v_L \approx e_g$, so that the field current is given by $I_f = e_g/r_f$. This relationship between e_g and I_f is represented by the linear curves in Fig. 2–10.

When the resistance of the field is less than the critical value r_{fc}, and when the field current is less than, for example, I_{fb}, the generated potential (curve a) is at all times greater than the potential required to overcome the resistance of the shunt field (line b), and so the field current builds up

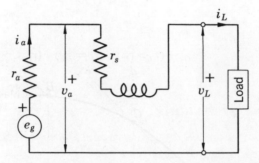

Fig. 2–11. Equivalent static circuit of a d-c series generator.

to I_{fb} until a steady-state condition is reached about the point of interception B. Curve c, which is tangential to the magnetization curve, gives the maximum acceptable value for the resistance of the field r_{fc}. If the resistance is greater than r_{fc}, equilibrium is reached at the intercept D, which is, however, at a low voltage; so the generator is in effect not self-exciting and the output voltage does not build up.

The characteristic of the series-excited generator differs considerably from that of the separately or shunt-excited machines. The generator equation for the series generator represented in Fig. 2–11 is

$$v_L = k\omega_m\phi_p - i_a(r_a + r_s) \tag{2–8}$$

Since the load current flows through the series field winding, the flux ϕ_p, and hence the generated voltage e_g, are dependent on the load. Under open-circuited conditions the voltage generated is a minimum, but as the load is increased the voltage builds up and has a form similar to that of the magnetizing curve, as shown by curve d in Fig. 2–8. As in the case of the shunt-excited generator, the combined resistance of the load and generator windings must be less than the critical value given by the magnetization curve if the voltage is to build up.

Example 2-1. A 440-volt, 115-amp, d-c long-shunt generator is operating under rated conditions. If the generator has the following characteristics

armature resistance	0.016 ohm
shunt field circuit resistance	62 ohms
series field resistance	0.018 ohm
interpole resistance	0.01 ohm
total brush drop	1.8 volts

find the internally generated voltage.

Referring to Fig. 2–7, the internally generated voltage is seen to be

$$e_g = v_L + (i_L + I_f)(r_a + r_i + r_s) + 1.8$$

where

$$I_f = \frac{v_L}{r_f + R_f} = \frac{440}{62} = 7.1 \text{ amp}$$

and so

$$e_g = 440 + (115 + 7.1)(0.016 + 0.01 + 0.018) + 1.8$$
$$= 447.2 \text{ volts}$$

2-10. COMPOUND EXCITATION

It is obvious from Fig. 2–8 that the external characteristic of the series-excited generator differs markedly from the others. Use is made of this fact in the compound generator, in which there are both shunt and series field windings. When the series ampere-turns predominate, the machine is said to be *overcompounded:* the output voltage increases as the load current increases, as shown by curve *e* in Fig. 2–8. A generator is said to be *flat-compounded* if it has a characteristic as in curve *f* of Fig. 2–8, when the no-load and full-load voltages are equal.

Example 2-2. A d-c shunt generator is to be flat-compounded by adding series field windings so that the existing winding is long-shunt. A test of the uncompounded generator, which has 750 shunt turns per pole, indicates that the rated field current of 2.2 amp is required to produce the rated voltage of 220 volts at no load, while 2.6 amp is required to produce the same voltage when the generator delivers a full-load rated current of 45 amp. Find the number of series turns required.

The test shows that additional ampere-turns are required to compensate for armature reaction and resistive effects at full load. The difference between full-load and no-load ampere-turns is

$$750(2.6 - 2.2) = 300 \text{ amp-turns}$$

This difference must be supplied by the series winding in order to flat-compound the generator.

At full load, $i_a = i_L + I_f = 45 + 2.2 = 47.2$ amp; and, since the current passes through the series winding, $300/47.2 = 6.3$ turns are required.

2-11. GENERATOR APPLICATIONS

Separately excited generators are important control-system elements, since the field winding can control the terminal voltage over a wide range. The separately excited generator is a power amplifier with an amplification factor in the 30–50 range. The input is applied to the field and the amplified output is obtained at the armature terminals.

Shunt generators are used where a slight decrease in terminal voltage is required as the load is increased. A common use is for battery charging.

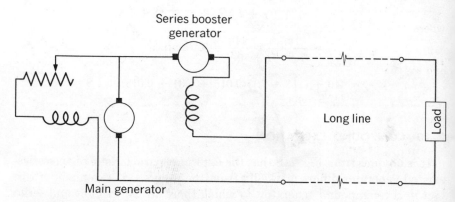

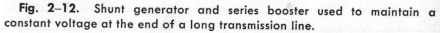

Fig. 2-12. Shunt generator and series booster used to maintain a constant voltage at the end of a long transmission line.

Series generators are frequently used as *boosters*, when power at constant voltage is required at a considerable distance from a generator. If a constant-voltage generator is used as the power source, then, due to the resistance of the transmission circuit, the load voltage decreases steadily as the load is increased. However, if a booster generator is placed in series with the line, as shown in Fig. 2–12, then the drop in voltage may be compensated for by the increase in output voltage of the series generator. As a result, an almost-constant voltage may be obtained at the other end of the line. This same result could, of course, be obtained by originally installing an overcompounded generator as the power source.

A flat-compounded generator is used when an almost-constant terminal voltage is required at all loads.

2-12. D-C MOTORS

There is no basic physical difference between a d-c generator and a d-c motor. If the output from the machine is electrical energy, it is acting as a generator; whereas if the output is mechanical energy, it is acting as a motor.

The principle of electrical-to-mechanical energy conversion in the d-c motor is dependent on the fact that a current-carrying conductor in a magnetic field is subjected to a force which is normal to both the direction of current flow and the direction of the magnetic field. The armature conductors carry a band of current along the rotor in an axial direction, while the poles provide a radial flux; as a result, a tangential force acts on

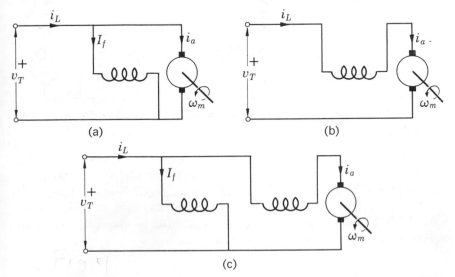

(a) (b) (c)

Fig. 2–13. (a) Schematic diagram of a shunt-excited d-c motor. (b) Schematic diagram of a series-excited d-c motor. (c) Schematic diagram of a compound-excited d-c motor.

the rotor. The commutator maintains the current direction in the conductors under the individual poles, so that the direction of the tangential force does not change as the rotor rotates.

As in the case of the generator, the armature currents generate a cross-magnetizing armature flux, which distorts the main flux distribution and produces armature reaction effects. Interpoles, or compensating windings, may again be used to neutralize the armature flux; however, their polarity is the reverse of that for the generator.

Direct-current motors may be shunt-, series-, or compound-excited, as shown in Fig. 2–13. Again the method of excitation is the factor which determines the external characteristics of the machine, and the compound machine combines the radically different characteristics of the shunt- and series-excited motors.

2–13. D-C MOTOR EQUATIONS AND CHARACTERISTICS

The equivalent circuit for a short-shunt compound d-c motor with interpoles is shown in Fig. 2–14. The symbols are as given in the case of the generator except for v_T, which is the d-c supply voltage.

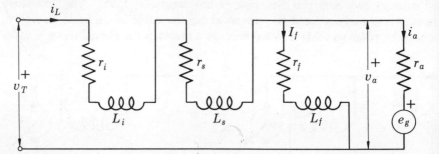

Fig. 2–14. Equivalent circuit of a short-shunt compound d-c motor with interpoles.

A source of voltage e_g is shown, which opposes the supply voltage v_T. This emf is called the *back-emf*, and is generated by virtue of the fact that the armature conductors are rotating in a magnetic field. Under equilibrium conditions, e_g is almost equal in magnitude to v_T and the relationship for the simple shunt motor of Fig. 2–13a is given by the *motor equation:*

$$v_T = e_g + i_a r_a \tag{2–9}$$

where e_g is given by Eq. 2–3. Note the similarity between Eq. 2–9 and the generator equation of Eq. 2–4.

The important external characteristic of a motor is the variation of speed with torque. This speed change is usually expressed in terms of *speed regulation*, which is defined as

$$\text{percentage speed regulation} = \frac{\text{no-load speed} - \text{full-load speed}}{\text{full-load speed}} \times 100$$

The electromagnetic torque T developed in a d-c motor is proportional to the armature current I_a and the effective flux per pole ϕ_p. When mks units are used, the constant of proportionality is k, as given by Eq. 2–3a. Thus

$$T = k\phi_p i_a \tag{2–10}$$

Substituting Eq. 2–3 for e_g, and Eq. 2–10 for i_a in Eq. 2–9 gives

$$v_T = k\omega_m \phi_p + \frac{T r_a}{k\phi_p} \tag{2–11}$$

Solving Eq. 2–11 for ω_m gives

$$\omega_m = \frac{v_T - Tr_a/k\phi_p}{k\phi_p} \qquad (2\text{–}12)$$

The external speed–torque characteristics may now be determined from Eq. 2–12.

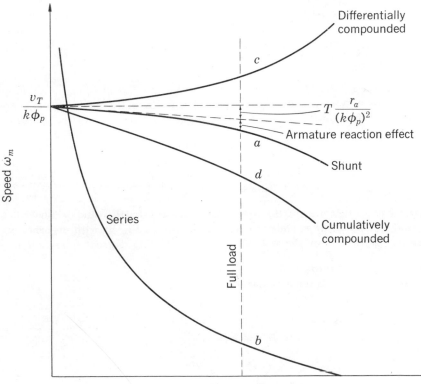

Fig. 2–15. External speed–torque characteristic of (a) shunt motor; (b) series motor; (c) differentially compounded motor; (d) cumulatively compounded motor.

In the case of the shunt motor with interpoles, or negligible armature reaction, the field current, and hence the flux, may be considered constant throughout the range of operation. Thus the speed of the shunt motor decreases linearly from a no-load speed of $v_T/k\phi_p$. When armature reaction causes a decrease in ϕ_p as the torque is increased, the rate at which the speed decreases becomes greater towards full load, and the characteristic is as shown by curve a of Fig. 2–15. In the case of the series generator, the speed equation is

$$\omega_m = \frac{v_T - T(r_a + r_s)/k\phi_p}{k\phi_p} \tag{2-13}$$

At no load when $T = 0$, $i_L = 0$ and so $\phi_p = 0$. Equation 2–13 indicates that the speed is infinite. In practice, of course, there will always be a windage and friction load on a motor, and so a small flux is generated by the current which supplies the no-load losses. However, an unloaded series motor may attain a dangerously high speed and should always be installed so that it is coupled directly, or through gears, to its load. Curve b of Fig. 2–15 shows a typical speed–torque characteristic for a d-c series motor.

Example 2–3. A 220-volt, series d-c motor has a full-load rating of 30 hp at 850 rpm and draws a current of 117 amp. The losses under rated conditions are expressed in terms of the rated output power as

resistive loss in armature	5.1 percent
resistive loss in field	4.8 percent
friction and windage loss	3.8 percent
other fixed losses	1.3 percent

It is assumed that within the operating range the friction and windage loss varies directly with speed and the resultant flux varies directly with the armature current. If the load on the motor is such that the input current is 90 amp, find

(a) The speed of rotation.
(b) The output power in horsepower.
(c) The output torque.

(a) Denote rated conditions with the subscript 1 and required conditions with the subscript 2. The armature resistive loss is

$$i_{a1}{}^2 r_a = 0.051 \times 30 \times 746$$

so that

$$r_a = \frac{0.051 \times 30 \times 746}{117^2} = 0.083 \text{ ohm}$$

Similarly

$$r_s = \frac{0.048 \times 30 \times 746}{117^2} = 0.0782 \text{ ohm}$$

Based on Eqs. 2–9 and 2–3,

$$k\phi_1\omega_1 = v_T - i_{a1}(r_a + r_s)$$
$$k\phi_2\omega_2 = v_T - i_{a2}(r_a + r_s)$$

so that

$$\omega_2 = \omega_1 \left(\frac{\phi_1}{\phi_2}\right) \left[\frac{v_T - i_{a2}(r_a + r_s)}{v_T - i_{a1}(r_a + r_s)}\right]$$

and since the flux is assumed proportional to the armature current, and speed and angular velocity is proportional, the relationship between speeds n_2 and n_1 is

$$n_2 = n_1 \left(\frac{i_{a1}}{i_{a2}}\right) \left[\frac{v_T - i_{a2}(r_a + r_s)}{v_T - i_{a1}(r_a + r_s)}\right]$$

$$= 850 \left(\frac{117}{90}\right) \left[\frac{220 - 90(0.083 + 0.0782)}{220 - 117(0.083 + 0.0782)}\right] = 1132 \text{ rpm}$$

(b) The output power is

$$P_{02} = v_T i_{a2} - i_{a2}{}^2(r_a + r_s) - 0.038 \left(\frac{n_2}{n_1}\right) P_{01} - 0.013 P_{01}$$

$$= 220 \times 90 - (90)^2 0.161 - 0.038 \left(\frac{1132}{850}\right) 30 \times 746 - 0.013 \times 30 \times 746$$

$$= 17{,}065 \text{ watts} = 22.9 \text{ hp}$$

(c) The output torque is

$$T_{02} = \frac{P_{02}}{\omega_2} = \frac{17{,}065 \times 60}{1132 \times 2\pi} = 144 \text{ newton-m}$$

The characteristics of the shunt and series motor may be combined in the compounded machine, which has both shunt and series field windings. If the series turns produce an mmf which opposes the mmf of the shunt turns, the motor is said to be *differentially compounded*. If the series turns provide a significant demagnetizing effect, the net flux decreases as the torque increases and, as seen from Eq. 2–13, the speed increases, as shown by curve c of Fig. 2–15. If the mmf of both the shunt and series turns reinforce each other, the motor is *cumulatively compounded* and has a characteristic similar in form to a shunt motor, but with a greater droop, as shown by curve d (Fig. 2–15).

2–14. SPEED CONTROL AND APPLICATIONS OF D-C MOTORS

Compared to the fixed-frequency a-c machine it is a relatively simple matter to vary the speed of the d-c motor. In fact, this is one of its greatest advantages. Equation 2–12 indicates that speed change may be accomplished by variation of ϕ_p, r_a or v_T, called *shunt field control, armature circuit resistance control*, and *armature terminal voltage control*, respectively.

Shunt field control is the most frequently used of the three methods. An external rheostat is inserted in the shunt field circuit to control the shunt field current and consequently the effective flux ϕ_p. Since at full load only a small percentage of the input power is supplied to the field, the additional power loss in the field rheostat is not significant. Shunt field control permits speed variation between maximum and base speed. When the resistance R_f of the external rheostat in the field circuit is zero, the flux is at its maximum; thus further reduction in speed is not possible with this form of control.

When speed variation between base and zero speed is required, armature terminal voltage control must be resorted to.

An important example of a system which utilizes both shunt field and armature voltage control is the Ward-Leonard system, shown in Fig. 2–16. It consist of a separately excited d-c generator which supplies a controllable voltage v_T to the armature of a d-c motor. The generator is usually driven by an induction motor. Below base speed, control is achieved by adjustment of the generator field current, which in turn

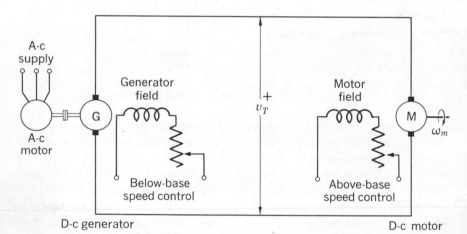

Fig. 2–16. Schematic diagram of the Ward-Leonard speed control system.

varies the armature voltage supplied to the motor. Above base speed, control is achieved by adjustment of the motor field current. In general, the d-c field supply is produced by a small d-c generator, called an *exciter*, which is mounted on the shaft of the motor-generator set.

Although such a system requires a large initial investment, it is particularly useful when large quantities of power must be controlled over an extensive speed range, since both control elements are located in the low-power circuits.

For small motors, or for larger ones when operation at other than rated speed is of short and infrequent duration, armature circuit resistance control may be effectively utilized. An external resistance, which reduces the armature voltage, is inserted in series with the armature. Although this is an inefficient method of control, it is simple and inexpensive for small motors and is frequently used with series motors.

2-15. MACHINE EFFICIENCY

The most obvious way to determine experimentally the efficiency of a machine is to measure the input and output power while operating under the desired conditions, and calculate the overall efficiency from

$$\text{efficiency} = \frac{\text{output power}}{\text{input power}} \qquad (2\text{-}14)$$

However, in many cases this is not the most satisfactory approach, especially in the case of large machines where it might be inconvenient to operate at about full load. If Eq. 2-14 is put in the form

$$\text{efficiency} = \frac{\text{input} - \text{losses}}{\text{input}} \qquad (2\text{-}15)$$

then the efficiency is determined from loss measurements. In fact, results obtained from Eq. 2-15 are more accurate than those from Eq. 2-14 since an error in the loss measurement typically results in an error of about one-tenth that value in the efficiency calculation. Machine losses may be broken down into four main categories:

1. Copper losses.
2. Mechanical losses.
3. No-load core losses.
4. Stray load losses.

2-15.1. Copper Losses. The calculation of i^2R losses in the armature and field windings is based on their d-c resistances at 75°C. In general, the brush-contact loss at the commutator is included in this category and the voltage drop is usually taken as a constant at 1.8 volts for carbon brushes.

2-15.2. Mechanical Losses. These arise from friction and windage; they may be determined by mechanically driving the rotor at the required speed, with the machine both unloaded and unexcited, and measuring the mechanical power required.

2-15.3. No-Load Core Losses. These are composed of *hysteresis* and *eddy-current* losses. Hysteresis losses are incurred in a magnetic material whenever the magnetic flux density is changed. In the d-c machine most of this loss is associated with the rotor iron due to the continual reversal of the flux density during rotation. An empirical equation for the hysteresis power loss is

$$P_h = k_h B_{\max}^m \omega_m \qquad (2\text{-}16)$$

where k_h is a constant, $B_{\max}$ is the maximum flux density, and m is usually taken as equal to 2.

The eddy-current loss is caused by the generation of currents in the rotor iron. Since the rotor iron, as well as the armature conductors which it supports, rotates in the magnetic field, voltages are generated and cause the eddy currents. Both the eddy-current and hysteresis losses are reduced by fabricating the rotor from thin laminated sheets of low-loss magnetic material. Eddy-current losses are expressed by

$$P_e = k_e(B_{\max}\omega_m\mathfrak{I})^2 \tag{2-17}$$

where k_e is a constant and $\mathfrak{I}$ is the thickness of the laminations.

The no-load core losses may be found by measuring the power required to drive the excited but unloaded machine. Since the mechanical losses are known, these may be deducted, giving the no-load core losses.

2–15.4. Stray Load Losses. These losses include those resulting from non-uniform current and magnetic flux distribution. They are difficult to evaluate and are often assumed to be 1 percent of the output power for d-c machines.

2–16. DYNAMIC PERFORMANCE OF D-C MACHINES

It was previously noted that the separately excited d-c machine is an important automatic control system element. Consequently, its behavior under conditions of changing input and output, or its dynamic characteristics, are often of greater interest than the steady-state, or static, characteristics already studied. In the design and analysis of control systems, the interaction between the various components is represented in the form of block diagrams. It is important therefore to analyze the dynamic performance of the d-c machine and then to develop the block diagram for both the d-c separately excited generator and motor.

2–17. DYNAMIC ANALYSIS OF THE D-C GENERATOR

Figure 2–17 shows the equivalent circuit for the separately excited generator. Note the presence of the inductances since we are now interested in the time-varying performance of the generator, and the use of lower case symbols representing instantaneous values. We now regard the generator as a control circuit element in which the field voltage v_f is the input signal and the armature, or load, current i_a is the output. Hence the block diagram must represent the relationship between the input v_f and the output i_a. The differential equation for the field circuit is

$$v_f = i_f r_f + L_f p i_f \tag{2-18}$$

The differential operator d/dt is replaced by p. If τ_f, the time constant of the field, is defined as

$$\tau_f = \frac{L_f}{r_f} \tag{2-19}$$

then Eq. 2–18 may be put in the form

$$i_f = v_f \frac{1}{r_f(1 + \tau_f p)} \tag{2-20}$$

It is assumed that operation is within the linear region of the magnetization curve so that, at a fixed speed ω_{m0}, the generated voltage e_{g0}

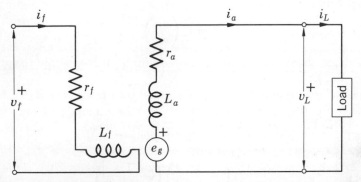

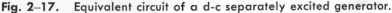

Fig. 2–17. Equivalent circuit of a d-c separately excited generator.

is proportional to the field current:

$$e_{g0} = k_f i_f \tag{2-21}$$

where k_f is the constant of proportionality. Substituting Eq. 2–20 in Eq. 2–21 gives the generated voltage for the fixed speed ω_{m0} as

$$e_{g0} = v_f\left(\frac{k_f}{r_f}\right)\left(\frac{1}{1 + \tau_f p}\right) \tag{2-22}$$

Since the generated voltage is proportional to speed, then at some other speed ω_m the generated voltage e_g is

$$e_g = e_{g0}\left(\frac{\omega_m}{\omega_{m0}}\right) \tag{2-23}$$

In order to evaluate e_g from Eq. 2–23, an expression for ω_m, the instantaneous speed of the machine, must be available. If the driving torque from the prime mover is T_m, and the electromagnetic torque which opposes rotation of the rotor is T, then the difference between the two torques is

$$T_m - T = Jp\omega_m + D\omega_m \tag{2-24}$$

where J is the inertia of the rotor and D is the damping coefficient. The left-hand side of Eq. 2–24 represents the excess mechanical torque provided, and this is used to accelerate the rotor and overcome the frictional torque $D\omega_m$.

Solving Eq. 2–24 for ω_m gives

$$\omega_m = (T_m - T)\frac{1}{D\left(1 + \dfrac{J}{D}p\right)} \tag{2-25}$$

From Eqs. 2–3 and 2–10, $e_{g0} = k\phi_p\omega_{m0}$ and $T = k\phi_p i_a$ and so the opposing electrical torque is

$$T = i_a\left(\frac{e_{g0}}{\omega_{m0}}\right) \tag{2-26}$$

Having determined ω_m, and an expression for T, it is possible to solve for e_g in Eq. 2–23.

If the load on the generator is represented by a resistance R_L and by an inductance L_L, then the output current may be calculated from

$$e_g = i_a[(r_a + R_L) + p(L_a + L_L)]$$

which yields

$$i_a = e_g\left(\frac{1}{r_a + R_L}\right)\left(\frac{1}{1 + \tau_{aL}p}\right) \tag{2-27}$$

where

$$\tau_{aL} = \frac{L_a + L_L}{r_a + R_L} \tag{2-28}$$

Equation 2–28 gives the combined time constant of the armature and load.

Example 2–4. A simple d-c generator is running unexcited at its rated speed. Initially it is assumed that the current is zero through the load, which consists of $R_L = 0.7$ ohm and $L_L = 2.1$ henrys. At $t = 0$, the field is excited with the rated voltage of $V_f = 220$ volts from a supply whose internal resistance is negligible. If

$$r_a = 0.02 \text{ ohm} \qquad r_f = 42 \text{ ohms}$$
$$L_a = 0.015 \text{ henry} \qquad L_f = 35 \text{ henrys}$$

and it may be assumed that $e_g = 41i_f$, find the variation of the field current and the output current as a function of time.

The voltage equation of the field circuit is

$$V_f = i_f r_f + L_f\frac{di_f}{dt}$$

Taking the Laplace transform

$$\frac{V_f}{s} = I_f r_f + L_f[sI_f - i_f(0)]$$

where the Laplace transform of i_f is I_f. Since $i_f(0) = 0$,

$$I_f = \frac{V_f}{L_f} \frac{1}{s(s + 1/\tau_f)} = \frac{V_f}{L_f} \left(\frac{\tau_f}{s} - \frac{\tau_f}{s + 1/\tau_f} \right)$$

and so the inverse Laplace transform gives

$$i_f = \frac{V_f}{L_f} (\tau_f - \tau_f e^{-t/\tau_f}) = \frac{V_f}{r_f} (1 - e^{-t/\tau_f})$$

$$= \frac{220}{42}(1 - e^{-1.2t})$$

$$= 5.24(1 - e^{-1.2t})$$

The voltage equation for the load circuit is

$$e_g = (r_a + R_L)i_a + (L_a + L_L) \frac{di_a}{dt}$$

or, since $e_g = 41i_f$,

$$\frac{41i_f}{r_a + R_L} = i_a + \tau_{aL} \frac{di_a}{dt}$$

where

$$\tau_{aL} = \frac{L_a + L_L}{r_a + R_L}$$

Upon taking the Laplace transform with $\mathcal{L}[i_a(t)] = I_a(s)$

$$\frac{41I_f}{r_a + R_L} = I_a + \tau_{aL}[sI_a - i_a(0)]$$

Substituting for I_f and setting $i_a(0) = 0$ gives

$$\frac{41V_f\tau_f}{L_f(r_a + R_L)} \left(\frac{1}{s} - \frac{1}{s + 1/\tau_f} \right) = I_a(1 + s\tau_{aL})$$

or

$$I_a = \frac{41V_f\tau_f}{L_f\tau_{aL}(r_a + R_L)} \left[\frac{1}{s(s + 1/\tau_{aL})} - \frac{1}{(s + 1/\tau_f)(s + 1/\tau_{aL})} \right]$$

After expanding in partial fractions, the inverse Laplace transform gives

$$i_a = \frac{41V_f}{r_f(r_a + R_L)} \left[1 - e^{-t/\tau_{aL}} - \left(\frac{\tau_f}{\tau_f - \tau_{aL}} \right) (e^{-t/\tau_f} - e^{-t/\tau_{aL}}) \right]$$

$$i_a = \frac{41 \times 220}{42 \times 0.72} \left[1 - e^{-0.34t} - \left(\frac{0.832}{0.832 - 2.95} \right) (e^{-1.2t} - e^{-0.34t}) \right]$$

$$i_a = 298(1 + 0.392e^{-1.2t} - 1.392e^{-0.34t}) \text{ amp}$$

In developing the block diagram representation, some of the important operations of block diagram algebra should be considered. Some of the frequently encountered symbols and operations are shown in Fig. 2–18. Each square, circle and triangle represents a mathematical operation and the interconnection of the blocks corresponds to the sequence of operations required to derive the output from the input quantities. Expressions within squares are called *transfer functions*, and as shown in Fig. 2–18a the output $C = GR$, where R is the input and G is the transfer function. Inputs may be added or subtracted, multiplied, or integrated, as shown

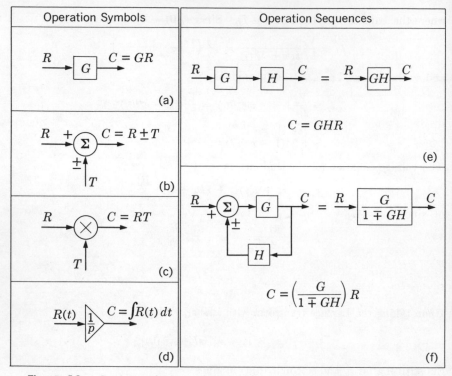

Fig. 2–18. Basic symbols and operations of block-diagram algebra.

in parts b, c, and d of Fig. 2–18. The operation in Fig. 2–18f is of particular importance: it represents a feedback system, in which a part of the output $\pm CH$ is returned to the input so that

$$C = G(R \pm CH)$$

or

$$C = R\left(\frac{G}{1 \mp GH}\right) \qquad (2\text{–}29)$$

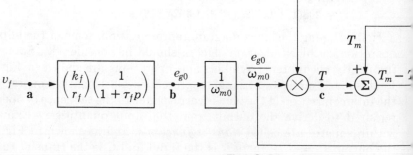

Fig. 2–19. Block diagram of

and so the feedback circuit may be represented by a single block with a transfer function

$$\left(\frac{G}{1 \mp GH}\right)$$

It is desired to develop a block diagram for a d-c generator with the input as v_f and the output i_a. The completed block diagram is shown in Fig. 2–19. In developing it, Eqs. 2–22, 2–26, 2–25, 2–23, and 2–27 are used, in that order. The complete diagram may be subdivided into sections corresponding to the different equations. For example, Eq. 2–22

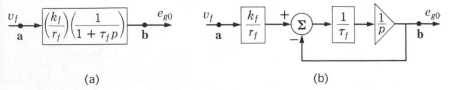

(a)   (b)

Fig. 2–20. (a) Block diagram. (b) Equivalent analog computer diagram.

corresponds to the section between (boldface) **a** and **b**, and Eq. 2–26 corresponds to that between **b** and **c**. Note that a feedback loop from the output is required to formulate the electromagnetic torque T. In deriving ω_m it is necessary to know the torque T_m supplied by the prime mover, so it is assumed that

$$T_m = G_m \omega_m \qquad (2\text{--}30)$$

where G_m is the function which relates the torque and speed of the prime mover. With G_m as a transfer function, a feedback loop is taken from ω_m and so the difference $T_m - T$ is obtained.

The block diagram in Fig. 2–19 may in turn be put into a more basic form suitable for use with an analog computer. For example, the section between **a** and **b** may be represented by a circuit containing a feedback loop and an integrator, as in Fig. 2–20.

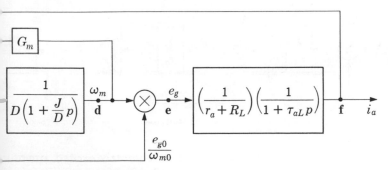

c separately excited generator.

2-18. DYNAMIC ANALYSIS OF THE D-C MOTOR

Figure 2–21 shows the equivalent circuit of a separately excited d-c motor. Assuming speed control is achieved by means of armature terminal voltage control, and the field current is held constant, the objective of this section is to develop the block diagram for the motor with v_T as the input and ω_m as the output.

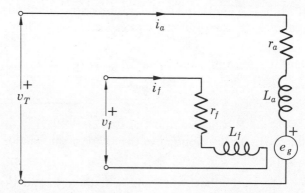

Fig. 2–21. Equivalent circuit of a d-c separately excited motor.

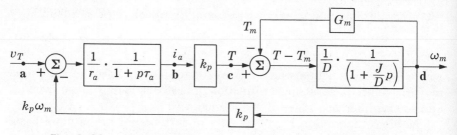

Fig. 2–22. Block diagram of a d-c separately excited motor.

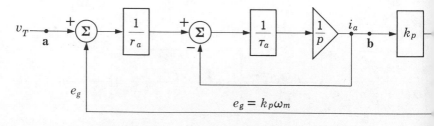

Fig. 2–23. Block diagram of a separately excited, armatur⋅

The dynamic motor equation is

$$v_T = i_a(r_a + L_a p) + e_g \qquad (2\text{--}31)$$

The generated voltage $e_g = k\phi_p \omega_m$, but since the field current is constant it may be assumed that $k\phi_p$ is given by a constant k_p, so that

$$e_g = k_p \omega_m \qquad (2\text{--}32)$$

Substituting Eq. 2–32 in Eq. 2–31, and solving for i_a gives

$$i_a = (v_T - k_p \omega_m)\, \frac{1}{r_a(1 + \tau_a p)} \qquad (2\text{--}33)$$

where the armature winding time constant

$$\tau_a = \frac{L_a}{r_a} \qquad (2\text{--}34)$$

Equation 2–33 is used in developing the first part (from **a** to **b**) of the block diagram in Fig. 2–22. Since the electromagnetic torque produced in the motor is given by $k\phi_p i_a$, and $k_p = k\phi_p$,

$$T = k_p i_a \qquad (2\text{--}35)$$

The torque is therefore directly proportional to i_a, and part **b** to **c** of the diagram may be drawn.

The torque equation governing the rotation of the rotor and load is

$$T - T_m = J p \omega_m + D \omega_m \qquad (2\text{--}36)$$

so that

$$\omega_m = (T - T_m)\, \frac{1}{D\left(1 + \dfrac{J}{D} p\right)} \qquad (2\text{--}37)$$

Again, if a function G_m relates the speed and torque of the load, then the remainder of the block diagram, from **c** to **d**, may be completed. As

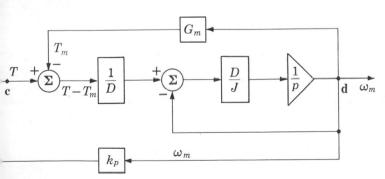

oltage-controlled d-c motor (analog computer circuit).

in the case of the generator, the blocks may be put in a form suitable for analog computer use. Figure 2–23 shows such a diagram.

Not only may the analog circuit of the d-c machine be used to represent it as a circuit element of a control system, but the circuit itself may be used to study machine response. Since the voltages throughout the circuit are proportional to the corresponding electromechanical quantities, it is possible to investigate any of the intermediate quantities. For example, in Fig. 2–23, the armature current, or the driving torque, may be monitored at points **b** or **c** respectively.

2–19. METADYNES AND AMPLIDYNES

The important properties of a d-c separately excited generator, when used as part of a control system, are its power amplification and response. Although power amplification of the order of 100 may be achieved from a single generator, in some cases this is not sufficient. An obvious solution is to place two generators in cascade as shown in Fig. 2–24. While

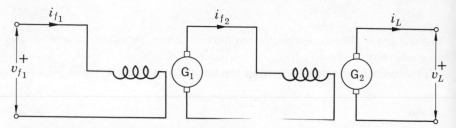

Fig. 2–24. Two d-c motors in cascade, used when high power gain is required and rapid response is not important.

such a system does provide a power gain approximately equal to the product of the individual gains, the response of the system is impaired, since the transmission of a signal from v_{f_1} to v_L is dependent on time constants of the first and the second field circuits. When rapid response to the input signal is not important, the cascaded generator arrangement may be used; however, when both large power gain and rapid response are required modifications must be made to the ordinary d-c machine. The *metadyne* and *amplidyne* are important examples of machines so modified.

2–19.1. **The Metadyne.** The metadyne consists of a separately excited d-c generator in which the regular quadrature-axis brushes qq' are shorted together and a new pair of direct-axis brushes dd' are added. The output is taken across these new brushes as shown in Fig. 2–25.

To understand the operation of the metadyne as a high-gain power amplifier, consider Fig. 2–26. Since the quadrature brushes are short-circuited, a large current flows in the armature winding and so produces a cross-flux ϕ_q. By suitable design, ϕ_q may be as large or larger than the field flux ϕ_m. As a result, if a set of brushes dd' is placed as shown in Figs. 2–25 and 2–27, an output associated with the rotation of the conductors through the ϕ_q field is obtained. The high power gain of the metadyne results from the fact that the magnitude of the short-circuit

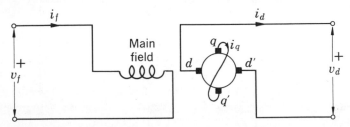

Fig. 2–25. Schematic diagram of a metadyne generator.

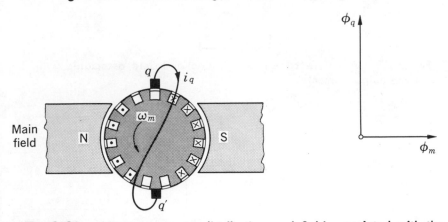

Fig. 2–26. Armature current distribution and field associated with the short-circuited current i_q.

current i_q, and consequently the flux ϕ_p, are particularly sensitive to small changes in the main field flux ϕ_m. Since the output voltage is dependent on ϕ_q, a small change in the main field excitation power causes a large change in the output power. As a result, power amplification of the order of 20,000 may be obtained, as compared to 100 for the ordinary generator.

2-19.2. The Amplidyne. A disadvantage of the metadyne in many cases is the fact that the output voltage v_d decreases as i_d increases. This may be seen from the i_d armature current distribution in Fig. 2–27. The current i_d produces a magnetic flux ϕ_d which is in opposition to the main flux ϕ_m. As a result the net value of the main flux decreases, and so do i_q and ϕ_q, as the output current i_d increases.

In order to correct for this demagnetizing effect a compensating winding, in series with the output, may be provided which produces a flux equal and opposite to ϕ_d, as shown in Fig. 2–28. Such a compensated metadyne is known as an *amplidyne*. Although the power gain is not as great as in the metadyne, the input to the field directly controls the output. As a

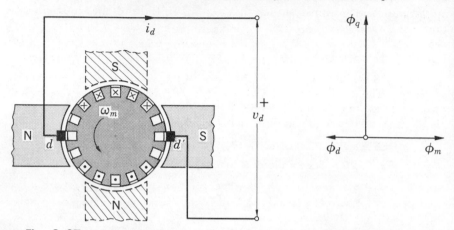

Fig. 2–27. Armature current distribution and field associated with the metadyne output current i_d.

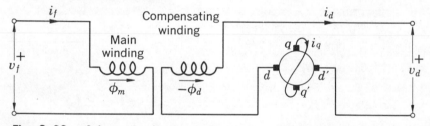

Fig. 2–28. Schematic diagram of a compensated metadyne, or amplidyne.

result the amplidyne may be considered as a voltage source, while the metadyne has the properties of a current source.

PROBLEMS

2–1. Determine the generated voltage required for the operation of a d-c generator at a terminal voltage of 220 volts and a load current of 120 amp when

armature resistance	=	0.03 ohm
shunt field winding resistance	=	45 ohms
series field winding resistance	=	0.025 ohm
interpole winding resistance	=	0.04 ohm
total brush drop	=	1.8 volts

The machine is connected as

   a. Long-shunt generator with interpoles.
   b. Short-shunt generator with interpoles.
   c. Short-shunt generator without interpoles.

2-2. The output of a compound generator is 60 kw. The Joule heating loss of the generator is 5500 watts, the friction and windage loss is 2000 watts, and the core loss is 2800 watts. What torque is required from the prime mover if the speed of the generator is 1500 rpm? Also, find the efficiency of the generator.

2-3. An 8-pole generator has an armature with 47 coils, each of which contains 4 turns. The armature is wave-wound, so that there are two parallel current paths through the winding. The flux per pole is 3.7×10^{-2} weber and the speed is 760 rpm. What is the internally generated voltage?

2-4. The full-load output power of a simple d-c, 4-pole, shunt generator is 4.27 kw when the load voltage is 225 volts and the speed is 850 rpm. The total resistance of the shunt field windings and of the armature windings is 450 ohm and 0.1 ohm, respectively. The flux per pole at full load is 4.2×10^{-2} weber, and there are 2 current paths through the armature winding. Find the number of conductors in the armature.

2-5. The data taken for the no-load magnetization curve of a 4-pole shunt generator operating at 2000 rpm are:

field current (amp)	0	1.0	2.0	3.0	4.0	5.0
generated voltage (volts)	4	75	133	160	172	182

Determine the no-load magnetization curve for the generator when operated at a speed of 1500 rpm. Plot both curves.

2-6. The following data are for the no-load magnetization curve of a shunt, 4-pole d-c generator, operating at 1800 rpm.

field current (amp)	0	0.5	1.0	1.5	2.0	2.5
generated voltage (volts)	3.6	67.5	119.5	144	155	164

Find the total resistance of the shunt field windings if a no-load output voltage of 180 volts is generated when the speed is 2100 rpm, and the armature resistance is 0.05 ohm.

2-7. To what no-load voltage will the generator of Prob. 2-5 build up if the total resistance of the shunt field circuit is 41 ohms and the speed is 2000 rpm?

2-8. If the generator of Prob. 2-5 is fitted with a compensating short-shunt series winding of 6 turns/pole and the number of turns in the existing shunt winding is 800/pole, find the generated voltage when the speed is 2000 rpm, the load current is 120 amp, the shunt field current is 3 amp, and the armature reaction effect causes a demagnetization of 480 amp-turns/pole. If the armature resistance is 0.06 ohm and the series field resistance is 0.004 ohm (total for all poles), find the output voltage at the terminals of the generator.

2–9. It is required to add compensating long-shunt series windings to a shunt generator in order to make it flat-compounded. The existing shunt winding has 900 turns/pole and a current of 1.8 amp is required to produce a terminal voltage of 245 volts at no load, while a current of 2.3 amp is required to produce a terminal voltage of 245 volts at full load. How many series turns are required if the full-load armature current is 38 amp?

2–10. A 220-volt generator whose full-load armature current is 36 amp has a shunt field with 1800 turns/pole. The relationship between armature and shunt field current, required to keep the terminal voltage constant, is found to be $I_f = 0.61 + 0.01i_a$. How many series turns per pole must be added to flat-compound the generator if the resistance of the series field is neglected in the calculation and the windings are short-shunt?

2–11. If the machine described in Prob. 2–1 is operated as a motor from a source of 250 volts at a source current of 120 amp, find the generated voltage when the connections are for long-shunt operation with interpoles.

2–12. A 220-volt shunt motor has an armature resistance of 0.128 ohm and a field resistance of 68.3 ohms. If the full-load current supplied to the motor is 89 amp, find the generated back emf, the total resistive loss in the motor, and the total mechanical output power at full load, when iron and frictional losses are 1000 watts.

2–13. The generated back emf of a shunt motor at full load is 220 volts. If the terminal voltage is 222 volts, the armature resistance including the brush drop is 0.028 ohm, and the shunt field resistance is 95 ohms, find the line current.

2–14. A 220-volt shunt motor draws an armature current of 4.5 amp when running at a speed of 1150 rpm. If the resistance of the armature, including the brush drop, is 0.06 ohm, find the operating speed of the motor when the armature current is 43 amp.

2–15. When developing a torque of 18 lb-ft a 120 volt d-c shunt motor takes a total current of 8 amp from the supply. The field current is held constant at 1.6 amp and flux is assumed constant.

    a. What total current will the motor take when developing a full-load torque of 56 lb-ft?

    b. The motor develops 5 hp when the output torque is 56 lb-ft. If the speed increases 6 percent when the load torque is reduced to 18 lb-ft, what is the armature resistance?

2–16. The armature resistance, including brush drop, of a series motor is 0.06 ohm and the field resistance is 0.015 ohm. The motor runs at a speed of 1160 rpm when the line voltage is 117 volts and the armature current is 28 amp. What is the speed of the motor when the armature current is 24 amp if operating over the linear part of the saturation curve?

2–17. The full-load rating of a d-c series 45-hp motor is 220 volts, 175 amp, at a speed of 700 rpm. The full-load losses are expressed in terms of the input power as

resistive loss in field	3.5 percent
resistive loss in armature (and brushes)	3.9 percent
friction and windage loss	2.0 percent
other fixed losses	1.0 percent

If the motor is operating in the linear part of the magnetization curve and the supply current is at 0.75 times the rated value, find

a. The speed.
b. The torque developed.
c. The output power in horsepower, assuming windage and friction losses vary directly with the speed.

2-18. A 220-volt d-c series motor runs at a speed of 730 rpm when the supply current is 75 amp. What is the speed when the current supplied drops to 32 amp, if the flux produced decreases by 40 percent from its value at 75 amp? The resistance of the series field is 0.13 ohm and the resistance of the armature, including brush drop, is 0.16 ohm.

2-19. A d-c generator is running unexcited at its rated speed. The electrical load on the generator consists of $R_L = 0.5$ ohm and $L_L = 1.3$ henrys and it is assumed that the generated voltage and current are both zero. At time $t = 0$ the field is connected to a constant supply of d-c potential $v_f = 200$ volts. Assuming that the speed is maintained constant as the generated voltage builds up and the internal resistance of the field power supply is negligible, determine an expression for the growth of field current and armature current as a function of time. The following values apply:

$$r_f = 38 \text{ ohms} \qquad r_a = 0.01 \text{ ohm}$$
$$L_f = 27 \text{ henrys} \qquad L_a = 0.012 \text{ henry}$$

Assume that operation is on the linear part of the magnetization curve so that $e_g = 41i_f$.

2-20. A d-c separately excited generator is driven at a constant speed of 1020 rpm with its field and armature circuits open. At time $t = 0$ the field circuit is connected to a constant source of 220 volts. Find an expression for generated voltage as a function of time if $e_g = 87i_f$ and the field and armature constants are

$$r_f = 83 \text{ ohms} \qquad r_a = 0.03 \text{ ohm}$$
$$L_f = 47 \text{ henrys} \qquad L_a = 0.004 \text{ henry}$$

After steady-state conditions have been reached, the generator is loaded by a resistance $R_L = 1.4$ ohms in series with an inductance of 0.002 henry. Determine an expression for the load current, load voltage, and the electromagnetic torque as a function of time.

2-21. A d-c separately excited generator is driven by a source whose speed is given by $\omega_m = (\omega_0 + K \sin \omega t)$. If the flux is kept constant and the armature resistance and inductance are r_a and L_a, respectively, and the load consists of a resistance R_L in series with an inductance L_L, determine an expression for the load current as a function of time. What is the instantaneous steady-state power output of the generator to the load?

2–22. A d-c separately excited motor is running unloaded with the supply voltage at v_L, and the no-load armature current approximately zero. At time $t = 0$ a load torque T_m is applied. If the self-inductance and resistance of the armature is L_a and r_a, respectively, and the inertia of the rotor is J, find an expression for the rotor speed after the load has been applied. The electromagnetically generated torque is given by $T = k_p i_a$. Assume that frictional damping is negligible.

2–23. A separately excited, 220-volt d-c motor is operating unloaded at 2000 rpm. If $k\phi_p = 0.96$ newton-m/amp and the armature resistance is 3.1 ohms, find the no-load damping coefficient D. If at time $t = 0$ an inertial load of J_L is suddenly connected to the rotor, which itself has an inertia of J_R, formulate the two differential equations, in terms of speed and armature current, which govern the transient behavior of the motor. Assume that the armature has an inductance of L_a and the load has an associated damping coefficient of D_L.

2–24. Figure P2–24 represents a Ward-Leonard system in which the speed is controlled by variation of v_f, the generator field voltage. Assuming the motor field is maintained constant and the speed at which the generator is driven is also constant, draw the block diagram for the system, with the generator field voltage as the input signal and the motor speed as the output. Assume that the load on the motor is represented by a torque $D\omega_m$, where D is the coefficient of frictional damping.

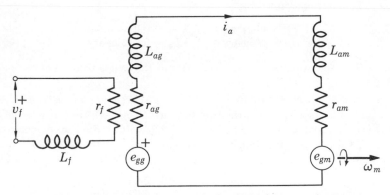

Fig. P2–24. Equivalent circuit of a Ward-Leonard system.

2–25. If the field of the motor in Prob. 2–24 has a resistance r_s and a self-inductance L_s and is placed in series with the armature, draw the block diagram with v_f as the input and ω_m as the output.

2–26. A closed-loop Ward-Leonard system is represented in Fig. P2–26, in which the generator field is supplied through an amplifier with gain A. The input to the amplifier is the difference between a fixed voltage E_0 and a voltage

$e_t = k_t\omega_m$, which is proportional to the output speed. Such negative feedback tends to maintain the speed constant as the load is varied. Draw a block diagram to represent such a closed-loop Ward-Leonard system.

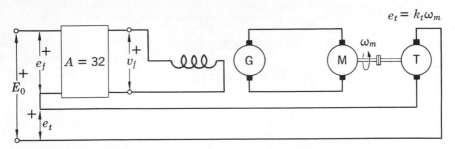

Fig. P2–26. Schematic of a closed-loop Ward-Leonard system.

In a particular system, $A = 32$ and $k_t = 2$ volt-sec and, with a field excitation of 200 volts, the no-load and full-load terminal voltages of the generator are 240 and 220 volts, respectively. When the input voltage to the motor is 220 volts, the no-load and full-load speeds of the motor are 730 and 670 rpm, respectively. Estimate the speed change, with and without feedback, when the full load is removed.

3

Synchronous Converters

When large quantities of electric power are transmitted over long distances it is desirable that the line current be as low as possible, since most of the loss is due to ohmic heating which varies with the square of the current. Therefore high voltages must be used (generally in the range from 10,000 to 500,000 volts). Such high voltages must be reduced to lower levels for distribution to the ordinary consumer. Transformers are used for this purpose and are also used at the generating station to step up the voltage prior to transmission. Since transformers can operate only with alternating current, almost all power is generated and transmitted as alternating current. Synchronous generators, or *alternators*, are used for the conversion of mechanical power into a-c electric power. The term "synchronous" is used because the frequency of the generated voltage is directly related to the speed of the rotor. Since the frequency of an electric power generation system is maintained constant, the speed of the rotor must also remain constant. Hence, synchronous machines generally operate under constant-speed conditions, and therefore the emphasis in this chapter will be on steady-state analysis.

3-1. THE BASIC ALTERNATOR

Figure 3–1 shows a cutaway view of a vertical waterwheel alternator, while Fig. 3–2a is a schematic of the basic alternator. The rotor contains the magnetic field winding, which is supplied with d-c current through slip rings. Usually a small d-c generator, or *exciter*, mounted on the rotor shaft is used to provide the field current. The stator contains the armature winding, which is represented by the concentrated coil aa'. In general, additional coils are placed about the stator and connected in series, thus more effectively utilizing the available stator space. The effect of such a distributed armature winding will be considered later.

If the angular flux distribution is sinusoidal, then the voltage induced in the coil aa' also varies sinusoidally as a function of time, as shown in

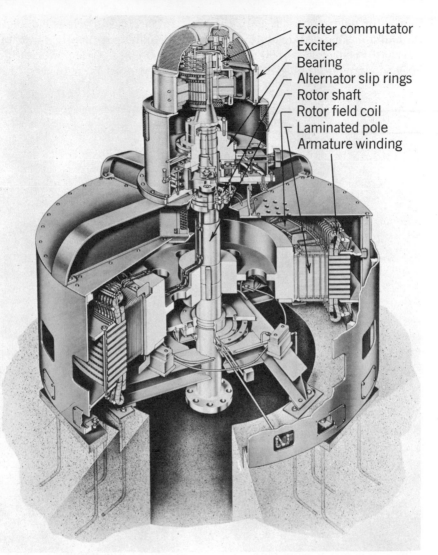

Exciter commutator
Exciter
Bearing
Alternator slip rings
Rotor shaft
Rotor field coil
Laminated pole
Armature winding

Fig. 3–1. Cutaway view of a vertical alternator. (Courtesy of Westinghouse Electric Corporation.)

Fig. 3 2b. The generated voltage goes through a complete cycle for each revolution of the rotor. Therefore if the frequency of the generated voltage is 60 cps then the rotor speed must be 60 rps, or 3600 rpm. If a gas or steam turbine is the prime mover then it is usually feasible to drive the rotor at this rather high speed. However, for other prime movers, such as a water turbine (Fig. 3–3), slower rotor speeds must be used. If four rotor poles are used, as in Fig. 3–4, an electrical cycle is completed for half a mechanical revolution of the rotor, and consequently a four-pole alternator is driven at 1800 rpm to produce 60-cps electric power. Similarly, if six poles are used, then the rotor speed must be reduced to 1200

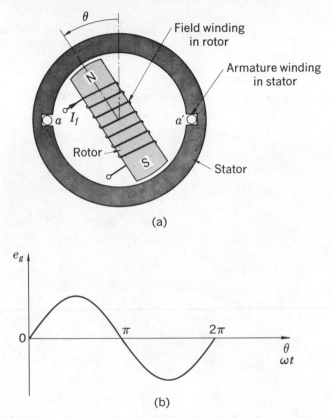

(a)

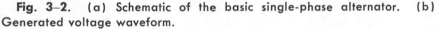

(b)

Fig. 3–2. (a) Schematic of the basic single-phase alternator. (b) Generated voltage waveform.

rpm. The relationship between the frequency f, the number of poles P, and the speed $\mathfrak{N}$ in rpm is therefore

$$f = \frac{P}{2} \frac{\mathfrak{N}}{60} \quad \text{cps} \tag{3-1}$$

It is important to differentiate between mechanical and electrical angles when the alternator has more than two poles. In mechanical terms, an angle of 360° is associated with a complete rotation of the rotor, as shown in Fig. 3–5; whereas, in electrical terms, an angle of 360° is associated with the angle between two adjacent north poles. Therefore if θ is an electrical

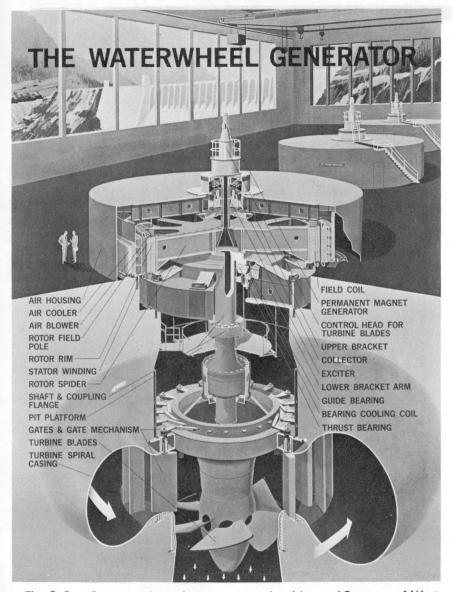

THE WATERWHEEL GENERATOR

AIR HOUSING
AIR COOLER
AIR BLOWER
ROTOR FIELD POLE
ROTOR RIM
STATOR WINDING
ROTOR SPIDER
SHAFT & COUPLING FLANGE
PIT PLATFORM
GATES & GATE MECHANISM
TURBINE BLADES
TURBINE SPIRAL CASING

FIELD COIL
PERMANENT MAGNET GENERATOR
CONTROL HEAD FOR TURBINE BLADES
UPPER BRACKET
COLLECTOR
EXCITER
LOWER BRACKET ARM
GUIDE BEARING
BEARING COOLING COIL
THRUST BEARING

Fig. 3–3. Cutaway view of alternator and turbine. (Courtesy of Westinghouse Electric Corporation.)

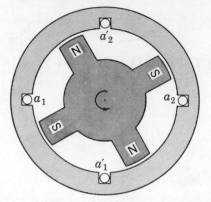

Fig. 3–4. Schematic of a four-pole single-phase salient-pole alternator.

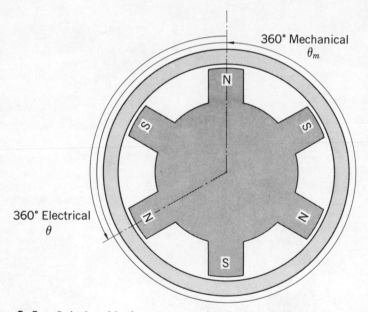

Fig. 3–5. Relationship between mechanical and electrical angles.

angle and θ_m a mechanical angle,

$$\theta = \theta_m \frac{P}{2} \qquad (3-2)$$

The rotors shown in Figs. 3–4 and 3–6 are said to be *salient-pole rotors* because the poles protrude from the periphery of the rotor.   Mechanically,

Fig. 3–6. Lowering a 590-ton salient-pole rotor into the stator of a 167,000-kva, 120-rpm, vertical waterwheel alternator. (Courtesy of Westinghouse Electric Corporation.)

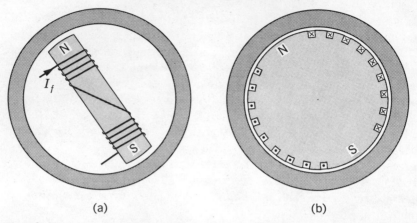

(a)   (b)

Fig. 3–7. (a) Two-pole salient rotor. (b) Two-pole non-salient, or cylindrical, rotor.

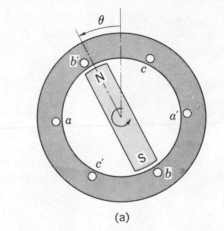

(a)

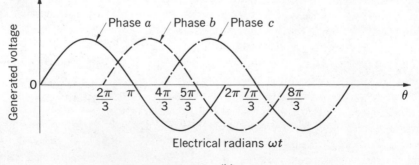

(b)

Fig. 3–8. (a) Cross-section of a basic three-phase alternator. (b) Voltage waveforms generated in the three phases.

this is usually unacceptable for two- or four-pole machines, whose high rotor speeds cause excessive centrifugal force. A non-salient, or cylindrical, rotor with the field winding embedded in peripheral slots, as shown in Fig. 3–7b, presents a more satisfactory mechanical design. However, magnetically, the cylindrical rotor is not as effective as the salient-pole rotor, since the individual magnetomotive forces produced by the peripheral coils are not unidirectional.

Most alternators generate three-phase power, that is, generate three separate alternating waveforms which are out of phase by 120 electrical degrees. Figure 3–8a shows the arrangement of the concentrated armature windings aa', bb', and cc' of a two-pole, three-phase alternator. The potentials induced in each of the three coils reach a maximum successively, as shown in Fig. 3–8b.

Three-phase power has advantages when compared with single-phase power. It is more economical to transmit using three wires, and provides a continuous rather than a pulsating source, since the instantaneous power is equal to the average power. Again, the consumer has a choice of voltages and may connect his equipment in wye or delta.

3–2. GENERATED VOLTAGE

As in the case of the d-c machine, the voltage induced in the windings of the synchronous machine is due to the relative motion between the magnetic field and the armature windings. In this section the voltage induced in one phase will be determined. Consider phase a of a P-pole alternator whose rotor is of effective length S and diameter d, as shown in Fig. 3–9a. The shaded region shows the projection onto the rotor of the area enclosed by the N-turn coil aa', whose pitch is π electrical radians. Figure 3–9b shows the sinusoidal rotor field flux-density distribution over 2π electrical radians on a developed diagram. It is assumed that at time $t = 0$, the axis of coil aa' and that of the north pole are coincident; then at time t the flux density wave has moved an angular distance ωt, where ω is the angular velocity in electrical radians/sec.

In order to calculate the voltage induced in coil aa', the instantaneous flux ϕ linking the coil must be evaluated.

Since there are P poles, the peripheral length between the opposite sides of a coil is $\pi d/P$; and since the axial length of the machine is S, the peripheral area enclosed by a coil is $\pi Sd/P$. Since the wave form of the flux density linking the coil aa' at time t is as shown in Fig. 3–9b, it is necessary to find the average value of the flux density linking the coil. This is

$$B_{av}(t) = \frac{1}{\pi} \int_{-\omega t}^{\pi - \omega t} B \sin \theta \, d\theta$$

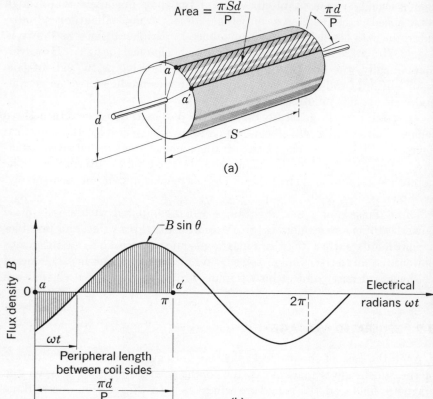

Fig. 3–9. (a) Schematic of rotor with shaded region showing area enclosed by coil aa', whose pitch is π electrical radians. (b) Developed flux density distribution over 2π electrical radians about the rotor pole face periphery, showing relative position of the coil aa' and the flux density wave after time t.

Therefore the flux linking the coil aa' at time t is

$$\phi(t) = \left(\frac{\pi Sd}{P}\right) B_{\mathrm{av}}(t) = \frac{\pi Sd}{P} \frac{1}{\pi} \int_{-\omega t}^{\pi - \omega t} B \sin \theta \, d\theta$$

$$= \frac{2SdB}{P} \cos \omega t = \Phi \cos \omega t \tag{3-3}$$

where

$$\Phi = \frac{2SdB}{P} \tag{3-4}$$

and is the total effective flux per pole. For an N-turn coil, the generated voltage is

$$e_g = N \frac{d\phi}{dt} \tag{3-5}$$

Substituting Eq. 3-3 in Eq. 3-5 gives

$$e_g = -\omega N\Phi \sin \omega t + N \frac{d\Phi}{dt} \cos \omega t \tag{3-6}$$

Under steady-state conditions the effective flux per pole is constant, and therefore the instantaneous voltage generated per phase is

$$e_g = -\omega N\Phi \sin \omega t \tag{3-7}$$

In the development of Eq. 3-7 it was assumed that the N turns of coil aa' were concentrated. However, in practice it is usual to distribute the winding through a number of adjacent slots in the stator. This results in a small decrease in the maximum generated voltage, since all the turns are no longer cut by the maximum flux at the same time. Therefore a winding distribution correction factor k_w is introduced. Consequently, for a distributed winding, the instantaneous voltage induced per phase is

$$e_g = -\omega k_w N\Phi \sin \omega t \tag{3-8}$$

The root-mean-square (rms) value of the voltage per phase is derived from

$$E_g = \frac{E_m}{\sqrt{2}}$$

where $E_m = \omega k_w N\Phi$ is the maximum value of the generated voltage per phase. Therefore, from Eq. 3-8,

$$E_g = \frac{\omega k_w N\Phi}{\sqrt{2}} = \frac{2\pi}{\sqrt{2}} f k_w N\Phi$$

Hence

$$E_g = 4.44 f k_w N\Phi \tag{3-9}$$

where f is the frequency of the generated voltage.

It is important to remember that Eq. 3-9 is an expression for the rms voltage generated *per phase*. In fact, it is common practice to work in terms of "per-phase" conditions whether the machine is single- or multiphase.

The winding distribution correction factor k_w may be determined by drawing a developed diagram of a section of the armature winding as in

Fig. 3–10a.   Consider phase a, which now has its N-turn winding distributed equally amongst four slots.   Since each of the other two phases also occupies four slots there are twelve slots within a space angle of 180° electrical, and therefore there is a space angle of 15° electrical between adjacent slots.   Since each winding is distributed, the voltages induced in

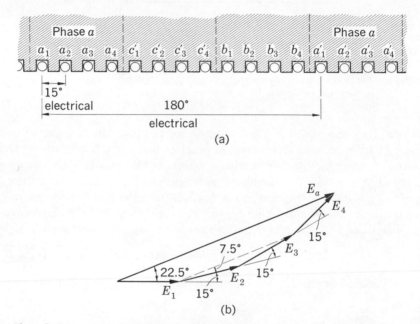

Fig. 3–10.   (a) Developed diagram of a distributed winding.   (b) Graphical sum of individual coil voltages.

a_1, a_2, a_3, and a_4 are each out of phase and the total voltage induced per phase is the vector sum of the separate voltages, E_1, E_2, E_3, E_4, induced in a_1, a_2, a_3, a_4, respectively.   The distribution correction factor for a four-slot distribution is defined as

$$k_w = \frac{|\mathbf{E}_1 + \mathbf{E}_2 + \mathbf{E}_3 + \mathbf{E}_4|}{E_1 + E_2 + E_3 + E_4} \qquad (3\text{--}10)$$

Figure 3–10b shows the graphical sum of $\mathbf{E}_1 + \mathbf{E}_2 + \mathbf{E}_3 + \mathbf{E}_4$.   For the particular case of a winding distributed over four slots, and $E_1 = E_2 = E_3 = E_4$,

$$k_w = \frac{2E_1(\cos 22.5° + \cos 7.5°)}{4E_1} = 0.958$$

3–3. EQUIVALENT CIRCUIT FOR A SYNCHRONOUS MACHINE

As in the case of the d-c machine, when drawing the equivalent circuit account is taken of the resistive and leakage reactive drop of the armature windings. Armature reaction must also be considered and in fact is a most significant factor.

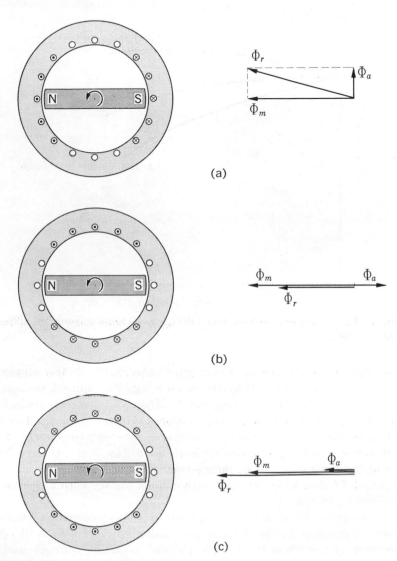

(a)

(b)

(c)

Fig. 3–11. Current distribution and flux phasor diagram for (a) unity power factor load; (b) zero lagging power factor load; (c) zero leading power factor load.

Consider the two-pole alternator of Fig. 3–11a, operating at a power factor of unity.   The current which flows in the armature is in phase with the generated voltage and produces an armature winding flux Φ_a which lags the main flux Φ_m by 90°.   The effect at unity power factor is therefore to cause the resultant flux Φ_r to lag the main flux.

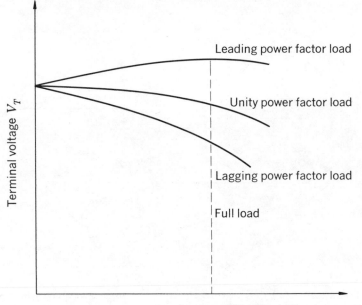

Fig. 3–12.   Variation of terminal voltage with load current for different power factors.

Consider the case of the alternator represented in Fig. 3–11b, supplying a purely inductive load.   Now the current lags the induced voltage by 90°, so that the armature winding flux Φ_a directly opposes the main flux. Therefore, armature reaction causes a decrease in the resultant flux and generated voltage as a lagging load current is increased; conversely, if the alternator is supplying a capacitive load, as in Fig. 3–11c, the resultant flux and the generated voltage increase as the load is increased.

Figure 3–12 shows the variation of terminal voltage with load current for different power factors.

To account for the rather complex effect of armature reaction, consider the phasor diagram in Fig. 3–13a for an inductive load. E_g is the generated voltage per phase at open circuit (the excitation voltage), and Φ_m is the flux per pole.   The fact that Φ_m leads E_g by 90° may be seen from Eqs. 3–3 and 3–7.   When the load is applied the lagging current I_a

produces an armature winding flux Φ_a in phase with itself. Thus the resultant flux is reduced to Φ_r and the generated voltage is reduced to E_r, where E_r lags Φ_r by 90°. The terminal voltage per phase V_T is found by

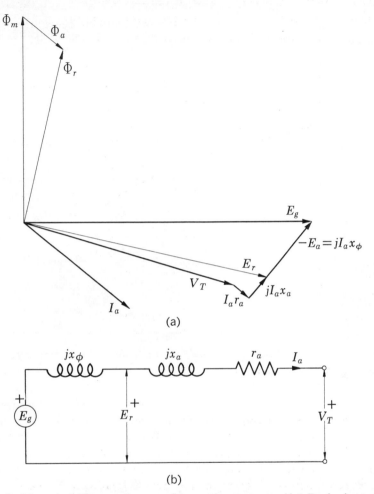

(a)

(b)

Fig. 3–13. (a) Phasor diagram for an alternator. (b) Equivalent circuit for one phase of an alternator.

subtracting the phasors jI_ax_a and I_ar_a from E_r, where x_a is the leakage reactance per phase and r_a is the winding resistance per phase.

In order to draw an equivalent circuit for the alternator, the effect of armature reaction must be represented. In other words, a circuit element must be incorporated which accounts for the phasor E_a. Such an element is an inductor with a reactance jx_ϕ carrying current I_a, as shown in Fig.

3–13b, where $jI_a x_\phi = -E_a$. The two inductive reactances jx_a and jx_ϕ are combined and the sum

$$\boxed{x_s = x_a + x_\phi} \tag{3–11}$$

is called the *synchronous reactance*. It is important to recognize that the synchronous reactance is only a convenient expression which accounts

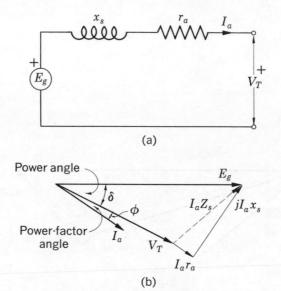

(a)

(b)

Fig. 3–14. (a) Equivalent circuit for one phase of an alternator. (b) Phasor diagram for an alternator.

for armature reaction effects and the leakage reactance of the armature winding. *Synchronous impedance* Z_s may be defined as

$$Z_s = r_a + jx_s \tag{3–12}$$

The equivalent circuit for one phase of a non-salient-pole alternator is shown in Fig. 3–14a, and the phasor diagram in Fig. 3–14b. The power-factor angle of the load is the angle between I_a and V_T, while the angle δ between V_T and E_g is called the *power angle*.

Example 3–1. A 20,000-kva, three-phase Y-connected alternator supplies a line-to-line voltage of 11,000 volts. The synchronous reactance and resistance per phase are 4.9 ohms and 0.68 ohm, respectively. If the rated voltage and current per phase are taken as base values, find the per-unit resistance and reactance of each phase.

Using per-unit quantities, find the no-load per-phase voltage E_g if the load is removed when the generator is delivering rated current at a lagging power factor of 0.8.

$$\text{base voltage per phase} = \frac{11,000}{\sqrt{3}} = 6350 \text{ volts}$$

$$\text{base current per phase} = \frac{(\text{rated kva per phase}) \times 1000}{\text{rated phase voltage}}$$

$$= \frac{20,000 \times 1000}{3 \times 6350} = 1050 \text{ amp}$$

$$\text{base ohm per phase} = \frac{\text{rated phase voltage}}{\text{rated phase current}}$$

$$= \tfrac{6350}{1050} = 6.05 \text{ ohms}$$

$$\text{per-unit resistance per phase} = \frac{\text{resistance per phase}}{\text{base ohm}} = \frac{0.68}{6.05} = 0.112$$

$$\text{per-unit reactance per phase} = \frac{\text{reactance per phase}}{\text{base ohm}} = \frac{4.90}{6.05} = 0.81$$

In per-unit quantities, with phasor I_a as reference,

$$V_T = 0.8 + j0.6$$
$$I_a = 1.00 + j0.00$$

Therefore from Fig. 3–15

$$E_g = V_T + I_a(r_a + jx_s)$$
$$= (0.8 + j0.6) + 1.00(0.112 + j0.81)$$
$$= 0.912 + j1.41$$

The rms value is

$$E_g = \sqrt{(0.912)^2 + (1.41)^2} = 1.68 \text{ per unit}$$
$$= 1.68 \times 6350 = 10,660/\underline{57°} \text{ volts}$$

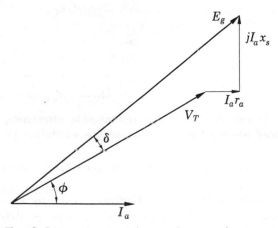

Fig. 3–15. Phasor diagram for an alternator.

The foregoing analysis is acceptable for non-salient-pole machines, where the variation of the air-gap reluctance about the periphery is negligible. However, in the case of salient-pole machines there is a significant difference between the reluctance of the air gap at a pole face and between poles. In order to account for this difference, the current I_a is divided

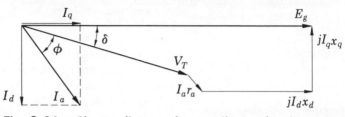

Fig. 3–16. Phasor diagram for a salient-pole alternator.

into two components: I_q, the *quadrature component*, which is in phase with E_g, and I_d, the *direct component*, which lags E_g by 90 electrical degrees. The synchronous reactance x_s is also split into two corresponding components x_q and x_d, the quadrature- and direct-axis synchronous reactances. As would be expected, due to the smaller air gap, the direct-axis reactance is in general greater than the quadrature-axis reactance. The phasor diagram for a salient-pole alternator is as shown in Fig. 3–16.

When using the phasor diagram of Fig. 3–16 the armature current I_a must be resolved into its components I_q and I_d. In order to do this it is assumed that the angle $(\phi + \delta)$ is known. But in many cases only the power factor, and hence ϕ, is explicitly known. However, based on the

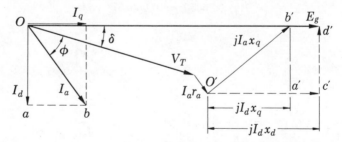

Fig. 3–17. Phasor diagram for a salient-pole alternator, showing construction required for the determination of the excitation phasor E_g.

geometric construction in Fig. 3–17 it is possible to derive the phasor diagram.

In order to complete the phasor diagram, assuming V_T, I_a, and ϕ are known, the angle δ and the magnitude of E_g must be determined. To evaluate δ, consider triangles Oab and $O'a'b'$. These triangles are similar since corresponding sides are perpendicular. Comparing Fig. 3–16 and Fig. 3–17, it is seen that the side $a'b'$ has to be jI_qx_q, and since triangles Oab and $O'a'b'$ are similar, side $O'b'$ is jI_ax_q. Since I_a and x_q are known, side $O'b'$ may be drawn, and Ob'determined. Again, since triangles Oab and $O'a'b'$ are similar, side $O'a'$ is jI_dx_q. But $O'c'$ is jI_dx_d. Therefore $a'c'$, or $b'd'$, is $jI_d(x_d - x_q)$. Therefore the magnitude of E_g is now known and the phasor diagram may be completed.

Example 3–2. The per-unit direct- and quadrature-synchronous reactances of a salient-pole alternator are 1.1 and 0.7 per phase, respectively, and the per-unit phase resistance is 0.05. Calculate the excitation voltage E_g when the alternator is operating under rated conditions and at a 0.8 lagging power factor.

Assuming V_T as reference

$$V_T = 1.00 + j0.00$$

and

$$I_a = 0.8 - j0.60$$

then

$$jI_ax_q = j(0.80 - j0.60)0.7 = 0.42 + j0.56$$

Therefore

$$\begin{aligned} Ob' &= V_T + I_ar_a + jI_ax_q \\ &= 1.00 + (0.80 - j0.60)(0.05) + 0.42 + j0.56 \\ &= 1.46 + j0.53 = 1.55\underline{/20°} \end{aligned}$$

Hence

$$\delta = 20°$$

and

$$\phi + \delta = 36.9° + 20° = 56.9°$$

The direct and quadrature components of the current may now be found:

$$I_d = 1.00 \sin 56.9°\underline{/20° - 90°} = 0.837\underline{/-70°}$$
$$I_q = 1.00 \cos 56.9°\underline{/20°} = 0.546\underline{/20°}$$

Therefore

$$E_g = ob' + jI_d(x_d - x_q) = 1.55\underline{/20°} + 0.837(1.1 - 0.7)\underline{/20°}$$
$$E_g = 1.885\underline{/20°}$$

3–4. STEADY-STATE POWER ANALYSIS

The output power per phase from an alternator is

$$P_0 = V_TI_a \cos \phi \tag{3 13}$$

In most cases the armature resistance is negligible compared to the synchronous reactance, so that for cylindrical-rotor alternators the phasor diagram may be drawn as in Fig. 3–18. The right-angle triangle $O'ab$ is added as construction so that Eq. 3 13 may be expressed in a more useful form.

From the geometry of Fig. 3–18, angle $aO'b = \phi$; therefore

$$O'b = I_a x_s \cos \phi = E_g \sin \delta$$

and so

$$I_a \cos \phi = \frac{E_g}{x_s} \sin \delta \qquad (3\text{--}14)$$

Substituting Eq. 3–14 in Eq. 3–13 gives

$$\boxed{P_0 = \frac{E_g V_T}{x_s} \sin \delta} \qquad (3\text{--}15)$$

It is apparent from Eq. 3–15 that for a certain excitation voltage E_g, the

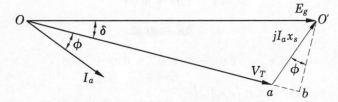

Fig. 3–18. Phasor diagram for a cylindrical rotor alternator when the resistance per phase is negligible.

maximum power per phase which the alternator can provide is

$$P_m = \frac{E_g V_T}{x_s} \qquad (3\text{--}16)$$

and maximum power is generated when $\delta = 90°$, that is, when the terminal voltage lags the excitation voltage by 90°. Any further power demand causes the alternator to slip a pole and consequently fall out of synchronism with the system.

Frequently it is convenient to include, with the synchronous reactance of the alternator, the impedance of the line and transformer bank to which the alternator is connected. If x_e is the effective reactance of the external line and V'_T is the terminal voltage at the end of the external circuit, the power delivered is

$$P = \frac{E_g V'_T}{x_e + x_s} \sin \delta' \qquad (3\text{--}17)$$

where δ' is the angle by which V'_T lags the excitation voltage E_g.

For the case of a salient-pole alternator, delivering power at voltage V'_T through a line of effective reactance x_e (Fig. 3–19a), the phasor diagram is shown in Fig. 3–19b.

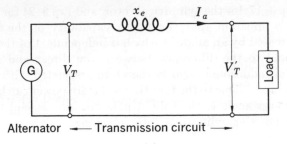

Alternator ⟵ Transmission circuit ⟶

(a)

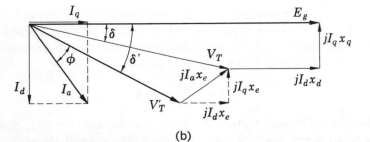

(b)

Fig. 3–19. (a) Alternator delivering power through a line of reactance x_e. (b) Phasor diagram for the alternator and line of Fig. 3–19a.

The power delivered per phase is

$$P = I_q V'_T \cos \delta' + I_d V'_T \sin \delta' \qquad (3\text{–}18)$$

From Fig. 3–19b,

$$I_q(x_e + x_q) = V'_T \sin \delta'$$

and

$$I_d(x_e + x_d) = E_g - V'_T \cos \delta'$$

so that

$$I_q = \frac{V'_T \sin \delta'}{x_e + x_q} \qquad (3\text{–}19)$$

and

$$I_d = \frac{E_g - V'_T \cos \delta'}{x_e + x_d} \qquad (3\text{–}20)$$

Substituting Eqs. 3–19 and 3–20 in Eq. 3–18 gives

$$P = V'^2_T \frac{\cos \delta' \sin \delta'}{x_e + x_q} - V'^2_T \frac{\cos \delta' \sin \delta'}{x_e + x_d} + \frac{E_g V'_T}{x_e + x_d} \sin \delta'$$

$$= \frac{E_g V'_T}{x_e + x_d} \sin \delta' + V'^2_T \frac{(x_d - x_q)}{2(x_e + x_q)(x_e + x_d)} \sin 2\delta' \qquad (3\text{–}21)$$

Comparing Eq. 3–17, for the cylindrical rotor, and Eq. 3–21 for the salient-pole rotor, it is apparent that the power capability of the salient-pole machine is increased by an amount which is independent of the excitation and proportional to the difference between the direct and quadrature reactance. This additional term is therefore associated with the simple reluctance machine. Due to the fact that a certain power can be delivered at a smaller power angle δ, the salient-pole machine is said to be *stiffer* than the corresponding cylindrical rotor machine.

3–5. CHARACTERISTIC CURVES

Some important relationships may be obtained by analysis of both the phasor diagram and the expression for generated power. Consider the simple cylindrical rotor machine in which armature resistance is negligible. The output power is given by Eq. 3–15 as

$$P_0 = \frac{E_g V_T}{x_s} \sin \delta$$

In general the terminal voltage V_T must remain constant and, since the synchronous reactance x_s is also constant, the magnitude of $E_g \sin \delta$ remains constant when the alternator is delivering a constant power. It is seen from Fig. 3–20a that, provided the phasor E_g moves along a locus ab parallel to V_T and spaced a distance $E_g \sin \delta$ from it, the output power remains constant. When the alternator is supplying a load at a specific power factor, the direction of $jI_a x_s$ is determined and so is the phasor E_g. Since the d-c field current I_f determines the magnitude of E_g, the curves in Fig. 3–20b show the variation of the armature current with the field current for different constant-power levels. These are called "V-curves." Also shown are the constant-power-factor curves.

Consider the case of the alternator delivering rated output power at unity power factor. In such a case $jI_a x_s$ is perpendicular to V_T. If the power factor becomes either leading or lagging and the output power is constant, then I_a must increase; hence the shape and name given to these curves. The limits imposed on the curves are those of zero output power, and the stability limit when $\delta = 90°$. The V-curves serve to correlate the output power, the output current, the power factor, and the field current.

In the case where the excitation current I_f is fixed, E_g is also fixed, so that the output power is governed by the magnitude of $\sin \delta$. Figure 3–21 shows the sinusoidal variation of output power with the power angle δ for different excitation levels. Maximum power is generated for $\delta = 90°$, and if more power is demanded then the alternator slips a pole and consequently falls out of phase with the system. In general, alternators are

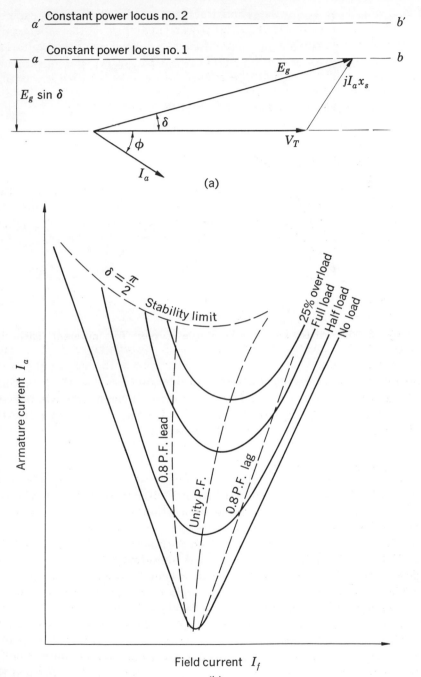

(a)

(b)

Fig. 3–20. (a) Phasor diagram, showing two constant-power loci, for an alternator. (b) Alternator V-curves.

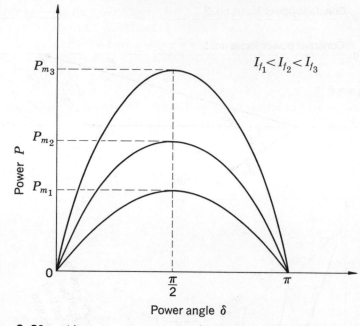

Fig. 3-21. Alternator power angle curves for different excitation levels.

operated at a power angle δ which is considerably less than the maximum, so that when a sudden demand for power arises it can be immediately and automatically supplied, and the additional demand does not cause the alternator to fall out of phase with the system.

3-6. DYNAMIC RESPONSE

From the considerations in Art. 3–5 it is obvious that the behavior of a synchronous machine under transient conditions is important when choosing a safe power angle at which to operate. The choice of such an angle of course depends on the type of load on the machine. If the load remains almost constant and any change in load is gradual then δ_∞, the operating power angle, may be quite large. However, if large and sudden load changes occur, then a considerable margin of stability must be provided and δ_∞ must be maintained at a low level.

When additional load is suddenly applied the rotor decelerates briefly so that the power angle may increase. During the period of deceleration the inertial energy of the rotor supplies a considerable amount of power to the system. However, when the required power angle is reached the rotor is decelerating and overshoots. As a result the rotor oscillates about the new power angle, providing the dynamic stability limit is not exceeded during the overshoot. In order to curtail such oscillation short-circuited copper bars are often inserted in the pole faces. The large currents induced in these bars during periods of oscillation are in such a direction that motion is opposed and so damping is provided.

In order to estimate the maximum swing of the power angle, which may be tolerated under transient conditions, consider the simple case of an

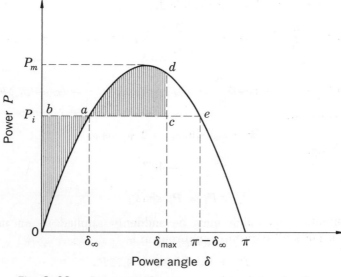

Fig. 3–22. Power angle curve used to determine δ_{max}.

alternator, with negligible damping, connected to a large system. Figure 3–22 shows the appropriate power angle curve. Assume the alternator is initially unloaded and a load P_i is suddenly applied. To take up the load the rotor must decelerate until the power angle becomes δ_∞. During this time, however, the applied load requires a power P_i which is at all times greater than that which the machine can develop electromagnetically. The energy deficiency, represented by the shaded area Oab, is provided by the inertial energy of the rotor while decelerating. (Since the speed is usually within 1 percent of the synchronous speed, even under severe transient conditions, it is acceptable to consider the power proportional to the developed torque and, since energy = $\int T \, d\delta$, the shaded area is proportional to energy.) Since the rotor is still decelerating when the power angle δ_∞ is reached, it continues to swing until the inertial energy deficiency is supplied. This energy is represented by area acd. Therefore the maximum swing of the power angle, δ_{max}, is given by the point at which area acd equals area Oab.

The maximum load which may be suddenly applied is determined by letting P_i increase until the area Oab is equal to the area ade. If a large load is applied, then area Oab is greater than area ade and it is not possible to return to the rotor all of the inertial energy which it lost, and the rotor fails to reach synchronous speed and falls out of phase with the system.

The maximum load which may suddenly be applied to an unloaded synchronous machine, when damping is negligible, will now be determined. If the power angle curve is represented by $P_m \sin \delta$, then for area Oab to equal area ade, the following must hold:

$$\delta_\infty P_i - \int_0^{\delta_\infty} P_m \sin \delta \, d\delta = \int_{\delta_\infty}^{\pi - \delta_\infty} P_m \sin \delta \, d\delta - P_i(\pi - 2\delta_\infty)$$

$$(3\text{--}22)$$

$$\delta_\infty P_m \sin \delta_\infty - P_m \left| \begin{matrix} \delta_\infty \\ \end{matrix} - \cos \delta \right|_0^{\delta_\infty} = P_m \left| \begin{matrix} \pi - \delta_\infty \\ \end{matrix} - \cos \delta \right|_{\delta_\infty}^{\pi - \delta_\infty} - (\pi - 2\delta_\infty) P_m \sin \delta_\infty$$

which reduces to

$$(\pi - \delta_\infty) \sin \delta_\infty = 1 + \cos \delta_\infty$$

Upon solving,

$$\delta_\infty = 46°$$

and since

$$P_i = P_m \sin \delta_\infty$$

the maximum load which may be suddenly applied to an unloaded alternator and still maintain synchronism is

$$P_i = P_m \sin 46° = 0.72 P_m \qquad (3\text{--}23)$$

The foregoing analysis may of course be modified for a machine which is already loaded when the additional load is suddenly applied.

The foregoing analysis is especially suited to a situation where the change in power angle is large and where the effective damping is negligible. In many cases, however, neither of the above conditions apply and the following linearized analysis is more appropriate.

At any particular instant the mechanical power P_r delivered to an alternator must be equal to the electromagnetic power developed, plus the power required to overcome inertia, plus the power dissipated in the damping system. Therefore

$$\boxed{P_r = P_m \sin \delta + P_j \frac{d^2\delta}{dt^2} + P_d \frac{d\delta}{dt}} \qquad (3\text{--}24)$$

where P_m is the maximum power generated when $\delta = \pi/2$, P_j is the power required to give one unit of acceleration to the rotor, and so

$$P_j = \frac{2}{\text{number of poles}} \frac{2\pi\mathfrak{N}}{60} J \text{ watt-sec}^2/\text{elect. radian}$$

where J is the inertia of the rotor in kg-m^2 and $\mathfrak{N}$ is the rotor speed in rpm. P_d is the power dissipated when the rotor speed departs from synchronous speed by one unit. In Eq. 3–24 the second term is called the *synchronous power* and the fourth term, the *damping power*.

When the variation of δ is within ± 30 electrical degrees $P_m \sin \delta$ may be approximated by $P_s \delta$, where P_s is called the *synchronizing power* and is equal to the slope of the power-angle curve at the origin. With the use of this approximation Eq. 3–24 becomes

$$P_j \frac{d^2\delta}{dt^2} + P_d \frac{d\delta}{dt} + P_s\delta = P_r \qquad (3\text{--}25)$$

Equation 3–25 is a linear second-order differential equation and associated with a damped oscillatory system where the driving function is P_r. The standard procedure in solving for δ is to rearrange the equation and substitute quantities having physical significance, namely: ω_n, the *undamped natural frequency*, and ξ, the *damping ratio*. Prior to solution for the instantaneous power angle it is apparent that under steady-state conditions the first two terms are zero, so that the steady-state power angle is

$$\delta_\infty = \frac{P_r}{P_s} \qquad (3\text{--}26)$$

The *complementary function*, which yields the transient part of the solution, is then

$$\frac{d^2\delta}{dt^2} + \frac{P_d}{P_j}\frac{d\delta}{dt} + \frac{P_s}{P_j}\delta = 0 \qquad (3\text{--}27)$$

where the constant term P_r is removed and Eq. 3–25 is divided by P_j. Substituting

$$\omega_n{}^2 = \frac{P_s}{P_j} \qquad (3\text{--}28)$$

and

$$\xi = \frac{P_d}{2\sqrt{P_j P_s}} \qquad (3\text{--}29)$$

in Eq. 3–27 gives

$$\frac{d^2\delta}{dt^2} + 2\xi\omega_n\frac{d\delta}{dt} + \omega_n{}^2\delta = 0 \qquad (3\text{--}30)$$

The characteristic equation for Eq. 3–30 is

$$m^2 + 2\xi\omega_n m + \omega_n{}^2 = 0 \qquad (3\text{--}31)$$

Equation 3–31 has roots

$$m_1, m_2 = -\xi\omega_n \pm \omega_n\sqrt{\xi^2 - 1} = -\xi\omega_n \pm j\omega_d$$

where $\omega_d = \omega_n \sqrt{1 - \xi^2}$.   Therefore the complete solution is

$$\delta(t) = \delta_\infty + C_1 e^{m_1 t} + C_2 e^{m_2 t}$$ (3–32)

where C_1 and C_2 are constants.

The nature of the solution is governed by the value of the damping ratio ξ.   If $\xi = 1$, then the machine is said to be *critically damped* and the variation of δ is exponential.   However, if $\xi < 1$ damped oscillations occur, and the machine is *underdamped*.   In this case, and when $\delta_\infty \neq 0$, the form of the solution is $\delta = \delta_\infty[1 + C_3 e^{-\xi \omega_n t} \sin (\omega_d t + \alpha)]$ where C_3 and α are constants which may be determined from the initial conditions, e.g., from $\delta(0) = 0$ and $d\delta(0)/dt = 0$.   When $\xi > 1$ no oscillations occur and the machine is *overdamped*.

In many cases only the undamped natural frequency of oscillation given by Eq. 3–28 and the damping ratio given by Eq. 3–29 may be required. The fact that the frequency of oscillation for an underdamped system, as derived from Eq. 3–32, is

$$\omega_d = \omega_n \sqrt{1 - \xi^2}$$ (3–33)

may also be of interest in certain cases.

3–7. BLOCK DIAGRAM REPRESENTATION

As in the case of the d-c machine, it is sometimes convenient to represent the synchronous machine by a block diagram, or analog computer circuit.   Such a representation may be required, for example, when a mathematical transient response analysis proves cumbersome, or when the synchronous machine is part of a larger system which is to be represented on an analog computer.

In order to develop the block diagram it is convenient to resolve the terminal phase voltage into components V_d and V_q, in phase with I_d and I_q, respectively, as shown in Fig. 3–23.   Resistance is assumed negligible and in order to represent the frequency f the reactances x_d and x_q are

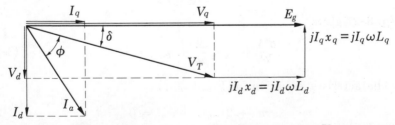

Fig. 3–23. Phasor diagram for an alternator, showing V_T resolved into direct and quadrature components.

written as ωL_d and ωL_q, where L_d and L_q are the *direct* and *quadrature inductances*, respectively. The excitation voltage is likewise expressed as $M\omega i_f$, where M is the maximum value of the mutual inductance between a stator phase winding and the field winding. Consequently, based on Fig. 3–23, the instantaneous voltage equations, for an alternator with a balanced three-phase load, may be written as

$$v_d = \omega L_q i_q \qquad (3\text{--}34)$$
$$v_q = \omega M i_f - \omega L_d i_d \qquad (3\text{--}35)$$

If v_f is the instantaneous voltage applied to the field and r_f and L_f are the field resistance and leakage inductance, respectively, then

$$v_f = r_f i_f + L_f p i_f - \tfrac{3}{2} M p i_d \qquad (3\text{--}36)$$

where it can be shown that the total voltage induced in the field winding

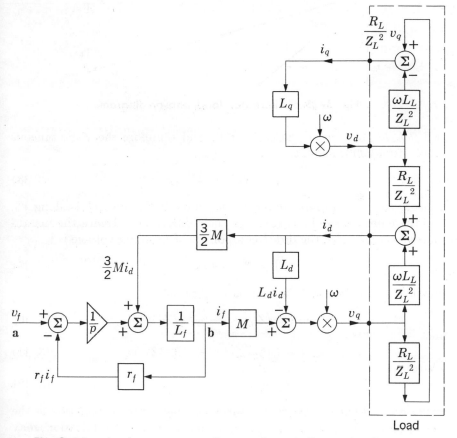

Load

Fig. 3–24. Analog computer diagram for a salient-pole alternator.

by the resultant flux of the three-phase armature winding is $-\frac{3}{2}Mpi_d$, and p is the differential operator d/dt.

Dividing Eq. 3–36 by p and rearranging gives

$$L_f i_f - \frac{3}{2} M i_d = \frac{1}{p}(v_f - r_f i_f) \qquad (3\text{--}37)$$

which enables the construction of part **ab** of the analog computer diagram in Fig. 3–24. The remainder of the alternator diagram may be completed using Eqs. 3–35 and 3–34.

The load, of resistance R_L and reactance ωL_L, must be represented in a form consistent with the direct and quadrature nature of the alternator output. Consider the load phasor diagram of Fig. 3–25. Phasors $R_L I_q$

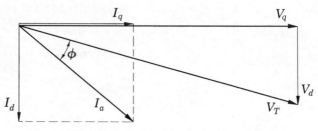

Fig. 3–25. Alternator load phasor diagram.

and $j\omega L_L I_d$ must be in phase along V_q and therefore the instantaneous quadrature voltage equation is

$$v_q = R_L i_q + \omega L_L i_d \qquad (3\text{--}38)$$

Phasors $R_L I_d$ and $jI_q\omega L_L$ are out of phase by 180°; but each is along V_d, and therefore phasor V_d is equal to their difference. Hence the instantaneous equation for the direct component of terminal voltage is

$$v_d = R_L i_d - \omega L_L i_q \qquad (3\text{--}39)$$

Solving Eqs. 3–38 and 3–39 for i_d and i_q gives

$$i_d = (R_L/Z_L{}^2)v_d + (\omega L_L/Z_L{}^2)v_q \qquad (3\text{--}40)$$

and

$$i_q = -(\omega L_L/Z_L{}^2)v_d + (R_L/Z_L{}^2)v_q \qquad (3\text{--}41)$$

where

$$Z_L{}^2 = R_L{}^2 + (\omega L_L)^2 \qquad (3\text{--}42)$$

Equations 3–40 and 3–41 are in a form suitable for the completion of the analog computer diagram for a synchronous machine. Modifications may be made to account for resistance and other conditions of operation.

3–8. THE POLYPHASE SYNCHRONOUS MOTOR

The polyphase synchronous motor may be considered as a machine of rather particularized application.   However, due to its distinctive characteristics, it is an important electromechanical device.

Consider the three-phase synchronous motor whose cross-section is represented in Fig. 3–26a.   The form of the motor is the same as that of the alternator.   An insight into its operation may best be obtained by considering the nature of the magnetic field produced when the balanced three-phase supply shown in Fig. 3–26b is connected to the armature

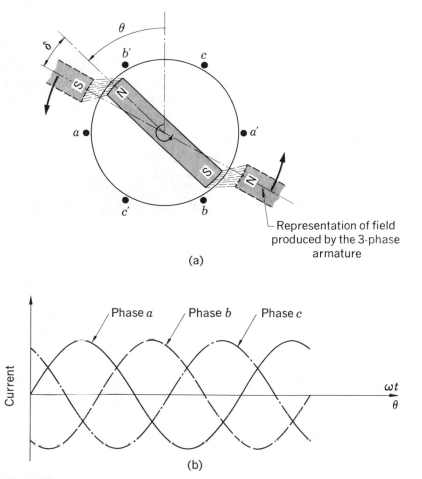

Representation of field produced by the 3-phase armature

(a)

(b)

Fig. 3–26.   (a) Schematic of a three-phase synchronous motor, with the field produced by the armature represented by the outer poles.   (b) Armature current waveforms.

windings. The objective of the following analysis, therefore, is to determine an expression for the mmf (which is produced by the three-phase currents flowing in the three windings) as a function of time t and angular location θ about the periphery of the stator.

Let the peak mmf produced along the axis of coil aa' at time t be

$$F_{ap}(t) = F_m \cos \omega t \tag{3-43}$$

where F_m is the maximum mmf produced per phase at time $t = 0$. Since the currents in the other coils are out of time-phase with that in coil aa', the peak mmf's of coils bb' and cc' are respectively

$$F_{bp}(t) = F_m \cos (\omega t - 120°) \tag{3-44}$$

and

$$F_{cp}(t) = F_m \cos (\omega t - 240°) \tag{3-45}$$

The peak mmf produced in each of the three coils is directed along the coil axis. Therefore the total resultant mmf $F(\theta,t)$ at some angle θ is found by summing the mmf components in the θ direction, as follows:

$$
\begin{aligned}
F(\theta,t) = {} & F_{ap}(t) \cos \theta + F_{bp}(t) \cos (\theta - 120°) + F_{cp}(t) \cos (\theta - 240°) \\
= {} & F_m \cos \omega t \cos \theta + F_m \cos (\omega t - 120°) \cos (\theta - 120°) \\
& + F_m \cos (\omega t - 240°) \cos (\theta - 240°) \quad (3\text{-}46) \\
= {} & \tfrac{1}{2}F_m \cos (\theta - \omega t) + \tfrac{1}{2}F_m \cos (\theta + \omega t) \\
& + \tfrac{1}{2}F_m \cos (\theta - \omega t) + \tfrac{1}{2}F_m \cos (\theta + \omega t - 240°) \\
& + \tfrac{1}{2}F_m \cos (\theta - \omega t) + \tfrac{1}{2}F_m \cos (\theta + \omega t - 480°)
\end{aligned}
$$

Therefore

$$\boxed{F(\theta,t) = \tfrac{3}{2}F_m \cos (\theta - \omega t)} \tag{3-47}$$

since the sum of the three terms containing $(\theta + \omega t)$ is zero. Therefore when balanced three-phase a-c current is supplied to three windings, which are displaced in space by 120 electrical degrees, a resultant mmf is produced which rotates at synchronous speed and has a constant maximum value equal in magnitude to three-halves the maximum mmf of a single phase. An equivalent effect is produced by the actual physical rotation of the synchronous motor rotor field. Under operating conditions, therefore, the rotor field locks with the field produced by the armature and both rotate at synchronous speed. The armature field is represented in Fig. 3–26a by the broken lines.

Under no-load conditions the axes of corresponding rotor and armature poles are coincident. As the motor is loaded the rotor field lags the armature field by an electrical angle δ, called the *torque angle* (corresponding to the power angle in the case of the alternator). The non-salient-pole motor delivers maximum torque when $\delta = 90$ electrical degrees.

Since the physical forms of a synchronous motor and alternator are basically the same, the analytical procedures developed for the alternator may be applied to the synchronous motor. Equation 3–1, which relates speed and frequency, holds, as does Eq. 3–9 for the excitation voltage E_g. In the case of the motor, E_g is the induced voltage which opposes the applied voltage V_T. The phasor difference is given by the phasor voltage drop across the resistance and synchronous reactance of the machine. Since in general the speed requirements of synchronous motors are low (compared to the 3600 rpm associated with a 60-cycle, two-pole motor), most have salient multipole rotors, and therefore both direct- and

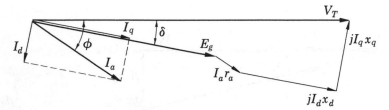

Fig. 3–27. Phasor diagram for a salient-pole synchronous motor.

quadrature-axis synchronous reactance must be accounted for. Figure 3–27 shows the phasor diagram of a salient-pole motor for which the phasor voltage equation is

$$V_T = E_g + I_a r_a + j(I_d x_d + I_q x_q) \qquad (3\text{–}48)$$

As in the case of the alternator, the resistance is generally negligible compared to the synchronous reactance, and the expression for power is derived as in Art. 3–4. Hence the output power for a cylindrical rotor synchronous motor is

$$P_0 = \frac{E_g V_T}{x_s} \sin \delta \qquad (3\text{–}49)$$

and for a salient-pole machine

$$P_0 = \frac{E_g V_T}{x_d} \sin \delta + V_T^2 \left(\frac{x_d - x_q}{2 x_d x_q}\right) \sin 2\delta \qquad (3\text{–}50)$$

where δ is called the *torque angle*. Equations 3–49 and 3–50 may be written as torque equations since the speed is constant and $P_0 = \omega_s T$, where T is the torque developed and ω_s is the mechanical synchronous speed in radians per second.

V-curves are also used to represent the relationship between excitation current, armature current, load, and power factor. The form of the V-curves for a synchronous motor is the same as for the alternator. However, the load refered to in Fig. 3–20b may now be considered as the mechanical shaft load and may be expressed in terms of output torque or power.

Example 3–3. A 3000-hp, 28-pole, 4000-volt, 3-phase, Y-connected synchronous motor is operating at unity power factor. The direct- and quadrature-axis reactances are 3.9 and 2.75 ohms, respectively. Neglecting resistance, determine the maximum output torque.

This problem is similar to that considered in the case of the alternator where the excitation voltage E_g is not explicitly known and must be evaluated from a knowledge of the phasor relationships.

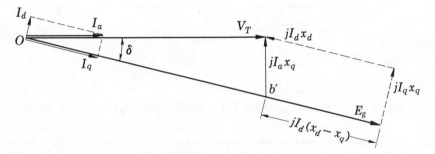

Fig. 3–28. Indirect determination of the phasor diagram for a synchronous motor.

The phasor diagram of Fig. 3–28 is similar to that for the alternator in Fig. 3–16. The torque angle may be determined from the phasor sum of V_T and $-jI_a x_q$.

$$I_a = \frac{3000 \times 746}{3 \times 2310} = 323 \text{ amp}$$

and

$$\begin{aligned} ob' &= V_T - jI_a x_q \\ &= 2310 - j323 \times 2.75 = 2310 - j890 \end{aligned}$$

Therefore

$$\delta = \tan^{-1}\frac{-890}{2310} = \tan^{-1} -0.385 = -21.1°$$

Therefore

$$I_d = 323 \sin 21.1°\underline{/90° - 21.1°} = 116\underline{/68.9°}$$

From Fig. 3–28

$$|E_g| = |ob'| + |I_d(x_d - x_q)|$$

Therefore

$$\begin{aligned} E_g &= [(2310^2 + 890^2)^{½} + 116(3.9 - 2.75)]\underline{/-21.1°} \\ &= 2614\underline{/-21.1°} \text{ volts} \end{aligned}$$

Maximum torque is produced at maximum output power and therefore Eq. 3–50 must be optimized with respect to δ, giving

$$\delta_{opt} = \cos^{-1}\left\{ -\frac{A}{8B} \pm \sqrt{\left(\frac{A}{8B}\right)^2 + \frac{1}{2}} \right\}$$

where

$$A = \frac{E_o V_T}{x_d} \qquad B = V_{T^2}\left(\frac{x_d - x_q}{2x_d x_q}\right)$$

Therefore

$$A = \frac{2614 \times 2310}{3.9} = 1.55 \times 10^6$$

and

$$B = \frac{(2310)^2 \times 1.15}{2 \times 3.9 \times 2.75} = 0.285 \times 10^6$$

Therefore

$$\delta_{opt} = \cos^{-1}(-0.68 \pm 0.98) = 72.6°$$

Hence

$$P_{max} = A \sin \delta_{opt} + B \sin 2\delta_{opt}$$
$$= 1.55 \times 10^6 \sin 72.6° + 0.285 \times 10^6 \sin 145.2°$$
$$= 1.64 \text{ megawatts per phase}$$

Since

$$\omega_{mech} = 2\pi n = 2\pi f \frac{2}{P} = \frac{2\pi 60}{14} = 26.9 \text{ rad/sec}$$

$$T_{max} = \frac{P_{max}}{\omega_{mech}} = \frac{1.64 \times 10^6}{26.9}$$
$$= 61 \times 10^3 \text{ newton-m per phase}$$

Therefore the total maximum output torque is $61 \times 3 \times 10^3$ or 0.183×10^6 newton-m.

The synchronous motor, being inherently a constant-speed machine, obviously presents problems when starting it is considered. If the stator and rotor windings are energized, while the rotor is at standstill, then the rotating field of the armature, sweeping past the rotor at synchronous speed, at one instant exerts a starting torque, but half an electrical cycle later exerts a torque of equal and opposite magnitude. As a result the time-average torque is zero and the rotor remains at standstill. This inherent starting problem, associated with synchronous motors, is overcome by utilizing the starting properties of other motors. For example, it may be convenient, in the case of a large synchronous motor, to use an auxiliary d-c motor, or induction motor, for starting purposes. However, the most common approach is to make the synchronous motor self-starting by incorporating short-circuited conductors about the periphery of the rotor and utilizing the starting properties of the squirrel-cage induction motor. The rotor can be brought to within a few percent of synchronous speed in this way, and when the rotor field is excited the motor *pulls into step*. The starting windings also serve to damp out the rotor oscillations which tend to occur when the load is changed.

Since the synchronous motor is inherently not self-starting, it is obviously best suited to continuous operation where large quantities of power are required at constant speed.   An important feature of the synchronous motor is its ability to draw power from the supply at leading, lagging, or

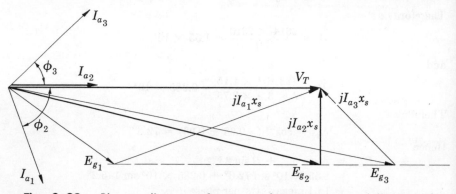

Fig. 3–29. Phasor diagrams for a synchronous motor delivering the same quantity of power at lagging, unity, and leading power factors.

unity power factor, as shown in Fig. 3–29.   Frequently, unloaded synchronous motors, excited to operate at a leading power factor, are incorporated in a system to compensate for the lagging power factor associated with induction motors and transformers, and so improve the overall power factor.   When a synchronous motor is used for power-factor correction exclusively, it is called a *synchronous condenser*.

The transient analysis developed for the alternator may be directly applied in the case of the synchronous motor.   The motor load is in general expressed in terms of torque or power, but since losses are neglected in the transient analysis, and the speed is at all times close to synchronous, a power-angle curve similar to that in Fig. 3–22 may be used for establishing stability criteria.   Expressions for rotor oscillation, torque, and power fluctuation may be derived from Eq. 3–25 in a manner similar to that discussed in Art. 3–6.

PROBLEMS

3–1. Calculate the rotor speed of the following alternators:

    a. 10 poles, 25 cps.
    b. 6 poles, 50 cps.
    c. 48 poles, 60 cps.

3-2. Three 50-cps alternators have the following speeds: 428, 750, 1000 rpm. How many poles has each?

3-3. Through how many mechanical degrees must the rotor of a 24-pole alternator rotate in order to generate 7 complete electrical cycles?

3-4. A 3-phase, 4-pole alternator has a 5-slot distributed winding with 2 conductors in each slot. All the conductors in each phase are connected in series, and the phases are then Y-connected, as shown in Fig. P3-4. The flux per pole

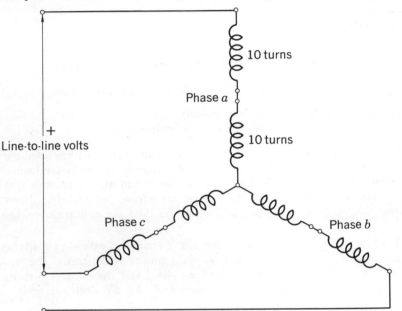

Fig. P3-4. Coil connection circuit of the alternator in Prob. 3-4.

is 0.25 weber and is sinusoidally distributed in space. If the rotor speed is 1500 rpm, find

a. The maximum voltage generated per phase.

b. The rms line-to-line voltage.

c. A consistent set of voltage equation for each phase, if it is assumed that the voltage induced in phase a is a maximum at time $t = 0$, and the phase sequence is abc.

d. A set of line-to-line voltage equations consistent with the phase equations derived in (c).

3-5. An 8-pole, 3-phase, 60-cps alternator has a Y-connected armature whose effective winding distribution factor $k_w = 0.95$. Each coil has 3 turns and the 4 coils associated with each phase are connected in series. The effective resistance of the field winding is 11 ohms, and the flux produced per pole may be taken as 0.03 times the field current. If the switch in the field circuit is closed at time $t = 0$, and a d-c voltage of 110 volts is applied to the field, what is the effective inductance of the field if the instantaneous generated voltage is at 0.5 of its steady state rms phase value at time $t = 0.0625$ sec?

3–6. A 3000-kva, 3-phase, 2-pole, 60-cps, Y-connected alternator has a rated line-to-line voltage of 6600 volts, rms. The resistance and synchronous reactance of each phase are 2.03 and 13.8 ohms, respectively. Determine the excitation voltage E_g required to develop rated terminal voltage and rated current when the power factor of the load is

    a. 0.7 lagging.
    b. Unity.
    c. 0.7 leading.

Use per-unit quantities and draw the phasor diagram in each case.

3–7. Draw the phasor diagram for a salient-pole alternator when

    a. The power factor of the load is unity.
    b. The power factor of the load is 0.8 leading.

3–8. A salient-pole, 800-kva, delta-connected alternator delivers rated current at the rated voltage of 2300 volts to a 0.9 leading power factor load. The resistance per phase is 1.65 ohms and the direct- and quadrature-axis synchronous reactances are 15.3 and 13.2 ohms per phase, respectively. Draw the phasor diagram, and using per-unit quantities, find the excitation voltage per phase.

3–9. The following parameters refer to a Y-connected salient-pole alternator: negligible armature resistance, $x_d = 45$ ohms, and $x_q = 30$ ohms. The terminal bus voltage $\sqrt{3}\, V_T = 13,600$ volts, line-to-line, and the per-phase excitation voltage is $E_g = 11,400$ volts. If the power angle δ is 25° electrical, find

    a. The power delivered to the load.
    b. The magnitude of the load current and the power factor.

3–10. For the alternator described in Prob. 3–8, determine the total output power to the load. If the terminal and excitation voltage remain constant, find the power angle δ at which the alternator supplies maximum power to the load, and also the maximum power supplied.

3–11. A salient-pole, Y-connected, 3-phase alternator delivers power to a load through two similar transmission circuits in parallel. The reactance per phase of each transmission circuit is 0.65 per unit and the direct- and quadrature-synchronous reactances per phase of the alternator are 1.00 and 0.70 per unit, respectively. All resistances are negligible. The phase voltage at the load end of the transmission circuits is 1.00 per unit. The excitation voltage per phase is 1.7 per unit and δ' is 30° electrical. What is the per unit power delivered to the load? What is the maximum power which could be delivered?

3–12. A cylindrical rotor alternator is delivering power to a load through a transmission circuit for which the steady-state overall power angle δ'_∞ is 20° electrical. What additional load may be suddenly applied without causing the alternator to fall out of phase? Give your answer in terms of an initial 1.00 per unit load.

3-13. A 300-kva, 4000-volt, 3-phase, 60-cps, Y-connected, 24-pole alternator is running unloaded at synchronous speed. The inertia of the rotor system is 600 kg-m², the synchronizing power is 18,000 watts/electrical degree, and the damping torque is 3400 newton-m-sec/mechanical radian. At time $t = 0$ the rated load of 300 kw is suddenly applied. Find

a. The natural frequency of oscillation.
b. The damping ratio and the damped frequency.
c. The power angle δ as a function of time.

3-14. A 50-cps, 3-phase, 36-pole alternator is to be synchronized with a large system. If, however, the magnitude and phase of the alternator voltage differ from that of the system, large transient power surges occur, as well as rotor oscillation. When synchronizing the above alternator the terminal voltage is adjusted to the correct value, so that the steady-state power would be zero, and the rotor is at synchronous speed, but the alternator voltage leads that of the system by 17° electrical. Determine an expression for the rotor oscillations as a function of time. The effective inertia of the rotating system is 0.5×10^5 kg-m², the synchronizing power is 2.1×10^5 watts/electrical degree and the damping power is 5.1×10^3 watt-sec/electrical degree.

3-15. Assuming the losses are negligible, determine an expression for the transient power surge between the alternator and system under the conditions described in Prob. 3-14. Also determine the transient output torque from the prime mover as a function of time.

3-16. If the alternator described in Prob. 3-14 is running 15 percent above synchronous speed, in addition to being out of phase by 17° electrical with the system, determine an expression for the surge of power between the alternator and the system as a function of time. Find the maximum value of the power angle.

3-17. Figure P3-17 shows the circuit diagram of an alternator whose terminal voltage is controlled by a feedback loop. The output voltage is rectified by means of a linear rectifier whose constant is k_r volts direct-current, per a-c volt, and the rectified voltage e_r is subtracted from a fixed voltage E_0. The difference is amplified by a linear amplifier with a voltage gain A, the output of which feeds

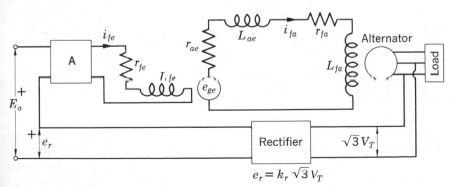

$$e_r = k_r \sqrt{3}\, V_T$$

Fig. P3-17. Alternator with terminal voltage control.

the field of the d-c exciter.   The output of the d-c exciter in turn feeds the field of the alternator.   Using standard notation, and assuming a linear relationship between field current and induced voltage, draw an analog computer diagram for the complete system, assuming the alternator is a salient-pole machine.

3–18. A 3000-kva, 3-phase, Y-connected, 2300-volt synchronous motor has per-phase armature resistance of 0.05 per unit and direct- and quadrature reactances of 0.95 and 0.6 ohm per unit respectively.   Find the per-phase excitation voltage for rated kva load at a lagging power factor of 0.8.

3–19. The rated output of a 440-volt, 6-pole, Y-connected, 3-phase, 60-cycle synchronous motor is 200 hp.   Assuming resistance is negligible and the machine may be treated as a cylindrical rotor motor with a synchronous reactance of 0.4 ohm per phase, operating at a leading power factor of 0.9, find the armature current when the motor is driving a load which requires a constant torque of 950 newton-m.   Also find the excitation voltage required for the motor to operate at a power factor of 0.9 leading.

3–20. A synchronous motor delivers power to a constant load of 1.0 per unit. The excitation voltage may be increased to 1.6 per unit, and the terminal voltage is assumed constant.   If the synchronous reactance of the machine is 0.9 per unit per-phase and losses may be assumed negligible, what are the limits imposed on the values of the leading and lagging power factors?   At both limits of power factor, find the per unit value of the armature current.

3–21. A 14-pole synchronous motor is rated at 1300 hp when operating from a 4000-volt, 3-phase, 60-cycle supply.   The motor is Y-connected, the effective synchronous reactance may be taken at 2.2 ohms per phase, and resistance is assumed negligible.   The rotational losses of the motor are 28 kw.

    a. If the per-phase excitation voltage is set at 2200 volts when the load is 1300 hp, what is the motor current and power factor?

    b. What is the current and power factor when $E_g = 2400$ volts and the load is 1300 hp?

3–22. A 4000-volt, 400-hp, 3-phase, 60-cps, 26-pole, Y-connected synchronous motor is operating in the steady state, but unloaded.   At time $t = 0$ the rated load is suddenly coupled to the motor shaft.   The inertia power of the rotating system is 35×10^3 watt-sec^2/electrical degree, the synchronizing power is 20 kw/electrical degree, and the damping power is 150 watt-sec/electrical degree. Find an expression for the transient oscillation of the rotor, and (assuming negligible losses) find the power supplied to the motor during the transient period. What is the minimum amount of additional damping required to prevent oscillation of the rotor?

3–23. If the expression for the power-angle curve of the motor described in Prob. 3–22 is given by $1141 \sin \delta$ kw, what is the maximum value of the power angle attained after a constant load of 10,000 hp is applied to the unloaded motor for a period of 1.75 sec?   Damping may be neglected when calculating the maximum value of δ.

3–24. The total input power to a plant is 490 kw at 2300 volts. The power factor is lagging at 0.7 and a synchronous condenser is to be installed to improve the overall power factor to 0.9 lag. Find the rating of the required machine in kvar.

3–25. A 200-hp, 3-phase, 60-cps, self-starting synchronous motor has a squirrel-cage winding which is used to bring the rotor speed to within a small percentage of synchronous speed. The main rotor field is then excited and the rotor locks into synchronism with the field.

If the rotor field winding has a negligible time constant and is excited at time $t = 0$, when the slip is constant at 1 percent and $\delta = -10$ electrical degrees, find an expression for δ as a function of time if the constant "no-load" load on the motor is 15 hp and the maximum possible output power is 300 hp.

Assume that

$$P_j = 6100 \text{ watt-sec}^2/\text{electrical degree}$$
$$P_d = 2180 \text{ watt-sec/electrical degree}$$
$$P_s = 3900 \text{ watts/electrical degree}$$

4

Inductive Energy Conversion

In this chapter two important energy conversion systems are considered: the transformer and the induction motor. It may appear surprising that the transformer, which is an electrical-to-electrical energy converter, and the induction motor, which is an electromechanical energy converter, should be considered jointly. However, it will be shown that the induction motor may be considered as a transformer whose secondary winding is permitted to rotate. Consequently, much of the analysis applied to the transformer may be modified and utilized in the analysis of the induction motor. Therefore, although the transformer is not an electromechanical device it is considered at this stage to provide a basis for investigating the characteristics of the induction motor.

4–1. TRANSFORMERS

The basic transformer is a device comprising two electrical circuits coupled by a common time-dependent magnetic field. Transformers have many applications; however, most of those of large capacity are used for "stepping up" or "stepping down" the voltage in transmission and distribution circuits. Since transmission of power at high voltage is economical, it is customary to "step up" the voltage at the generators and again "step down" the voltage at the receiving end for safe local distribution. Smaller transformers are used as circuit elements where their impedance-matching and isolating properties, rather than their energy conversion properties, are of interest.

Physically, the simple two-winding transformer may be constructed as a core-type transformer, as shown in Fig. 4–1a, in which two coils, the primary and secondary, are wound about an iron core. If insulation is not a major problem, and it is desired that a high percentage of the flux produced in the primary link the turns of the secondary, then the shell-type design shown in Fig. 4–1b may be used. In this, insulated coils of the primary and secondary windings are placed alternately about a central limb of an iron core, which encloses both windings.

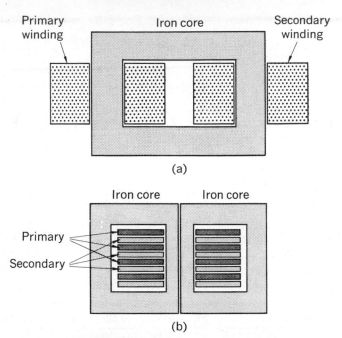

(a)

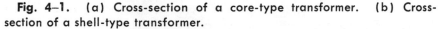

(b)

Fig. 4–1. (a) Cross-section of a core-type transformer. (b) Cross-section of a shell-type transformer.

To reduce losses, the core is built up from thin sheets of steel with high permeability and low hysteresis loss. Transformers which are rated above about one kilowatt are generally immersed in oil to improve the insulation and also provide a cooling medium.

4–2. TRANSFORMER EQUIVALENT CIRCUIT

Consider the simple transformer of Fig. 4–2, in which a voltage v_1 is applied to a coil of N_1 turns and negligible resistance. An exciting current i_e flows, a flux ϕ is produced, and an equal and opposite voltage e_1 is induced, where

$$e_1 = N_1 \frac{d\phi}{dt} = v_1 \qquad (4\text{--}1)$$

Assuming there is no flux leakage, then the same flux ϕ links the N_2 turns of the secondary, so that a voltage

$$e_2 = N_2 \frac{d\phi}{dt} = v_2 \qquad (4\text{--}2)$$

is induced. Therefore from Eq. 4–1 and Eq. 4–2

$$\frac{e_1}{e_2} = \frac{N_1}{N_2} \tag{4-3}$$

Since the unloaded transformer represents a purely inductive load, the exciting current lags the impressed voltage v_1 by 90°. An equivalent circuit for the transformer is shown in Fig. 4–2b in which the exciting current flows through an equivalent inductive reactance x_e. The remainder

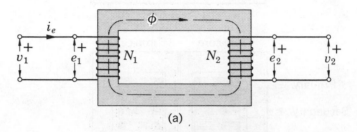

(a)

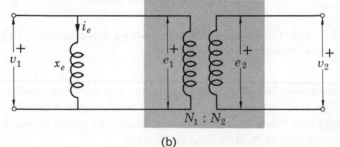

(b)

Fig. 4–2. (a) Schematic of a simple transformer. (b) Equivalent circuit.

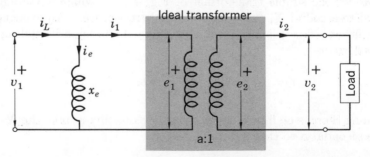

Fig. 4–3. Equivalent circuit for a transformer with negligible leakage and resistive loss.

of the circuit may be considered as an ideal transformer in which the primary current is zero when the secondary current is zero.

If a load drawing a current i_2 is connected to the secondary then a current i_1 flows in the primary winding of the ideal transformer as shown in Fig. 4–3. The current ratios may be found by observing that the power

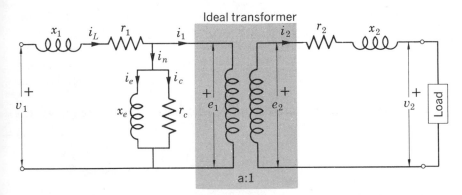

Fig. 4–4. Equivalent circuit for a transformer.

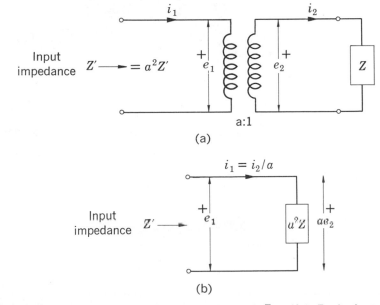

(a)

(b)

Fig. 4–5. (a) Ideal transformer with load Z. (b) Equivalent circuit with respect to the primary.

losses in an ideal transformer are zero and therefore

$$e_1 i_1 = e_2 i_2 \qquad (4\text{-}4)$$

and so from Eqs. 4–3 and 4–4

$$\boxed{\frac{i_2}{i_1} = \frac{e_1}{e_2} = \frac{N_1}{N_2}} \qquad (4\text{-}5)$$

Since inductance is defined as flux linkage per unit current, the fact that all the flux produced in one coil does not link the other may be accounted for by primary and secondary leakage reactances, x_1 and x_2, respectively, placed as shown in Fig. 4–4. The winding resistances are also accounted for by r_1 and r_2. Even under no-load conditions power is dissipated, due to hysteresis and eddy-current loss. Consequently, a resistance r_c with a current i_c is incorporated in the equivalent circuit, so that the power loss

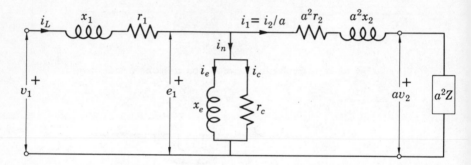

(a)

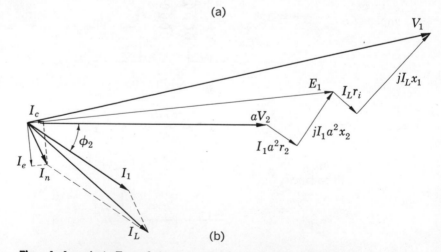

(b)

Fig. 4–6. (a) Transformer equivalent circuit referred to the primary. (b) Transformer phasor diagram referred to the primary.

in the core is given by $i_c{}^2r_c$. Therefore under no-load conditions the total current i_n is the phasor sum of i_e and i_c.

To simplify transformer calculations, it is convenient to express all quantities with respect to either the primary or secondary side. Consider the ideal transformer of Fig. 4–5a with a load of impedance Z, and a primary-to-secondary turns ratio a. The impedance as seen from the supply is

$$Z' = \frac{e_1}{i_1} = \frac{ae_2}{i_2/a} = \frac{a^2e_2}{i_2}$$

Therefore

$$\boxed{Z' = a^2Z} \qquad (4\text{–}6)$$

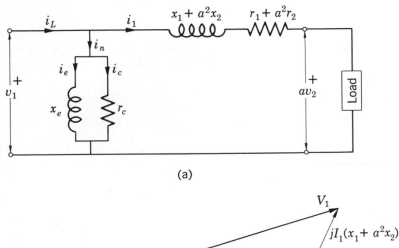

(a)

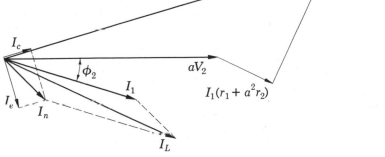

(b)

Fig. 4–7. (a) Approximate equivalent circuit for a transformer referred to the primary. (b) Approximate phasor diagram for a transformer.

Hence, if the ideal transformer is removed and the load is replaced by a load of impedance a^2Z, as in Fig. 4–5b, the input impedance and powers remain unaltered. Similarly, an impedance in the primary circuit may be expressed in terms of the secondary circuit parameters.

Figures 4–6a and 4–6b show the equivalent circuit and the phasor diagram, respectively, of a transformer referred to the primary. When the no-load current is small, an approximation may be made by moving the shunt circuit to the terminals and then combining the resistive and also the reactive elements, as shown in Fig. 4–7a. The phasor diagram simplifies to that in Fig. 4–7b.

Example 4–1. A 10-kva transformer has a 10:1 turns ratio, and the following parameters at 60 cps:

$$r_1 = 8 \text{ ohms} \qquad r_2 = 0.08 \text{ ohm}$$
$$x_1 = 9.5 \text{ ohms} \qquad x_2 = 0.095 \text{ ohm}$$
$$x_e = 6000 \text{ ohms} \qquad 1/r_c \approx 0$$

If the transformer is supplying rated kva at 240 volts and a power factor of 0.8 lag, draw the approximate equivalent circuit and phasor diagram for the transformer with respect to the primary, and find the input current, voltage and power factor.

The current is

$$I_1 = \frac{\text{kva} \times 1000}{aV_2} = \frac{10 \times 1000}{10 \times 240} = 4.17 \text{ amp}$$

Working in per unit quantities with $aV_2 = 2400$ volts and $I_1 = 4.17$ amp as the base voltage and current, respectively, the base resistance is

$$\frac{aV_2}{I_1} = \frac{2400}{4.17} = 575 \text{ ohm}$$

Since $a = 10$,

$$x_1 + a^2x_2 = 9.5 + 100 \times 0.095 = 19 \text{ ohm} = \tfrac{19}{575} = 0.033 \text{ per unit}$$
$$r_1 + a^2r_2 = 8 + 100 \times 0.08 = 16 \text{ ohm} = \tfrac{16}{575} = 0.0278 \text{ per unit}$$

and

$$x_e = \tfrac{6000}{575} = 10.4 \text{ per unit}$$

From Fig. 4–8b

$$V_1 = aV_2 + I_1[(r_1 + a^2r_2) + j(x_1 + a^2x_2)]$$

With I_1 as reference,

$$V_1 = 0.8 + j0.6 + 1(0.0278 + j0.033)$$
$$= 0.8278 + j0.633 \text{ per unit} = 1.04\underline{/37.3°} \text{ per unit}$$
$$= 2400 \times 1.04 = 2495 \text{ volts}$$

and

$$I_e = \frac{V_1}{jx_e} = -j\frac{0.8278 + j0.633}{10.4} = 0.061 - j0.0797 \text{ per unit}$$

Therefore

$$I_L = I_1 + I_e = 1 + 0.061 - j0.0797 = 1.061\underline{/-4.3°} \text{ per unit}$$
$$= 4.17 \times 1.061 = 4.43 \text{ amp}$$

Therefore

$$\phi_1 = 37.3° + 4.3° = 41.6°$$

and the input power factor $\cos \phi_1 = \cos 41.6° = 0.75$.

4-3. STEADY-STATE OPERATION OF POLYPHASE INDUCTION MOTORS

The induction motor is the simplest and most widely used a-c motor. The squirrel-cage motor is exceptionally rugged, since there are no insulated windings on the rotor, and in addition no slip rings or commutator are needed. Consequently when an essentially constant speed motor is required the induction motor is usually the choice. If, however, speed

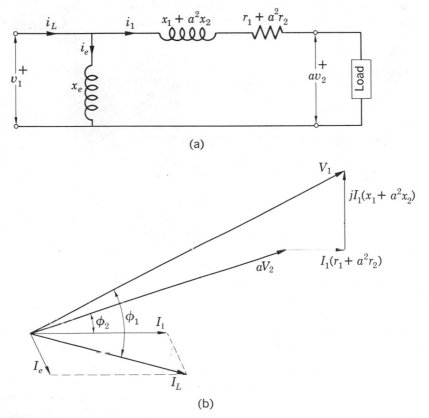

(a)

(b)

Fig. 4-8. (a) Approximate transformer equivalent circuit. (b) Approximate phasor diagram for a transformer.

variation is required, a wound-rotor induction motor may be used.   The operation and characteristics of both the squirrel-cage and wound-rotor induction motors are now considered.

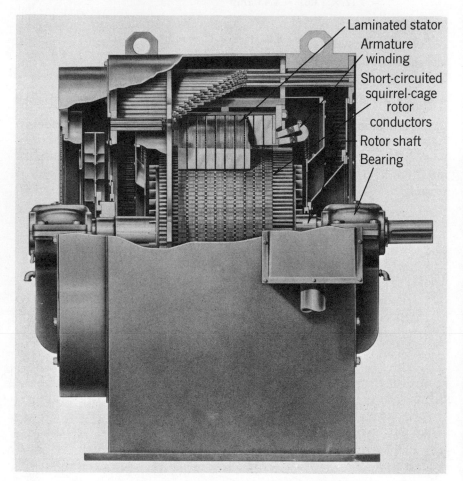

Fig. 4–9. Cutaway view of squirrel-cage induction motor.   (Courtesy of Westinghouse Electric Corporation.)

The stator of the induction motor is similar to that of the synchronous motor.   In the case of a three-phase motor separate windings aa', bb', and cc' are placed about the stator so that when they are connected to a three-phase supply a synchronously rotating constant-magnitude mmf wave is produced, as discussed in Art. 3–8.   The rotor winding of the squirrel-cage machine consists of either copper or aluminum-alloy conductors which are short-circuited by end rings as shown in cutaway Fig. 4–9.

The operation of the induction motor may be visualized by considering a short-circuited coil in a magnetic field, as in Fig. 4–10. If the field is held stationary, and the coil is rotated clockwise, a voltage is induced and a current flows in the coil as shown. If, on the other hand, the coil is held stationary and the field is rotated counterclockwise, the direction of current flow is unchanged. The motor rule now indicates that the current-carrying coil tends to rotate in the counterclockwise direction. It therefore tends to rotate in the same direction as the field. The coil speed will

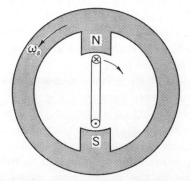

Fig. 4–10. Short-circuited coil in a magnetic field.

always be less than that of the field; otherwise, there would be no relative motion between the coil and the field, and so no induced current or motor action. In the induction motor the rotating field is produced by the polyphase supply applied to the stator windings. However, the effect on the short-circuited rotor turns is the same, and so a torque is produced in the direction of rotation of the stator field.

The form of the stator winding is the same as that in the synchronous motor, and therefore the synchronous speed of the field is determined by the frequency of the supply and the number of "poles" for which the stator is wound. Therefore, from Eq. 3–1, for a P-pole stator winding the synchronous speed of the field is

$$\mathfrak{N}_s = \frac{120f}{P} \, rpm \tag{4-7}$$

Under steady-state operation of the induction motor, the rotor speed $\mathfrak{N}$ is always less than the synchronous speed of the field. The relative difference in speed is called the *fractional slip* and is defined as

$$s = \frac{\mathfrak{N}_s - \mathfrak{N}}{\mathfrak{N}_s} \tag{4-8}$$

Therefore, as the rotor speed decreases, the slip increases and becomes unity at standstill. Equation 4–8 may also be written in the form

$$\mathfrak{N} = \mathfrak{N}_s(1 - s) \tag{4-9}$$

and it is apparent that, as the relative slip approaches zero, the rotor speed approaches synchronous speed.

The relative motion between the field and the short-circuited rotor conductors induces rotor voltages at a frequency sf, called the *slip frequency*. At standstill $s = 1$, and so the rotor frequency is the same as the stator frequency. Under these conditions the machine is electrically similar to a transformer with a short-circuited secondary winding, and the energy which is transferred across the stator-rotor air gap is converted to electrical energy and then dissipated as heat.

The equivalent circuit of an induction motor at standstill is therefore that of the short-circuited transformer in Fig. 4–11a, where a is the effective turns ratio between the stator and rotor. The equivalent circuit may be referred to the primary (or stator side) as in Fig. 4–11b, where r_2 and x_2 are the effective resistance and reactance of the rotor, respectively, referred to the stator. If the rotor is now permitted to rotate at a relative slip s, the induced voltage in the rotor decreases to sE_1. The frequency decreases to sf, and consequently the effective reactance of the rotor also decreases, to sx_2. The equivalent circuit for an induction motor operating with a relative slip s is therefore as shown in Fig. 4–11c. If the rotor voltage sE_1 in the equivalent circuit is decreased by a factor s and the rotor circuit impedance is also decreased by a factor s, then the current I_2 is unaltered and the equivalent circuit of Fig. 4–11d results.

When the induction motor is operating, some of the power which crosses the stator-rotor air gap is converted to mechanical power and the remainder, $I_2{}^2r_2$, is converted to electrical power and dissipated as heat. With this in mind, the resistance r_2/s of Fig. 4–11d is split into $r_2 + r_2(1 - s)/s$ and the final form of the induction motor equivalent circuit is shown in Fig. 4–11e. Since the total power transferred to the rotor is $I_2{}^2[r_2 + r_2(1 - s)/s]$ and the electrical power dissipated is $I_2{}^2r_2$, the remainder $I_2{}^2r_2(1 - s)/s$ must be the mechanical output power. Therefore, of the power transferred to the rotor, a fraction $(1 - s)$ is converted to mechanical power and a fraction s is dissipated as heat in the rotor.

4–4. STEADY-STATE INDUCTION MOTOR CHARACTERISTICS

As in the case of the transformer, the equivalent circuit of Fig. 4–11e may be approximated by that of Fig. 4–12, in which the excitation reactance x_e has been moved to the input terminals and the current through r_c is considered negligible.

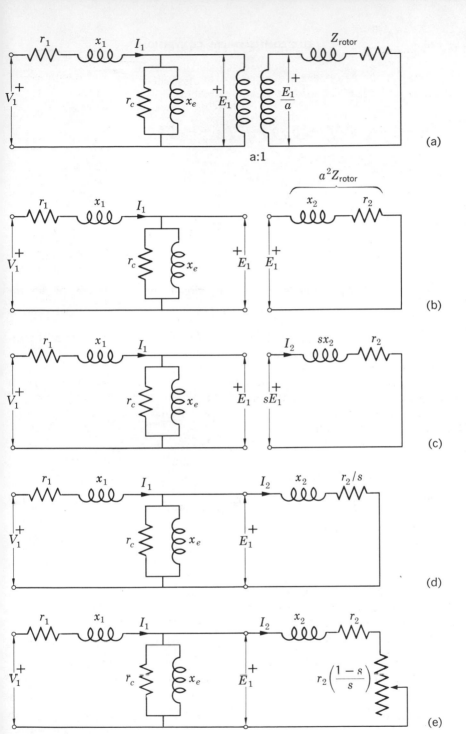

Fig. 4–11. Equivalent circuit for one phase of an induction motor (a) at standstill; (b) at standstill referred to the stator; (c) at a relative slip s; (d) at a relative slip s; (e) in final form at relative slip s.

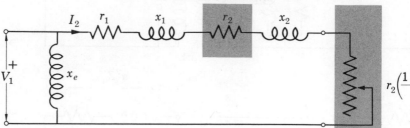

Fig. 4–12. Approximate equivalent circuit for one phase of an induction motor.

The fraction of the power transferred to the rotor per phase and converted into mechanical power is

$$P = I_2{}^2 r_2 \left(\frac{1 - s}{s}\right) \tag{4–10}$$

Since

$$I_2 = \frac{V_1}{\sqrt{(r_1 + r_2/s)^2 + (x_1 + x_2)^2}} \tag{4–11}$$

upon substituting Eq. 4–11 in Eq. 4–10

$$P = V_1{}^2 \frac{(r_2/s)(1 - s)}{(r_1 + r_2/s)^2 + (x_1 + x_2)^2} \tag{4–12}$$

The torque developed per phase is

$$T = \frac{P}{\omega_s(1 - s)}$$

where ω_s is the synchronous speed of the rotor in mechanical radians/sec. Therefore

$$\boxed{T = \frac{V_1{}^2}{\omega_s} \frac{r_2/s}{(r_1 + r_2/s)^2 + (x_1 + x_2)^2}} \tag{4–13}$$

The form of the torque–slip curves for various applied voltages expressed by Eq. 4–13 is shown in Fig. 4–13. Maximum torque is produced at a particular slip s_m which is independent of the applied voltage, and as is apparent from Eq. 4–13 the magnitude of the maximum torque varies directly with the square of the applied voltage.

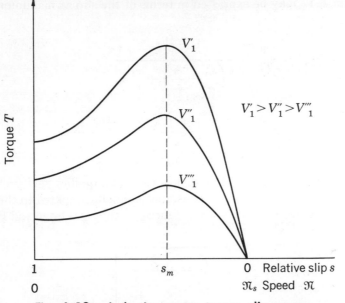

Fig. 4-13. Induction motor torque–slip curves.

The starting torque per phase of the induction motor is given by Eq. 4–13 with $s = 1$, and is

$$T_0 = \frac{V_1{}^2}{\omega_s} \frac{r_2}{(r_1 + r_2)^2 + (x_1 + x_2)^2} \tag{4-14}$$

Upon differentiating Eq. 4–13 with respect to s and setting the result equal to zero, the slip at maximum torque is

$$\boxed{s_m = \frac{r_2}{\sqrt{r_1{}^2 + (x_1 + x_2)^2}}} \tag{4-15}$$

Substituting Eq. 4–15 in Eq. 4–13 gives the maximum torque per phase:

$$\begin{aligned}
T_m &= \frac{V_1{}^2}{\omega_s} \frac{\sqrt{r_1{}^2 + (x_1 + x_2)^2}}{[r_1 + \sqrt{r_1{}^2 + (x_1 + x_2)^2}]^2 + (x_1 + x_2)^2} \\
&= \frac{V_1{}^2}{\omega_s} \frac{0.5}{r_1 + \sqrt{r_1{}^2 + (x_1 + x_2)^2}}
\end{aligned} \tag{4-16}$$

From Eqs. 4–13 and 4–16,

$$\frac{T}{T_m} = \frac{2r_2}{s} \cdot \frac{r_1 + \sqrt{r_1{}^2 + (x_1 + x_2)^2}}{\left(r_1 + \dfrac{r_2}{s}\right)^2 + (x_1 + x_2)^2} \tag{4-17}$$

Equation 4–17 may be expressed in terms of the slip at maximum torque s_m as

$$\frac{T}{T_m} = \frac{1 + \dfrac{r_1}{r_2} s_m}{\dfrac{1}{2}\left(\dfrac{s_m}{s} + \dfrac{s}{s_m}\right) + \dfrac{r_1}{r_2} s_m} \tag{4–18}$$

or as

$$\frac{T}{T_m} = \frac{1 + 1/\sqrt{1 + Q^2}}{\dfrac{1}{2}\left(\dfrac{s_m}{s} + \dfrac{s}{s_m}\right) + 1/\sqrt{1 + Q^2}} \tag{4–19}$$

where $Q = (x_1 + x_2)/r_1$ and is analogous to the quality factor of circuit theory. In general, the stator resistance is small compared to the sum of the equivalent stator and rotor reactances, so that Q is large and Eq. 4–19 may be approximated by

$$\boxed{\frac{T}{T_m} = \frac{2}{\dfrac{s_m}{s} + \dfrac{s}{s_m}}} \tag{4–20}$$

From Eq. 4–15 it is apparent that the slip at which maximum torque occurs is independent of the applied voltage and varies directly with the

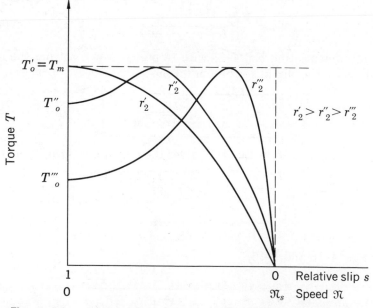

Fig. 4–14.   Torque–slip curves for different rotor resistances.

rotor resistance. In the case of the squirrel-cage machine, the rotor resistance cannot be varied and consequently maximum torque is always produced at the same slip. In general, the resistance of a squirrel-cage rotor is relatively low and consequently maximum torque occurs at a small slip, or, in other words, maximum torque occurs at a speed close to synchronous speed.

Frequently it is desirable that a large torque be provided at starting. The starting torque may be increased, as shown in Fig. 4–14, if it is possible to increase the rotor resistance. In fact, it is seen from Eq. 4–15 that the maximum torque may be provided at starting (i.e., when $s = 1$) if the rotor resistance is increased so that

$$r_2 = \sqrt{r_1{}^2 + (x_1 + x_2)^2} \qquad (4\text{--}21)$$

Although such a large rotor resistance provides the required starting torque, the machine efficiency is low due to the large $I_2{}^2 r_2$ copper loss in the rotor, and in addition, due to the form of the torque–slip curve, the speed regulation of the machine is poor.

Wound-rotor induction motor

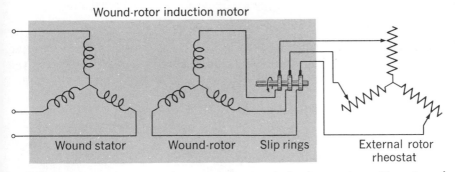

Fig. 4–15. Schematic of a wound rotor induction motor with external rotor rheostat.

A wound-rotor induction motor provides a solution to the foregoing problems. The conductors are now insulated and placed in slots, and in order to vary the effective rotor resistance the windings are connected through slip rings to external variable rheostats, as shown in Fig. 4–15. With this arrangement it is possible to select the speed at which maximum torque occurs. For starting purposes all the external resistance is put in circuit and as the rotor gains speed the resistance may be reduced to zero, so that under operating conditions the effective rotor resistance is that of the rotor windings. The wound-rotor induction motor is not as robust as the squirrel-cage machine due to the insulated rotor windings and the presence of slip rings. In general, also, the rotor resistance is greater than that of the squirrel cage and as a result the speed regulation is not as good.   However, when speed and torque variation is required the wound rotor machine competes favorably with the d-c motor.

Example 4–2.   A 440-volt, 3-phase, 60-cps, Y-connected, 4-pole, wound-rotor induction motor has a total effective stator and rotor leakage reactance at standstill of 4 ohms/phase, referred to the stator, and a full-load slip of 10 percent. The rotor and stator resistances in ohms/phase, when referred to the stator, are respectively 0.8 and 0.75.

(a) Find the maximum output torque if the windage and friction loss is considered constant at 500 watts.

(b) If maximum torque is required at a speed of 1000 rpm, how much resistance, referred to the stator, must be added to the rotor winding per phase?

(c) What is the percentage change, in sign and magnitude, in the starting torque when the additional resistance, as determined in part b, is added?

(d) What is the frequency of the voltage induced in the rotor at a speed of 1600 rpm?

(a) From Eq. 4–16 the maximum torque per phase is

$$T_m = \frac{(440/\sqrt{3})^2}{30 \times 2\pi} \times \frac{0.5}{0.75 + \sqrt{0.75^2 + 4^2}} = 35.5 \text{ newton-m}$$

and so the total torque developed internally is $3T_m = 3 \times 35.5 = 106.5$ newton-m.   From Eq. 4–15, the slip at maximum torque is

$$s_m = \frac{0.8}{\sqrt{0.75^2 + 4^2}} = 0.197$$

and the power developed internally is

$$P_m = 3T_m\omega_m = 3T_m\omega_s(1 - s_m)$$
$$= 106.5 \times 30 \times 2\pi \times 0.803$$
$$= 16,200 \text{ watts}$$

The output power is therefore $(16,200 - 500) = 15,700$ watts and the output torque is $15,700/(30 \times 2\pi \times 0.803) = 104$ newton-m.

(b) From Eq. 4–15 the rotor resistance for maximum torque at a slip s_m should be

$$r'_2 = s_m \sqrt{r_1{}^2 + (x_1 + x_2)^2}$$

When the speed is 1000 rpm the slip is $(1800 - 1000)/1800 = 0.445$.   Therefore the total rotor resistance should be $0.445\sqrt{0.75^2 + 4^2} = 1.82$ ohm and so $(1.82 - 0.8) = 1.02$ ohm/phase should be added to the rotor winding.

(c) Equation 4–14 permits the ratio between the starting torque with the additional resistance (T'_0) and without the additional resistance (T_0) to be written as

$$\frac{T'_0}{T_0} = \frac{r'_2}{r_2} \cdot \frac{(r_1 + r_2)^2 + (x_1 + x_2)^2}{(r_1 + r'_2)^2 + (x_1 + x_2)^2}$$
$$= \frac{1.82}{0.8} \times \frac{(1.55)^2 + 4^2}{(2.57)^2 + 4^2} = 1.85$$

The additional resistance therefore results in an additional 85-percent starting torque.

(d) A speed of 1600 rpm corresponds to a slip $s = (1800 - 1600)/1800 = 0.111$ and so the frequency of the voltage induced in the rotor is

$$f_2 = sf = 0.111 \times 60 = 6.66 \text{ cps}$$

4–5. TRANSIENT ANALYSIS OF THE POLYPHASE INDUCTION MOTOR

In this section two transient situations are considered. In the first case, the electrical behavior of the induction motor is examined when a three-phase short circuit at the stator takes place under steady-state conditions; and secondly, the dynamic behavior of the machine is considered.

4–5.1. Transient Behavior Under Short-Circuited Conditions. The equivalent circuit referred to the primary of an induction motor operating under steady-state conditions is shown in Fig. 4–16a, where V_1 and I_1 are

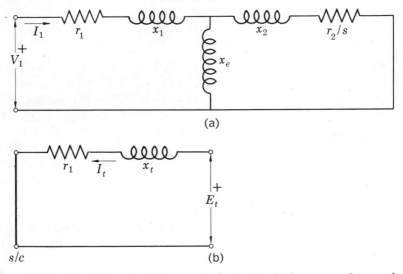

(a)

(b)

s/c

Fig. 4–16. (a) Steady-state equivalent circuit for one phase of an induction motor. (b) Induction motor transient equivalent circuit for one phase with a short circuit across the input terminals.

the rms stator voltage and current per phase respectively. At time $t = 0$ the input is short-circuited and the equivalent circuit is now given by Fig. 4–16b, where the initial value of the *"voltage behind the transient reactance,"* E_t, is given to a close approximation by

$$E_{t0} = V_1 - \left(x_1 + \frac{x_2 x_e}{x_2 + x_e} \right) I_1$$

since in general the voltage drop across r_1 is negligible. The initial transient current which flows into the short circuit is

$$I_{t0} = \frac{E_{t0}}{x_t} \qquad (4\text{-}22)$$

where the transient reactance is

$$x_t = x_2 + \frac{x_1 x_e}{x_1 + x_e} \qquad (4\text{-}23)$$

The time constant of the transient equivalent circuit is

$$\tau_t = \frac{x_t}{\omega r_1} \qquad (4\text{-}24)$$

and therefore the short-circuit current as a function of time is

$$\boxed{I_t(t) = \frac{E_{t0}}{x_t} e^{-t/\tau_t}} \qquad (4\text{-}25)$$

In practice the time constant τ_t is generally small, and therefore electrical transients in the induction motor are of short duration and often neglected.

When examining rotor oscillation of the synchronous machine, it was pointed out that short-circuited conductors are frequently placed about the periphery of the rotor to damp out oscillation. In effect the induction machine principle is used, in that any excursion from synchronous speed causes relative motion between the rotor conductors and the stator flux, and consequently a restoring torque. It is therefore apparent that rotor oscillation in the induction motor is not a problem and any disturbance is rapidly damped out.

4-5.2. Time for an Induction Motor To Reach Steady-State Speed from Standstill. In considering the dynamic behavior of the induction motor, the time taken to attain steady-state operating speed from standstill is of interest. Consider an induction motor with a purely inertial load, where the total inertia of the rotating system is J. Then the torque-balance equation for the rotor is

$$3T = J \frac{d\omega}{dt} = J \frac{d}{dt} [\omega_s (1 - s)]$$

where T is the torque developed per phase in a three-phase induction motor and therefore

$$3T = -J\omega_s \frac{ds}{dt} \qquad (4\text{-}26)$$

Substituting the approximate value for T from Eq. 4–20 in Eq. 4–26 gives

$$-J\omega_s \frac{ds}{dt} = \frac{6T_m}{\dfrac{s_m}{s} + \dfrac{s}{s_m}}$$

From which

$$t = \frac{-J\omega_s}{6T_m}\left(s_m \int_1^{s_\infty} \frac{ds}{s} + \frac{1}{s_m}\int_1^{s_\infty} s\,ds\right)$$

and therefore

$$t = \frac{J\omega_s}{6T_m}\left[s_m \ln\frac{1}{s_\infty} + \frac{1}{2s_m}(1 - s_\infty{}^2)\right] \tag{4-27}$$

where s_∞ is the steady-state relative slip.

Example 4–3. A 4-pole, 3-phase, 60-cps, 350-hp, Y-connected induction motor is supplied through a feeder of impedance $0.002 + j0.025$ ohm per phase. The line-to-line voltage at the input to the feeder is 440 volts and the resistances and reactances of the machine in ohms per phase referred to the stator are: $r_1 = 0.006$; $r_2 = 0.008$; $x_e = 3.1$; $x_1 = x_2 = 0.06$. At full load the power factor at the input to the feeder is 0.89 and the efficiency of the combined feeder and motor is 86 percent.

(a) Determine an expression for the current in the motor as a function of time if a 3-phase short circuit occurs at the input to the feeder, when the motor is operating at rated load.

(b) If the moment of inertia of the rotating system is 50 kg-m², what period of time is required to bring the rotor speed up to 1728 rpm from standstill, if the load is purely inertial?

(a) Accounting for the impedance of the feeder the equivalent phase circuit is shown in Fig. 4–17. Since the efficiency is 86 percent, the input power per

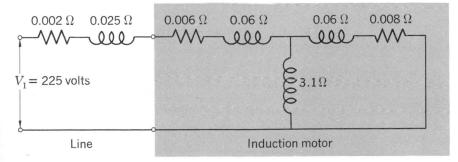

Fig. 4–17. Equivalent circuit for one phase of an induction motor with a feeder line.

phase from the source is

$$P_1 = \frac{350 \times 0.746}{3 \times 0.86} = 101 \text{ kw}$$

and since

$$P_1 = V_1 I_1 \cos \phi$$

$$I_1 = \frac{101 \times 10^3}{255 \times 0.89} = 447 \text{ amp}$$

The voltage behind the transient reactance is

$$E_{t0} = V_1 - I_1 \left(x'_1 + \frac{x_e x_2}{x_e + x_2} \right) = 255 - 447 \left(0.085 + \frac{3.1 \times 0.06}{3.16} \right)$$
$$= 190.8 \text{ volts}$$

where x'_1 is the combined reactance of the feeder and stator per phase. From Eq. 4–23, the transient reactance is

$$x_t = x_2 + \frac{x'_1 x_e}{x'_1 + x_e} = 0.06 + \frac{0.085 \times 3.1}{3.1 + 0.085}$$
$$= 0.143 \text{ ohm}$$

From Eq. 4–24, the transient time constant is

$$\tau_t = \frac{x_t}{\omega r'_1} = \frac{0.143}{377 \times 0.008} = 0.047 \text{ sec}$$

where r'_1 is the combined resistance of the feeder and stator per phase. Therefore, from Eq. 4–25, the short-circuit current as a function of time is

$$I_t(t) = \frac{E_{t0}}{x_t} e^{-t/\tau_t} = \frac{190.8}{0.143} e^{-t/0.047}$$

Therefore

$$I_t(t) = 1340 e^{-21t} \text{ amp}$$

As expected the time constant is small and the transient short-circuit current is of short duration.

(b) From Eq. 4–15, the slip at maximum torque is

$$s_m = \frac{r_2}{\sqrt{r_1'^2 + (x'_1 + x_2)^2}} = \frac{0.008}{\sqrt{(0.008)^2 + (0.145)^2}}$$
$$= 0.055$$

and from Eq. 4–16, the total maximum torque is

$$3T_m = 255^2 \times \frac{60}{2\pi \times 1800} \times \frac{0.5 \times 3}{0.008 + \sqrt{(0.008)^2 + (0.145)^2}} = 3400 \text{ newton-m}$$

It should be noted that when calculating the torque the term ω_s is expressed in mechanical radians per second.

From Eq. 4–27, the time taken to reach a relative slip of 0.04, which corresponds to a speed of 1728 rpm, is

$$t = \frac{50 \times 188.2}{2 \times 3400} \left[0.055 \ln \frac{1}{0.04} + \frac{1}{2 \times 0.055} (1 - 0.04^2) \right]$$
$$= 12.8 \text{ sec}$$

4–6. INDUCTION MOTOR STARTING AND SPEED CONTROL

Two important factors of interest, when considering the starting of induction motors, are the starting torque and starting current. A large starting torque is desirable, while the starting current should be as small as possible. Such characteristics are attained in the wound-rotor induction motor by the insertion of external rotor resistance during starting.

However, in the case of the squirrel-cage motor, no such provision is made. Yet with special rotor design it is possible to achieve a large effective rotor resistance at standstill, which increases the starting torque

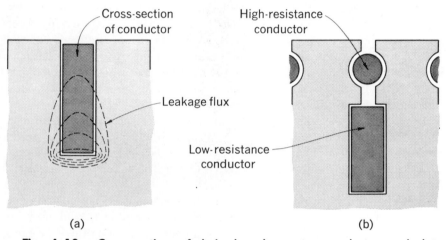

(a)   (b)

Fig. 4–18. Cross-section of (a) deep-bar rotor conductor and slot; (b) double squirrel-cage rotor conductors and slot.

and limits the starting current. The increased effective resistance at starting depends on the *skin effect*. Consider the conductor of a deep-bar rotor, as in Fig. 4–18a, in which the leakage flux distribution is as shown. The conducting material at the bottom of the slot is linked by more of the reactive flux then that at the top, and consequently has a greater leakage reactance. Therefore most of the current flows in the low-leakage reactance area at the top of the bar and, due to the non-uniform current distribution, the effective resistance is larger than the d-c value. However, when the motor is started and attains full-load speed the frequency of the rotor current decreases, in the case of a 60-cps motor, to 3 or 4 cps. At such a low frequency the skin effect is negligible, the current distribution becomes almost uniform, and the effective rotor resistance decreases towards its d-c value. Essentially the same result is achieved in the case of the double squirrel-cage rotor, which has two layers of rotor conductors. A typical cross-section of a rotor slot is shown in Fig. 4–18b. At standstill most of the current is forced to flow through the high-resistance conductor at the top of the slot, while at rated speed the leakage reactance effect is negligible and the current also flows freely through the low resistance conductor at the bottom of the slot.

When a high starting current is a problem it may be necessary to reduce the applied voltage. This may be done conveniently by connecting the stator windings in wye for starting and then switching, so that they are connected in delta. In this way the applied voltage per phase is reduced by a factor of $\sqrt{3}$; however, the starting torque is reduced by a factor of 3. Autotransformers may also be used for stepping down the supply voltage while starting.

Speed control in the wound-rotor induction motor may be achieved by variation of the rotor resistance. The range of speed variation depends of course on the particular torque–speed characteristic of the load. If the load characteristic is as in Fig. 4–19a and the rotor resistance may be increased from r_2 to r'_2, then the speed may be varied between the limits $\mathfrak{N}$ and $\mathfrak{N}'$. If operation at low speed is required for lengthy periods, then this means of speed variation is inefficient.

In the case of the squirrel-cage induction motor, rotor-resistance speed control is not possible. In small machines, when efficiency is not of prime importance, the applied voltage may be varied by means of external rheostats. Since the torque is proportional to the square of the applied voltage, the curves in Fig. 4–19b are obtained.

Pole changing is an important means of speed control for squirrel-cage motors. The number of poles for which the stator is wound may be changed by switching from one set of connections to the other. Figure 4–19c shows the speed variation attained by increasing the number of poles by a factor of two.

As seen from Eq. 4–7, the synchronous speed varies directly with the frequency. Prior to the development of large-capacity silicon-controlled rectifiers a variable-frequency supply was usually ruled out for economic or efficiency reasons, but with the developments in solid-state technology it appears that this means of speed control will be used more extensively in the future.

In addition to the methods of speed control already discussed, there are numerous other ingenious systems. Several of them depend on auxiliary machines which serve to control the mechanical output power, and hence the speed, by feeding back to the supply a controllable portion of the rotor energy. In other words, rather than permitting the usual dissipation of electrical energy in the rotor, this energy is returned to the supply at a controlled rate.

The *Leblanc system*, shown in Fig. 4–20, is but one of the many possible arrangements. Here the wound rotor of the induction motor is connected through slip rings, and through a commutator, to another similar rotor mounted on the same shaft. Since both rotor speeds are $(1 - s)$ times the synchronous speed, and the frequency of the input to the auxiliary rotor is sf, its field rotates at synchronous speed relative to the rotor

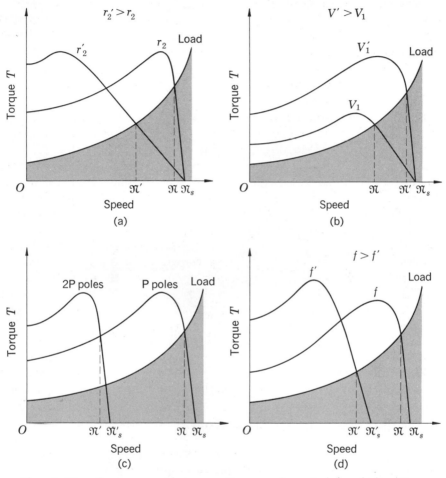

Fig. 4–19. Torque–speed curves for speed control by (a) rotor resistance variation; (b) applied voltage variation; (c) pole changing; (d) frequency variation.

windings provided the connections are such that the rotor and field rotate in opposite directions.   The auxiliary rotor therefore acts as a frequency-changing device which restores the frequency of the induction motor rotor to that of the source.   Power may be returned to the supply via slip rings and a variable-ratio three-phase transformer.   To decrease the speed, additional power is returned to the source by increasing the voltage difference between the transformer and the supply. Variation of the brush location on the commutator may be used for control of the relative phase

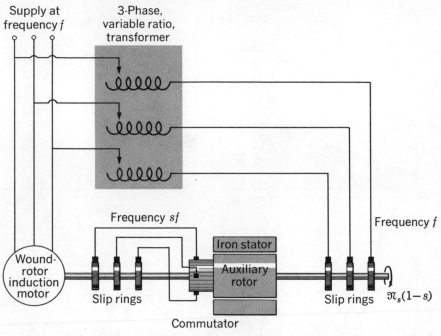

Fig. 4–20. Schematic diagram of the Leblanc system.

difference between the supply and the feedback circuit, and hence for control of the overall power factor of the system.

4–7. SINGLE-PHASE INDUCTION MOTORS

Single-phase induction motors are used extensively in business, industry, and in the household when a three-phase supply is not available or when only small (up to 5 hp) quantities of power are required. Structurally, the single-phase motor is similar to the squirrel-cage machine except it has a single-phase distributed winding in the stator (an additional stator winding, used for starting the motor, is discussed below). If an alternating current flows through the distributed winding, then, as in the case of the polyphase winding, the instantaneous mmf $F(\theta,t)$ is both a function of position and time, and from Eq. 3–46

$$F(\theta,t) = F_m \cos \omega t \cos \theta \qquad (4\text{–}28)$$

where F_m is the maximum mmf which occurs at time $t = 0$ and position $\theta = 0$. Equation 4–28 indicates that the flux distribution is stationary and sinusoidal with an alternating amplitude. Therefore, due to the stationary nature of the flux wave, no starting torque is exerted on the rotor.

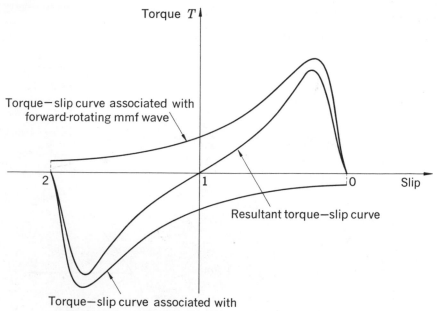

Torque T

Torque–slip curve associated with forward-rotating mmf wave

Resultant torque–slip curve

Torque–slip curve associated with backward-rotating mmf wave

Fig. 4–21. Single-phase induction motor torque–slip curve.

Equation 4–28 may be more fully interpreted if it is expanded trigonometrically into

$$F(\theta,t) = \frac{F_m}{2} \cos (\omega t - \theta) + \frac{F_m}{2} \cos (\omega t + \theta) \qquad (4\text{--}29)$$

Comparing Eq. 4–29 with Eq. 3–47 indicates that the mmf wave may be considered as composed of one wave which rotates in the positive θ direction with an angular velocity ω, and a second wave which rotates in the negative θ direction with the same angular velocity. A torque–slip curve may be associated with each rotating mmf wave, the resultant torque exerted on the rotor being the sum of the individual torques, as shown in Fig. 4–21. As expected from Eq. 4–28, the net torque at standstill is zero. However, it is apparent that once the rotor has been set in motion a net torque is exerted and the rotor tends to rotate in the direction of initial motion.

In order to make the single-phase motor self-starting, the basic properties of the self-starting polyphase motors are introduced, namely, the addition of a starting winding out of space-phase with the main winding and
carrying a current out of time phase with the main current. Therefore
a starting winding is placed at 90 electrical degrees to the main winding

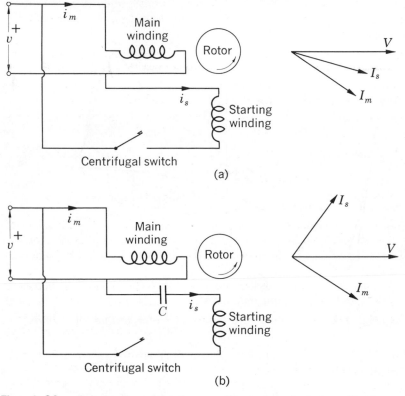

Fig. 4–22. Schematic and phasor diagrams of (a) split-phase induction motor; (b) capacitor start induction motor.

and the time-phase difference between the currents in the two windings is
achieved by making the starting circuit less inductive, or even capacitive,
with respect to the main circuit, as shown in Fig. 4–22. Maximum starting torque is produced if the two currents are out of phase by 90 electrical
degrees, and this may be achieved in the capacitor-start motor. It is
common practice to incorporate a centrifugal switch which disconnects
the starting winding when the motor has reached 70 to 80 percent of
synchronous speed.

PROBLEMS

4-1. For transformers whose losses are negligible:

a. Is the voltage across each turn of the primary winding more, less, or equal to the voltage across each turn of the secondary winding?
b. The secondary has 1800 turns. If it is desired to step down voltage from 440 to 110 volts, how many turns must the primary winding have?
c. If a 3-ohm load is connected to the secondary of the transformer in part (b), what is the primary current?

4-2. Two instrument transformers are used in conjunction with a wattmeter to measure power in a 2400-volt line. The voltage transformer has a turns ratio of 15:1, while the current transformer has a turns ratio of 1:50. If the wattmeter reads 430 watts, what is the power flow in the circuit?

4-3. If the transformer considered in Example 4-1 is operated on a 50-cps supply, find the input current, voltage, and power factor.

4-4. A 16-kva transformer has a 15:1 turns ratio, and the following parameters at 60 cps:

$$r_1 = 2.25 \text{ ohms} \qquad r_2 = 0.01 \text{ ohm}$$
$$x_1 = 4.5 \text{ ohms} \qquad x_2 = 0.02 \text{ ohm}$$
$$x_e = 4000 \text{ ohms} \qquad r_c = 7000 \text{ ohms}$$

If the transformer is supplying rated kva at 110 volts, and at a power factor of 0.8 lag, draw the approximate equivalent circuit and phasor diagram for the transformer with respect to the primary. Find the input current, voltage, and power.

4-5. A single-phase load is supplied through a feeder whose impedance is $(105 + j360)$ ohm and a transformer with a step-down turns ratio of 13.8:1 and an equivalent impedance of $(0.26 + j1.08)$ ohm referred to its low-voltage side. The feeder is at the high-voltage side, and a load of 180 kw at 0.85 leading power factor and 2250 volts is at the low-voltage side.

a. Assuming negligible no-load current, draw an equivalent circuit and phasor diagram of the combined feeder and transformer with respect to the high-voltage side.
b. Calculate the magnitude of the input voltage to the feeder.

4-6. Draw the complete equivalent circuit of an induction motor and indicate what each of the elements represents.

4-7. A 6-pole, 3-phase, 60-cps induction motor has a full-load relative slip of 0.04 and a no-load relative slip of 0.006. Find

a. The full-load speed.
b. The no-load speed.
c. The frequency of the voltage induced in the rotor conductors at no load, standstill, and full load.

4-8. a. In what important respect does the variation of torque with speed for the induction motor differ with that for the d-c shunt motor?

    b. Why in general is the slip of the squirrel-cage motor low?

    c. What type of rotor would you use in an induction motor where large starting torque as well as small slip at running speed is required?

4–9. An aircraft gyroscope, whose rotating mass is in fact the rotor of an induction motor, operates on the standard frequency of 400 cps.

    a. What is the rotor speed of a 115-volt, 3-phase, 2-pole gyroscope rotor when the slip is 0.12?

    b. What is the frequency of the voltage induced in the rotor conductors?

    c. The maximum torque on the rotor is to be developed at a rotor speed of 18,200 rpm. The rotor is wound with 50 turns of silver wire per phase, where the mean length of each turn is 0.1 m. The inductance of the winding is 1.66×10^{-4} henry/phase. If it is assumed that $a = 1$ and $r_1 \approx x_1 \approx 0$, find the diameter of the wire if the resistivity of silver at the operating temperature is 1.629×10^{-8} ohm-m.

4–10. An 8-pole, 3-phase, 60-cps, Y-connected, 220-volt induction motor has stator and rotor resistances of 0.25 and 0.15 ohm per phase, and a stator and rotor reactance of 0.6 ohm and 0.23 ohm per phase, respectively, at 60 cps, where all quantities are referred to the stator. The excitation reactance is 23 ohm per phase. At a slip of 0.03, find

    a. The output power if 3 percent of the mechanical power developed is dissipated by windage and friction.

    b. The heat dissipated by the rotor conductors.

    c. The output torque.

    d. The total electrical input power and the starting current.

4–11. For the induction motor described in Prob. 4–10, determine the speed at which maximum torque is produced and the maximum output torque. To what value should the rotor resistance be changed so that maximum torque is produced at standstill? What is the starting current with the additional rotor resistance in circuit?

4–12. The induction motor of Prob. 4–10 is to be supplied from a constant 220-volt source through a feeder with an impedance of $(0.3 + j0.2)$ ohm per phase. Under such a condition, what is the maximum output torque? What is the starting torque?

4–13. A 10-pole, 3-phase, 60-cps, 220-volt, Y-connected induction motor has stator and rotor resistances of 0.3 ohm and 0.3 ohm per phase, and stator and rotor reactances of 0.7 ohm and 0.28 ohm per phase, respectively, where all quantities are referred to the stator. The excitation reactance is 23 ohm per phase. At a slip of 0.04, find

    a. The output power, if 4 percent of the mechanical power developed is dissipated by windage and friction.

    b. The heat dissipated by the rotor conductors.

    c. The output torque.

    d. The total electrical input power.

    e. The approximate starting current.

4-14. A 6-pole, 220-volt, 3-phase, 60-cps, Y-connected, wound-rotor induction motor has a total reactance at standstill of 3 ohm per phase, referred to the stator, and a full-load slip of 12 percent. The rotor and stator resistance in ohms per phase, when referred to the stator, are respectively 0.7 and 0.6.

a. Find the maximum output torque if the windage and friction loss is considered constant at 400 watts.

b. If maximum torque is required at a speed of 400 rpm, how much resistance, referred to the stator, must be added to the rotor winding per phase?

c. What is the percentage change, in sign and magnitude, in the starting torque when the additional resistance, as determined in part (b), is added?

d. What is the frequency of the voltage induced in the rotor at a speed of 200 rpm?

4-15. A 4-pole, 220-volt, 60-cps, 3-phase, wound-rotor induction motor has a combined stator and rotor leakage reactance of 4 ohms per phase, referred to the stator, and a full-load slip of 10 percent. If the stator reactance is five times greater than the stator resistance, and the stator and rotor reactances when referred to the stator are equal, find the maximum torque developed.

4-16. A 12-pole, 3-phase induction motor is operated from a 180-cps source and directly drives an 8-pole, 3-phase, Y-connected alternator. The windings of the alternator are distributed with 4 turns per phase and a distribution factor of 0.95. The flux per pole is 0.25 weber.

a. Find the frequency of the output voltage from the alternator if the open-circuit line-to-line rms value is 850 volts.

b. What is the speed of rotation of the coupling shaft?

c. What is the percentage slip of the induction motor?

4-17. A 6-pole, 220-volt, 60-cps, 3-phase, Y-connected, wound-rotor induction motor has rotor and stator resistances in ohms per phase, referred to the stator, of 0.01 and 0.013. The leakage reactances $x_1 = x_2 = 0.09$ ohm per phase and $x_e = 5.2$ ohm per phase. The motor is fed at rated terminal voltage through a transformer bank and feeder with equivalent series impedance of $(0.005 + j0.05)$ ohm per phase. When operating at an output power of 75 hp, a power factor of 0.85, and an overall efficiency of 84 percent, a three-phase short circuit occurs at the input to the transformer bank. Determine the rms value of the short-circuit current in the motor as a function of time.

4-18. A 6-pole, 3-phase, 60-cps, 400-hp, Y-connected induction motor is supplied at 440 volts. The resistances and reactances of the machine in ohms per phase referred to the stator are: $r_1 = 0.005$, $r_2 = 0.006$, $x_e = 3.5$, $x_1 = x_2 = 0.05$. At full load, the power factor is 0.9 and the efficiency of the combined feeder and motor is 86 percent.

a. Find the variation of the rms current input to the motor as a function of time if a three phase short circuit occurs at the input at $t = 0$.

b. If the motor load is purely inertial so that the moment of inertia of the rotating system is 70 kg-m², how much time is required to bring the speed up to 1000 rpm from standstill?

Bibliography: Part I

FITZGERALD, A. E., and KINGSLEY, C., JR. *Electric Machinery*, 2d ed. New York: McGraw-Hill Book Co., Inc. 1961.

GOURISHANKAR, V. *Electromechanical Energy Conversion*. Scranton, Pa.: International Textbook Co. 1965.

KIMBARK, E. *Power System Stability*. New York: John Wiley & Sons, Inc. 1948.

KRON, G. *Application of Tensors to the Analysis of Rotating Electrical Machinery*, 2d ed. Schenectady, N.Y.: *General Electric Review*. 1942.

LEVI, E., and PANZER, M. *Electromechanical Power Conversion*. New York: McGraw-Hill Book Co., Inc. 1966.

MAJMUDAR, H. *Electrochemical Energy Converters*. Rockleigh, N.J.: Allyn & Bacon, Inc. 1965.

MEISEL, J. *Principles of Electromechanical Energy Conversion*. New York: McGraw-Hill Book Co., Inc. 1966.

PUCHSTEIN, A. F., LLOYD, T. C., and CONRAD, A. G. *Alternating-Current Machines*, 3d ed. New York: John Wiley & Sons, Inc. 1954.

SCHILLING, E. W. *Electrical Engineering*. Scranton, Pa.: International Textbook Co. 1958.

SCHMITZ, N. L., and NOVOTNY, D. W. *Introductory Electromechanics*. New York: The Ronald Press Co. 1965.

SEELY, S. *Dynamic Systems Analysis*. New York: Reinhold Publishing Corp. 1964.

SEELY, S. *Electromechanical Energy Conversion*. New York: McGraw-Hill Book Co., Inc. 1962.

WHITE, D. C., and WOODSON, H. H. *Electromechanical Energy Conversion*. New York: John Wiley & Sons, Inc. 1959.

II

Direct Thermal-Electrical Conversion

5

Thermoelectric Conversion

5-1. CHARGE CARRIERS AND MATERIALS

Of the early theories regarding the electronic structure of metals the *free-electron theory*, as presented at the beginning of the twentieth century by Drude, is the most important. The theory, which was later modified by Lorentz, postulates that all except the outer (valence) electrons of the atoms are tightly bound. The free electrons, however, were assumed to move through the atomic lattice and to obey many of the gas laws, as described by kinetic theory. In particular it was assumed that the energy is distributed among the free electrons as determined from the classical Maxwell-Boltzmann law.

The free-electron theory explains many properties of metals. For example, when an external electric field is applied across a metal the resultant electron current is proportional to the potential gradient and is limited by electron-atom collisions. It also explains the Wiedemann-Franz law, which relates electrical and thermal conductivity.

However, the Drude-Lorentz theory predicts specific heats of metals which are at variance with those observed; it also fails to account for the fact that some substances are better electrical conductors than others. In view of these and other discrepancies it became apparent that some of the assumptions were in error. After the development of *quantum mechanics*, Sommerfeld found that most of the failings of the free-electron theory could be removed by replacing the classical Boltzmann statistics with the Fermi-Dirac quantum statistics. According to classical mechanics all electrons can have the same energies, so that at absolute zero they would all occupy the lowest available energy level. However, quantum theory specifies that electrons can reside only in discrete energy states, each of which is determined by three quantum numbers; and the Pauli exclusion principle states that there can be no more than two electrons in any one state and that these must have spins of opposite sign. As a result, at absolute zero, not only are the lowest possible energy states filled but

147

electrons occupy states of relatively large quantum number. Consequently if $f(E)$ is the probability that a particular quantum state is filled, then, at a temperature of absolute zero, the probability distribution as a function of energy is as shown in Fig. 5–1, where E_0 is the *Fermi energy* and is the highest energy level occupied at 0°K. At higher temperatures, electrons occupying states near the Fermi energy receive sufficient thermal

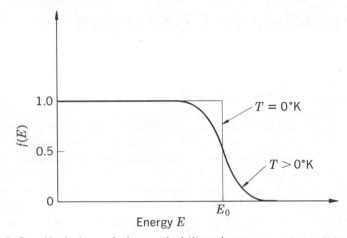

Fig. 5–1. Variation of the probability that a quantum state is filled as a function of state energy when the temperature is at absolute zero, and also $T°$K.

energy to move into higher unoccupied states. As a result there are unoccupied states below the Fermi energy, and the probability distribution is as shown in Fig. 5–1. The *Fermi function* represents this distribution and gives the probability that an allowed quantum state at energy E is filled when the material is at a temperature $T°$K.

$$f(E) = \frac{1}{1 + \exp\left[\dfrac{e(E - E_0)}{kT}\right]} \tag{5-1}$$

When $E = E_0, f(E_0) = 0.5$; therefore the Fermi energy may be defined as that energy at which the probability of a state being filled is one-half.

The allowed energy levels for the electrons of a particular isolated atom are represented in Fig. 5–2a. When two similar atoms having the same allowed energy levels are a distance d apart, the result is as shown in Fig. 5–2b. The individual energy levels split into two separate levels which move apart as the distance between the atoms decreases. The result is similar when two circuits of the same resonant frequency are brought together: the combined system has two resonant frequencies and the spacing between the frequencies increases as the coupling is increased.

In general, a large number of atoms in a material interact so that the discrete allowed energy levels split up into many energy levels and form an essentially continuous band as shown in Fig. 5–2c. Consequently, it is customary to talk of *allowed bands* separated by *forbidden zones*.

At this point it is possible to examine the band structure of electrical insulators, conductors, and semiconductors. A good electrical insulator is characterized by a filled valence band and a large band gap between this

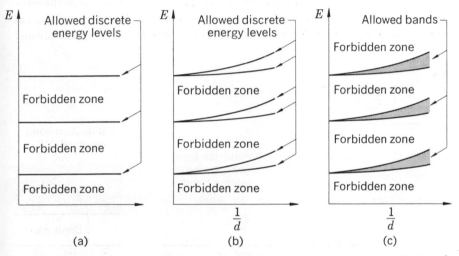

Fig. 5–2. (a) Allowed energy levels for the electrons of an isolated atom. (b) Allowed energy levels for the electrons of two atoms separated by a distance d. (c) Allowed energy bands for the electrons of an atomic lattice with a mean separation distance d.

and the next band, as in Fig. 5–3a. At operating temperatures, electrons in the valence band do not receive sufficient thermal energy to cross the large forbidden zone and reach the conduction band. As a result, the electrons are tightly bound to their atoms and the conductivity of such materials is low.

Conversely, a good conductor is characterized by a conduction band which overlaps the valence band and so enables the electrons to move throughout the material.

A *semiconductor* is a material which has a filled valence band at $0°K$ but has a small band gap between the valence and conduction band, so that an appreciable number of electrons receive sufficient thermal energy at room temperatures to rise into the conduction band. This is called an *intrinsic semiconductor*. The number of free electrons per unit volume in the conduction band n_i is a function of the absolute temperature and the energy gap E_g, and is given by

$$n_i{}^2 = A_0 T^3 \exp\left(-eE_g/kT\right) \tag{5-2}$$

where

$$A_0 = 2.33 \times 10^{43} \text{ m}^{-6}\text{-}^\circ\text{K}^{-3}$$

Most semiconductor materials have controlled amounts of impurity materials added. n-Type materials are characterized by an allowed energy level, or *donor level*, near the top of the forbidden zone. At room temperatures, almost all of the electrons from the donor atoms are thermalized into the conduction band and, since the number of impurity electrons at operating temperature is greater than the number of intrinsic electrons,

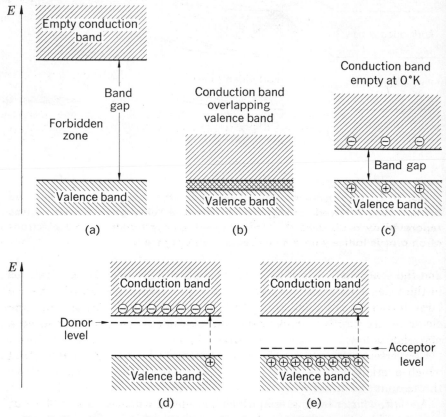

Fig. 5–3. Energy level diagrams for (a) an insulator; (b) a conductor; (c) an intrinsic semiconductor; (d) an n-type semiconductor; (e) a p-type semiconductor.

the electrical properties of the material are essentially determined by the quantity and form of impurity introduced. In a p-type material an acceptor impurity with an electron deficiency and an allowed energy level close to the valence band is introduced. At room temperatures, electrons are easily thermalized from the valence band to the acceptor level and fill most of the available energy states, leaving a deficiency of electrons in the valence band. The absence of an electron is called a hole, to which is attributed all the properties of a positively charged particle, so that conduction in a p-type material is mainly due to the movement of holes in the valence band. As with n-type materials at room temperature, the density of holes is in general very close to the density of acceptor impurity atoms, and for negligible intrinsic effects the electrical properties are controlled by the impurity concentration.

Even though a p-type material may contain a large number of holes per unit volume p, there are still some electrons generated as they were in the pure material. At all doping levels, and for both p- and n-type materials, it is found that

$$np = n_i^2 \tag{5-3}$$

where n is the number of free electrons per unit volume and n_i is given by Eq. 5-2. This relationship is convenient for calculating the minority carrier concentrations, once the doping level, and hence the majority carrier concentration, is known.

5-2. THERMOELECTRIC EFFECTS

In 1822, five years before Ohm's law was enunciated, the German physicist Seebeck discovered that a voltage is produced in a loop of two different materials if the junctions are at different temperatures. Twelve years later the French physicist Peltier discovered that when a current is passed through a loop of two different materials one junction becomes hot, while the other becomes cold. Finally, in 1854, the British physicist Thomson (Lord Kelvin) discovered that when a current passes through a conductor in which there is a temperature gradient, heat is either absorbed or liberated, depending on the current direction. In addition, he formulated two equations (the Kelvin relations) which relate the Seebeck, Peltier, and Thomson effects.

The cause of the three effects is now examined. Consider the loop in Fig. 5-4a, composed of materials A and B, which are p- and n-type materials, respectively. Junction 1 is maintained at an elevated temperature $T + \Delta T$ relative to junction 2, which is at temperature T, and consequently a greater number of electrons in the n-type material and holes in the p-type material are raised from the valence to the conduction band at junction 1. The excess of charge carriers diffuses to the lower density region at the cooler junction, where the holes and electrons recombine, and liberate heat. The flow of both holes and electrons from one junction to the other constitutes the circulation of a current i about the loop.* Provided the heat, which is required to raise the charge carriers

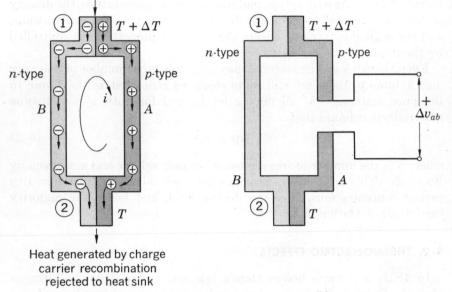

Heat supplied from source
for charge carrier generation

Heat generated by charge
carrier recombination
rejected to heat sink
(a)   (b)

Fig. 5–4. (a) Flow of charge carriers in a basic thermoelectric system. (b) Open-circuited thermoelectric system.

to the conduction band, is supplied at junction 1, and the heat of recombination is removed at junction 2, the current will continue to flow.

If the loop is open-circuited, a voltage Δv_{ab} develops, as shown in Fig. 5–4b. This is called the *Seebeck voltage*, and, for a given material combination, is proportional to the temperature difference ΔT. The temperature-dependent constant of proportionality S_{ab} for a small temperature difference is termed the *Seebeck coefficient* for the particular material combination, and

$$\Delta v_{ab} = S_{ab}\,\Delta T$$

* Negative charge flows in the opposite direction to positive current, while positive charge flows in the same direction as the current.

or, for a differential temperature difference

$$\frac{dv_{ab}}{dT} = S_{ab}$$ (5-4)

The Seebeck coefficient is dependent on material properties, and is also temperature-dependent, but it should be realized that the Seebeck voltage is independent of the geometry of the materials forming the loop, and also of the junction geometry. S_{ab} *is defined as positive if the current flows* *from material A to material B at the junction where the heat of recombination* *is rejected.*

If the heat sources and sinks are removed from the junction, and a voltage source applied across the gap in material B, so that a current continues to flow in the same direction as in Fig. 5-4a, then the flow of charge carriers remains unaltered. Therefore, electrons and holes continue to recombine at junction 2 and liberate heat, while being generated at junction 1 and absorbing heat from the surrounding material. As a result junction 2 becomes hot while junction 1 becomes cold. The rate of heat flow q at a junction is proportional to the current i, where the temperature-dependent constant of proportionality is called the *Peltier* *coefficient* Π_{ab}. Therefore

$$q = \Pi_{ab}i$$ (5-5)

As with the Seebeck coefficient Π_{ab} is dependent on temperature and on the materials at the junction, but is not dependent on the geometry of these materials. Π_{ab} *is defined as positive if heat is generated by the recom-* *bining charge carriers when current flows from material A to material B.* Therefore

$$\Pi_{ab} = -\Pi_{ba}$$ (5-6)

The Thomson effect may be examined by considering a p-type material in which there is a temperature gradient as shown in Fig. 5-5. If a current is passed from 2 to 1, then holes are moving into material which is at a higher temperature and therefore tend to cool it. The rate at which heat is absorbed by the holes in a differential length dx is proportional to the current i and also to the temperature gradient dT/dx. The temperature-dependent constant of proportionality, τ, is called the Thomson coefficient. Therefore the heat absorbed in a differential length dx is

$$dq_{\tau} = \tau i \frac{dT}{dx} dx$$

and the total Thomson heat absorbed is

$$q_\tau = i \int_2^1 \tau \frac{dT}{dx} \, dx$$

Therefore

$$q_\tau = i \int_{T_2}^{T_1} \tau \, dT \tag{5-7}$$

If the current direction is reversed, heat is liberated rather than absorbed. The Thomson coefficient is usually defined as positive if heat

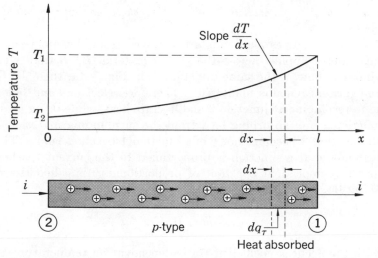

Fig. 5–5. Heat absorption in a current-carrying conductor with a temperature gradient.

is absorbed when the current flows from a low- to a higher-temperature region. *The Thomson coefficient is therefore defined as positive for* p-*type material and negative for* n-*type material.* It must be emphasized that this absorption, or liberation of heat is a reversible effect which is independent of the Joule heating. In practice, therefore, the total heat liberated in a given conductor is greater or less than i^2R, depending on whether the Thomson heat is liberated or absorbed, respectively.

In 1854 Thomson (Lord Kelvin) postulated that the Seebeck and Peltier coefficients are related by the equation

$$S = \frac{\Pi}{T} \tag{5-8}$$

This relationship (the *second Kelvin relation*) has been verified by precise experiment and there is no doubt that it holds. However, it is not possible to derive it unequivocally from the basic laws of thermodynamics. As a result, efforts were made to reformulate the basic laws of physics to encompass the Kelvin relation and, in 1931, Onsager satisfactorily formulated the principles underlying irreversible processes.

5–3. BASIC THERMOELECTRIC ENERGY CONVERSION

Now that the thermoelectric effects have been examined and it is apparent that fundamental relationships exist between thermal and electrical phenomena, a basic thermoelectric energy conversion system is considered. Figure 5–6 shows an arrangement in which heat is supplied

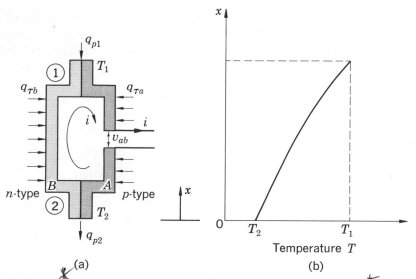

Fig. 5–6. (a) Schematic of idealized thermoelectric generator. (b) Temperature distribution between the heat sink and source.

at a rate q_{p1} and temperature T_1 at junction 1, and rejected at a rate q_{p2} and temperature T_2 at junction 2. A load current i is drawn from the system. For this initial analysis, Joule heating and heat loss by direct conduction of heat between reservoirs 1 and 2 is not considered.

Under steady-state conditions the electrical output power is equal to the net thermal input power. The thermal input is composed of the Peltier heat at the junctions plus the absorbed Thomson heat. (At present it is assumed that the heat intake associated with the Thomson effect is supplied by distributed heat reservoirs placed around the loop.) Therefore the steady-state power-balance equation is—

$$v_{ab}i = q_{p1} - q_{p2} + q_{\tau a} + q_{\tau b} \qquad (5\text{--}9)$$

where q_{ra} and q_{rb} are the rates at which Thomson heat is absorbed by materials A and B, respectively. Keeping in mind the definitions of positive heat flow, the terms of Eq. 5–9 may be expressed as follows:

$$-q_{p1} = \Pi_{ba1}i = -\Pi_{ab1}i \qquad (5\text{--}10)$$

$$q_{p2} = \Pi_{ab2}i \qquad (5\text{--}11)$$

From Eq. 5–7,

$$q_{rb} = i \int_{T_2}^{T_1} \tau_b \, dT \qquad (5\text{--}12)$$

and

$$q_{ra} = (-i) \int_{T_2}^{T_1} \tau_a \, dT \qquad (5\text{--}13)$$

where Π_{ab1} and Π_{ab2} are the Peltier coefficients evaluated at temperatures T_1 and T_2, respectively, and τ_a and τ_b are the Thomson coefficients expressed as functions of temperature for materials A and B, respectively.

Substituting for the terms in Eq. 5–9 and dividing across by i gives

$$v_{ab} = \Pi_{ab1} - \Pi_{ab2} + \int_{T_2}^{T_1} (\tau_b - \tau_a) \, dT \qquad (5\text{--}14)$$

Upon differentiating Eq. 5–14 with respect to T_1, the so-called *first Kelvin relation* may be established:

$$\frac{dv_{ab}}{dT_1} = \frac{d\Pi_{ab1}}{dT_1} + \tau_{b1} - \tau_{a1} \qquad (5\text{--}15)$$

where $d\Pi_{ab2}/dT_1$ is zero since Π_{ab2} is a function of T_2 only, and τ_{a1} and τ_{b1} are the Thomson coefficients of materials A and B, respectively, evaluated at a temperature T_1. Upon substituting S_{ab} and dropping the subscript 1, Eq. 5–15 becomes

$$S_{ab} = \frac{d\Pi_{ab}}{dT} + \tau_b - \tau_a \qquad (5\text{--}16)$$

and upon differentiating Eq. 5–8 with respect to T,

$$\frac{d\Pi_{ab}}{dT} = T \frac{dS_{ab}}{dT} + S_{ab} \qquad (5\text{--}17)$$

Substituting Eq. 5–17 in Eq. 5–16 and rearranging gives

$$\boxed{T \frac{dS_{ab}}{dT} = \tau_a - \tau_b} \qquad (5\text{--}18)$$

This is the *first Kelvin relation,* which relates the Seebeck and Thomson coefficients.

It should be apparent that both the Seebeck and Peltier coefficients have so far been expressed for the combination of two materials at a junction, while the Thomson effect is associated with a single material. Equation 5–18 may be used to attribute an absolute Seebeck coefficient to a single material. Integrating Eq. 5–18 from absolute zero to temperature T gives

$$S_{ab} = \int_0^T \frac{\tau_a}{T} \, dT - \int_0^T \frac{\tau_b}{T} \, dT$$

So that

$$\boxed{S_{ab} = S_a - S_b} \tag{5–19}$$

where S_a and S_b are defined as the absolute Seebeck coefficients of materials A and B, respectively, and

$$S_a = \int_0^T \frac{\tau_a}{T} \, dT \qquad S_b = \int_0^T \frac{\tau_b}{T} \, dT$$

The absolute Seebeck coefficient of a material may be found by joining it to another which is at a temperature in the superconducting region and has a Seebeck coefficient of zero. Such an experiment has been conducted for lead and its absolute Seebeck coefficient is accurately known over a wide temperature range. It is therefore possible to evaluate the absolute Seebeck coefficient of any other material by simply joining it to lead, measuring the combined Seebeck coefficient, and solving Eq. 5–19.

For a single material, the absolute Seebeck coefficient may be written as

$$S_a = \frac{dv_a}{dT} \tag{5–20}$$

where v_a is the Seebeck voltage associated with material A. Also, the Kelvin relations for a single material become

$$T \frac{dS_a}{dT} = \tau_a \tag{5–21}$$

and

$$S_a = \frac{\Pi_a}{T} \tag{5–22}$$

where Π_a is the absolute Peltier coefficient of material A.

When considering the basic system of Fig. 5–6, no mention was made of the junction effects which occur at the points where the electrical contacts are made. With this in mind, the effect of introducing an intermediate material C as in Fig. 5–7a, between materials A and B is now examined. The intermediate material and the junctions with the other two conductors are maintained at reservoir temperature T_1.

The voltage v_{ab} is composed of the individual Seebeck voltages, so that

$$v_{ab} = v_6 - v_5 = (v_6 - v_2) + (v_2 - v_3) + (v_3 - v_4) + (v_4 - v_5) \tag{5–23}$$

From Eq. 5–20

$$v_6 - v_2 = \int_{T_2}^{T_6} S_a \, dT$$

$$v_2 - v_3 = \int_{T_1}^{T_2} S_b \, dT$$

$$v_3 - v_4 = \int_{T_1}^{T_1} S_c \, dT = 0$$

$$v_4 - v_5 = \int_{T_5}^{T_1} S_a \, dT$$

Substituting these equations in Eq. 5–23 gives

$$v_{ab} = \int_{T_2}^{T_6} S_a \, dT + \int_{T_1}^{T_2} S_b \, dT + \int_{T_5}^{T_1} S_a \, dT \qquad (5\text{–}24)$$

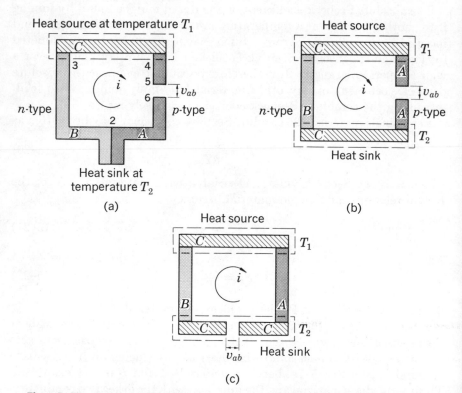

Fig. 5–7. Thermoelectric generator (a) with intermediate conductor at heat source; (b) with intermediate conductors at source and sink; (c) with electrical output terminals in the intermediate conductor at the heat sink.

Assuming the temperature is continuous in material A, then $T_5 = T_6$ and Eq. 5–24 may be written

$$v_{ab} = \int_{T_2}^{T_1} (S_a - S_b)\, dT \qquad (5\text{–}25)$$

which is independent of the properties of the material C. Therefore the important conclusion is reached: that an intermediate material, maintained at a fixed temperature throughout, may be introduced into a thermoelectric loop without altering the net Seebeck voltage. Consequently if terminal leads, made from a given material, are connected at points 5 and 6, for the purpose of making an electrical connection, and both of these leads are at the same temperature, then the Seebeck voltage v_{ab} remains unaltered.

The introduction of one or more intermediate conductors is of practical importance, since it is now possible to present a large surface area at the high temperature through which the input heat may pass. Likewise the junction at temperature T_2 may be effectively enlarged, so that a high heat rejection rate is possible. Such an arrangement is shown in Fig. 5–7b. Now that an intermediate material has been introduced at the cold reservoir, it is convenient, in practice, to place the connections to the external electrical circuit in this material, and the loop is opened as shown in Fig. 5–7c.

5–4. OPTIMIZED DESIGN

Having introduced some practical modifications, it is now appropriate to consider the steps which must be taken in order to optimize the thermal efficiency of the system. In the following analysis, some simplifying assumptions are made which in practice lead to results which are very close to the true values. The assumptions are the following:

1. The thermoelectric materials have resistivities and thermal conductivities which are independent of temperature.
2. All energy transfer between the heat source and sink is by way of the thermoelectric materials.
3. There is no heat loss from the surface of the thermoelectric materials.
4. There is negligible contact resistance.
5. The absolute Seebeck coefficients are averaged over the operating temperature range, and the constant average value of the Seebeck coefficient ($\bar{S}$) is used.

Consider the system in Fig. 5–8. The thermoelectric converter supplies a current i at a voltage v_L to a load R_L. Both of the thermoelectric materials A and B have constant cross-section with areas A_a, A_b, lengths l_a, l_b, resistivities ρ_a, ρ_b, and thermal conductivities k_a, k_b, respectively.

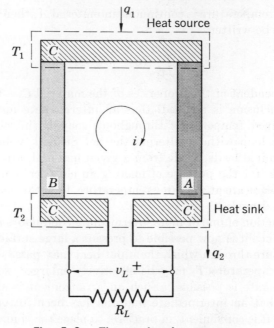

Fig. 5–8. Thermoelectric generator.

The effective internal resistance of the generator is then

$$r_g = \frac{\rho_a l_a}{A_a} + \frac{\rho_b l_b}{A_b}$$

or

$$r_g = \frac{\rho_a}{\gamma_a} + \frac{\rho_b}{\gamma_b} \tag{5–26}$$

where

$$\gamma_a = \frac{A_a}{l_a} \quad \text{and} \quad \gamma_b = \frac{A_b}{l_b}$$

The thermal conductance between the source and sink is

$$K = k_a \frac{A_a}{l_a} + k_b \frac{A_b}{l_b}$$

or

$$K = k_a \gamma_a + k_b \gamma_b \tag{5–27}$$

The average value of the Seebeck coefficient within the temperature range ΔT $(= T_1 - T_2)$, is evaluated by integration as

$$\bar{S} = \frac{1}{\Delta T} \int_{T_2}^{T_1} S_{ab}(T) \, dT$$

and the Peltier heat rates at the source and sink are, from Eqs. 5–5 and 5–22, respectively,

$$q_{p1} = \bar{S}T_1 i \tag{5-28}$$

and

$$q_{p2} = \bar{S}T_2 i \tag{5-29}$$

For the temperature range under consideration, the output voltage

$$v_L = v_{ab} - ir_g$$

Therefore

$$v_L = \bar{S}\,\Delta T - ir_g \tag{5-30}$$

The fact that the average absolute Seebeck coefficients for the range of operation are independent of temperature, that is, $dS_a/dT = dS_b/dT = 0$, means (from Eq. 5–21) that the effective average Thomson coefficients are zero. As a result it can be assumed that, under steady-state conditions, the total rate of heat input from the source q_1, at temperature T_1, is the sum of the Peltier heat rate q_{p1}, and the rate of heat conduction through materials A and B to the heat sink, q_c.

Now that the resistance of the materials is considered, account must be taken of the Joule heating. The assumption that half of the Joule heat produced in materials A and B is returned to each reservoir is found to be a close approximation. Therefore if q_r is the rate at which Joule heat is produced, the net rate of heat input from the source is

$$q_1 = q_{p1} + q_c - \tfrac{1}{2}q_r \tag{5-31}$$

Therefore

$$q_1 = \bar{S}T_1 i + K\,\Delta T - \tfrac{1}{2}i^2 r_g \tag{5-32}$$

Similarly, the rate at which heat is removed by the heat sink is

$$q_2 = \bar{S}T_2 i + K\,\Delta T + \tfrac{1}{2}i^2 r_g \tag{5-33}$$

The thermal efficiency is

$$\eta_t = \frac{\text{power out}}{\text{power in}} = \frac{i^2 R_L}{\bar{S}T_1 i + K\,\Delta T - \dfrac{1}{2}\,i^2 r_g} \tag{5-34}$$

Example 5–1. The following properties apply to a thermoelectric generator operating between 310 and 610°K:

$$\bar{S} = 440 \times 10^{-6} \text{ volt/°K}$$
$$K = 25 \times 10^{-3} \text{ watt/°K}$$
$$r_g = 3.1 \times 10^{-3} \text{ ohm}$$

(a) Calculate the open-circuit voltage.
(b) Calculate the current, output voltage, and efficiency at maximum power.

(c) Calculate the input power and the current when the terminals are short-circuited.

(a) The Seebeck voltage, or the internal voltage, developed is

$$v_{ab} = \bar{S}\,\Delta t$$
$$= 440 \times 10^{-6} \times 300$$
$$= 0.132 \text{ volt}$$

(b) For maximum power output $R_L = r_g$, so that the current is

$$i = \frac{v_{ab}}{2r_g} = \frac{0.132}{2 \times 3.1 \times 10^{-3}} = 21.3 \text{ amp}$$

The output voltage is

$$v_L = \tfrac{1}{2}v_{ab}$$
$$= 0.066 \text{ volt}$$

The maximum output power is

$$P_m = v_L i = 0.066 \times 21.3$$
$$= 1.41 \text{ watts}$$

The input power, from Eq. 5–32, is

$$q_1 = (440 \times 10^{-6} \times 610 \times 21.3) + (25 \times 10^{-3} \times 300)$$
$$- (0.5 \times 21.3^2 \times 3.1 \times 10^{-3})$$
$$= 12.53 \text{ watts}$$

Therefore the thermal efficiency at maximum power is

$$\eta_t = \frac{P_m}{q_1} = \frac{1.41}{12.53} = 11.2 \text{ percent}$$

(c) Under short-circuited conditions the current is

$$i_{sc} = \frac{v_{ab}}{r_g} = \frac{0.132}{3.1 \times 10^{-3}} = 42.6 \text{ amp}$$

The input power from the heat source is

$$q_1 = (440 \times 10^{-6} \times 610 \times 42.6) + (25 \times 10^{-3} \times 300)$$
$$- (0.5 \times 42.6^2 \times 3.1 \times 10^{-3})$$
$$= 16.1 \text{ watts}$$

It is apparent from the foregoing example that the thermoelectric generator is a low-voltage, high-current device. Therefore it is usual to connect a number of generators in series so that larger overall voltages are available.

Upon examining the various terms of the thermal efficiency expression, it is obvious that the geometry should be optimized so that a compromise is reached between the Joule heating loss and the thermal conduction loss between the hot and cold reservoirs.

To visualize the steps which must be taken in optimizing the geometry, the expression for thermal efficiency must be put in a more convenient form. Upon multiplying the numerator and denominator of Eq. 5–34 by $\Delta T / i^2 r_g T_1$ and making the substitution

$$M = \frac{R_L}{r_g} \tag{5–35}$$

we have

$$\eta_t = \frac{\dfrac{\Delta T}{T_1} M}{\dfrac{1}{i} \dfrac{\bar{S} \, \Delta T}{r_g} + \dfrac{1}{i^2} \dfrac{K(\Delta T)^2}{r_g T_1} - \dfrac{1}{2} \dfrac{\Delta T}{T_1}} \tag{5–36}$$

The current is

$$i = \frac{\bar{S} \, \Delta T}{r_g + R_L} \tag{5–37}$$

and upon substituting Eq. 5–37 in Eq. 5–36,

$$\eta_t = \frac{\dfrac{\Delta T}{T_1} M}{(1 + M) + \dfrac{K r_g}{\bar{S}^2} \dfrac{(1 + M)^2}{T_1} - \dfrac{1}{2} \dfrac{\Delta T}{T_1}} \tag{5–38}$$

In this form it is apparent that if $\bar{S}^2/K r_g$ is made as large as possible, then, under conditions of constant M and temperature, the thermal efficiency is optimized. In fact, this particular combination of terms is called the *figure of merit* and is denoted by

$$\boxed{Z = \frac{\bar{S}^2}{K r_g}} \tag{5–39}$$

For two particular materials operating within a fixed temperature range, $\bar{S}$ is fixed; therefore Z may be optimized by making the product $K r_g$ a minimum.

From Eqs. 5–26 and 5–27,

$$K r_g = (k_a \gamma_a + k_b \gamma_b) \left(\frac{\rho_a}{\gamma_a} + \frac{\rho_b}{\gamma_b} \right)$$

Therefore,

$$K r_g = k_a \rho_a + k_b \rho_b + k_a \rho_b \Gamma + \frac{k_b \rho_a}{\Gamma} \tag{5–40}$$

where

$$\Gamma \equiv \frac{\gamma_a}{\gamma_b} \tag{5–41}$$

Upon differentiating Eq. 5–40 with respect to Γ and setting the result equal to zero, the minimum value of Kr_g is found to occur for

$$\Gamma = \sqrt{\frac{\rho_a k_b}{\rho_b k_a}} \tag{5–42}$$

Substituting Eq. 5–42 in Eq. 5–40 gives

$$(Kr_g)_{\min} = k_a \rho_a + k_b \rho_b + 2\sqrt{k_a \rho_b k_b \rho_a}$$

or

$$(Kr_g)_{\min} = (\sqrt{k_a \rho_a} + \sqrt{k_b \rho_b})^2 \tag{5–43}$$

Therefore the figure of merit, with optimized geometry, becomes

$$\boxed{Z_0 = \left(\frac{\bar{S}}{\sqrt{k_a \rho_a} + \sqrt{k_b \rho_b}} \right)^2} \tag{5–44}$$

and the thermal efficiency with optimized geometry is

$$\eta_{t0} = \frac{\dfrac{\Delta T}{T_1} M}{(1 + M) + \dfrac{(1 + M)^2}{Z_0 T_1} - \dfrac{1}{2}\dfrac{\Delta T}{T_1}} \tag{5–45}$$

Now that the geometry has been optimized, the load which results in maximum efficiency may be found by differentiating Eq. 5–45 with respect to M, and setting the result equal to zero. This gives

$$M_0 = \sqrt{Z_0 \left(T_1 - \frac{\Delta T}{2} \right) + 1}$$

or

$$\boxed{M_0 = \sqrt{Z_0 \bar{T} + 1}} \tag{5–46}$$

where $\bar{T}$ is the mean temperature between the source and sink. Then the maximum value of the thermal efficiency with optimized geometry is

$$\eta_{mt0} = \frac{\dfrac{\Delta T}{T_1} M_0}{(1 + M_0) + \dfrac{(1 + M_0)^2}{Z_0 T_1} - \dfrac{1}{2}\dfrac{\Delta T}{T_1}} \tag{5–47}$$

For application in space the power output per unit weight, or per unit volume, is usually of more importance than the operation at maximum efficiency. Maximum output power P_m is provided when the resistance of the load is equal to the internal resistance of the generator, and therefore

$$P_m = \frac{(\bar{S} \, \Delta T)^2}{4r_g} \tag{5-48}$$

The power per unit volume is

$$\frac{P_m}{V} = \frac{(\bar{S} \, \Delta T)^2}{4 \left(\rho_a \dfrac{l_a}{A_a} + \rho_b \dfrac{l_b}{A_b} \right) (l_a A_a + l_b A_b)} \tag{5-49}$$

and obviously this may be increased by making the lengths of the thermo-electric materials as short as possible. The practical limit is reached when the material resistance approaches the value of the contact resistance. The material area ratio which maximizes Eq. 5–49 is found by differentiating the denominator with respect to A_a/A_b and setting the result equal to zero:

$$\rho_b l_a l_b - \left(\frac{A_b}{A_a} \right)^2 \rho_a l_a l_b = 0$$

Therefore, for maximum power output per unit volume,

$$\frac{A_a}{A_b} = \sqrt{\frac{\rho_a}{\rho_b}} \tag{5-50}$$

Upon substituting Eq. 5–50 in Eq. 5–49,

$$\left(\frac{P_m}{V} \right)_m = \left[\frac{\bar{S} \, \Delta T}{2(l_a \sqrt{\rho_a} + l_b \sqrt{\rho_b})} \right]^2 \tag{5-51}$$

The thermal efficiency, under conditions of maximum power output per unit volume, is obtained from Eq. 5–38 by setting $M = 1$ and setting $Kr_g = (Kr_g)_{mp}$, the value determined by the use of Eq. 5–50;

$$\eta_{mp} = \frac{\dfrac{\Delta T}{T_1}}{2 + \dfrac{4}{\bar{S}^2 T_1} (Kr_g)_{mp} - \dfrac{1}{2} \dfrac{\Delta T}{T_1}} \tag{5-52}$$

Example 5–2. A thermoelectric power supply is to be designed for space use. The source of heat is a nuclear reactor which is cooled by a liquid metal (NaK-78). Thermoelectric generators are connected to pipes through which the metal circulates, giving a mean heat source temperature of 728°K. Heat is radiated into space at a mean heat sink temperature of 588°K. An output power of 500 watts at 50 volts is required. The design is to be carried out for maximum efficiency. The materials selected are p-type AgSbTe$_2$ and n-type 75% PbTe–25% SnTe, since the figure of merit for both materials attains a maximum within the specified temperature range. The following data are for the mean operating temperature.

Material A	Material B
p-type AgSbTe$_2$	n-type PbTe–SnTe
$\bar{S}_a = 242 \times 10^{-6}$ volt/°K	$\bar{S}_b = -120 \times 10^{-6}$ volt/°K
$\bar{Z}_a = 1.92 \times 10^{-3}$/°K	$\bar{Z}_b = 1.15 \times 10^{-3}$/°K
$\bar{\rho}_a = 4.1 \times 10^{-5}$ ohm-m	$\bar{\rho}_b = 1 \times 10^{-5}$ ohm-m
Maximum permissible current	Maximum permissible current
density $= 10^5$ amp/m^2	density $= 2 \times 10^5$ amp/m^2

The thermal conductivities may be calculated from $\bar{Z} = \bar{S}^2/\bar{\rho}\bar{k}$, so that

$$\bar{k}_a = \frac{(242)^2 \times 10^{-12}}{4.1 \times 10^{-5} \times 1.92 \times 10^{-3}} = 0.748 \text{ watt/m-°K}$$

$$\bar{k}_b = \frac{(120)^2 \times 10^{-12}}{1 \times 10^{-5} \times 1.15 \times 10^{-3}} = 1.25 \text{ watts/m-°K}$$

From Eq. 5–44

$$Z_0 = \left(\frac{(242 + 120) \times 10^{-6}}{\sqrt{0.748 \times 4.1 \times 10^{-5}} + \sqrt{1.25 \times 10^{-5}}} \right)^2 = 1.6 \times 10^{-3}/\text{°K}$$

From Eq. 5–46

$$M_0 = \sqrt{1 + 1.6 \times 10^{-3} \times 658} = 1.43$$

From Eq. 5–42

$$\Gamma = \sqrt{\frac{4.1 \times 1.25}{1 \times 0.748}} = 2.62$$

The average Seebeck coefficient for the couple is

$$\bar{S} = \bar{S}_a - \bar{S}_b = (242 + 120) \times 10^{-6} = 362 \times 10^{-6} \text{ volt/°K}$$

Therefore within the temperature range of operation the internally generated Seebeck voltage is

$$v_{ab} = \bar{S}\,\Delta T = 362 \times 10^{-6} \times 140$$
$$= 0.0507 \text{ volt}$$

The output voltage is

$$v_L = v_{ab} \left(\frac{R_L}{R_L + r_g} \right) = v_{ab} \left(\frac{M_0}{1 + M_0} \right)$$
$$= 0.0507 \left(\frac{1.43}{1 + 1.43} \right) = 0.0296 \text{ volt}$$

Since a total output voltage of 50 volts is required, $50/0.0296 = 1690$ generators must be connected in series, and since the total load must be $50^2/500 = 5$ ohms,

$$P_L = \frac{5}{1690} = 2.96 \times 10^{-3} \text{ ohm}$$

From Eq. 5–35

$$r_g = \frac{2.96 \times 10^{-3}}{1.43} = 2.07 \times 10^{-3} \text{ ohm}$$

Since

$$r_g = \frac{\rho_a}{\gamma_a} + \frac{\rho_b}{\gamma_b} \quad \text{and} \quad \gamma_b = \frac{\gamma_a}{\Gamma}$$

then

$$\gamma_a = \frac{\rho_a + \Gamma\rho_b}{r_g}$$

$$= \frac{(4.1 + 2.62 \times 1) \times 10^{-5}}{2.07 \times 10^{-3}} = 3.24 \times 10^{-2} \text{ m}$$

and

$$\gamma_b = \frac{\gamma_a}{\Gamma} = \frac{3.24 \times 10^{-2}}{2.62} = 1.23 \times 10^{-2} \text{ m}$$

The minimum cross-sectional areas are specified by the current densities, and since $i = 500/50 = 10$ amp,

$$A_a \geq \frac{i}{J_a} = \frac{10}{10^5} = 10^{-4} \text{ m}^2$$

and

$$A_b \geq \frac{i}{J_b} = \frac{10}{2 \times 10^5} = 0.5 \times 10^{-4} \text{ m}^2$$

If the maximum current densities are used, then since $\gamma_a = A_a/l_a$ and $\gamma_b = A_b/l_b$,

$$l_a = \frac{10^{-4}}{3.24 \times 10^{-2}} = 0.31 \times 10^{-2} \text{ m}$$

$$l_b = \frac{0.5 \times 10^{-4}}{1.23 \times 10^{-2}} = 0.405 \times 10^{-2} \text{ m}$$

It should be noted that if it is specified that $l_a = l_b$, then A_a may be increased to 1.315×10^{-4} m so that l_a is then 0.405×10^{-2} m and γ_a remains at its optimum value of 3.24×10^{-2} m.

From Eq. 5–27,

$$K = [(0.748 \times 3.24) + (1.25 \times 1.23)] \times 10^{-2}$$
$$= 3.95 \times 10^{-2} \text{ watt/}^\circ\text{K}$$

and from Eq. 5–32,

$$q_1 = (362 \times 10^{-6} \times 728 \times 10) + (39.5 \times 10^{-3} \times 140)$$
$$\qquad\qquad\qquad\qquad\qquad - (0.5 \times 10^2 \times 2.07 \times 10^{-3})$$
$$= 2.64 + 5.51 - 0.104$$
$$= 8.05 \text{ watts}$$

and the total heat input is $8.05 \times 1690 = 13.6 \times 10^3$ watts.   The thermal efficiency is therefore

$$\eta_t = \frac{500 \times 10^2}{13.6 \times 10^3} = 3.68 \text{ percent}$$

The maximum possible thermal efficiency is the Carnot efficiency:

$$\eta_C = \frac{\Delta T}{T_1} = \frac{140 \times 100}{728}$$
$$= 19.2 \text{ percent}$$

and the relative Carnot efficiency is therefore

$$\eta_{rc} = \frac{3.68}{19.2} = 0.192$$

5-5. THERMOELECTRIC REFRIGERATION

As observed when considering the Peltier effect, the passage of current through a thermoelectric couple causes cooling at one junction and heat rejection at the other.   This cooling effect may be used in refrigeration. Although the cost of thermoelectric refrigeration is relatively high, it has certain advantages.   It is well suited to small-scale applications where compactness, simplicity, silence, and long life are desirable.   In addition, it is particularly easy to control the cooling rate, or even introduce automatic temperature cycling, by current variation.   If required, the temperature may also be raised above ambient by current reversal.

In refrigeration design an important quantity is the *coefficient of performance* ϕ, which is defined as the net rate of heat removal from the cold reservoir q'_1, divided by the electrical power input P; therefore

$$\boxed{\phi = \frac{q'_1}{P}} \qquad (5\text{-}53)$$

The net rate at which heat is removed from the cold reservoir is equal to the Peltier cooling rate, less the rate of heat conduction from the hot to the cold reservoir, less one-half of the Joule heat which flows back to the cold reservoir.   Therefore

$$q'_1 = \bar{S}T_1 i - K \Delta T - \tfrac{1}{2}i^2 r_g \qquad (5\text{-}54)$$

The applied voltage required to overcome the Seebeck voltage and the ir_g rise is

$$v_T = \bar{S} \Delta T + ir_g$$

Therefore

$$P = \bar{S} \Delta T i + i^2 r_g \qquad (5\text{-}55)$$

Upon substituting Eq. 5-54 and Eq. 5-55 in Eq. 5-53,

$$\phi = \frac{\bar{S}T_1 i - K\,\Delta T - \frac{1}{2}\,i^2 r_g}{\bar{S}\,\Delta T i + i^2 r_g} \tag{5-56}$$

In order to optimize the coefficient of performance, Eq. 5-56 is put into a suitable form by multiplying its numerator and denominator by $r_g/\bar{S}^2$ and then substituting

$$N = \frac{ir_g}{\bar{S}} \tag{5-57}$$

so that

$$\phi = \frac{T_1 N - \dfrac{1}{2}\,N^2 - \dfrac{\Delta T}{Z}}{N\,\Delta T + N^2} \tag{5-58}$$

Equation 5-58 has its maximum optimum value when the figure of merit $Z = Z_0$ (Eq. 5-44), and N is such that $d\phi/dN = 0$. The latter requirement gives the optimum value of N as

$$\boxed{N_0 = \frac{\Delta T}{\sqrt{1 + Z_0\bar{\bar{T}}} - 1}} \tag{5-59}$$

Therefore the maximum value of the optimized coefficient of performance is

$$\phi_{m0} = \frac{T_1 N_0 - \dfrac{1}{2}\,N_0{}^2 - \dfrac{\Delta T}{Z_0}}{N_0\,\Delta T + N_0{}^2} \tag{5-60}$$

and the current under such conditions, obtained from Eq. 5-57 and Eq. 5-59, is

$$i_0 = \frac{\bar{S}}{r_g} \cdot \left(\frac{\Delta T}{\sqrt{1 + Z_0\bar{\bar{T}}} - 1}\right) \tag{5-61}$$

If it is desired to remove heat at the maximum rate, then the current required i_q is obtained by taking the derivative of Eq. 5-54 with respect to i, and equating the result to zero to obtain

$$i_q = \frac{\bar{S}T_1}{r_g} \tag{5-62}$$

The maximum heat-pumping rate, as found by substituting Eq. 5-62 into Eq. 5-54, is therefore

$$q'_{1m} = \frac{(\bar{S}T_1)^2}{2r_g} - K\,\Delta T \tag{5-63}$$

The maximum temperature difference between the hot and cold reservoirs is achieved when the net rate of heat removal from the cold reservoir becomes zero. Therefore, with $q'_{1m} = 0$ in Eq. 5-63,

$$\Delta T_m = \frac{(\bar{S}T_1)^2}{2Kr_g} \qquad (5\text{-}64)$$

When $\bar{S}^2/Kr_g$ has its optimum value Z_0, the maximum optimized temperature difference,

$$\Delta T_{m0} = \tfrac{1}{2}Z_0T_1^2 \qquad (5\text{-}65)$$

is achieved.

5-6. EVALUATION OF THERMOELECTRIC DEVICES

Although there are obvious advantages associated with the use of thermoelectric systems for both generation and refrigeration, the fact that both efficiency and coefficient of performance compare unfavorably with those of conventional systems limits their adoption for all but small-capacity or specialized systems.

In order to compete with a conventional steam-generating plant, with an overall efficiency of 40 percent, and working between the same temperatures of 300°K and 850°K, the value of $Z\bar{T}$, as determined from Eq. 5-47, must be almost 6.

The possibility of realizing large values of $Z\bar{T}$ is now considered. For ordinary metals the resistivity and thermal conductivity are related by the Wiedemann-Franz law:

$$\rho_m k_m = \frac{\pi^2}{3}\left(\frac{k}{e}\right)^2 \bar{T}$$

or, in mks units,

$$\rho_m k_m = 2.45 \times 10^{-8}\bar{T} \qquad (5\text{-}66)$$

where k_m, k, and e are respectively the thermal conductivity, the Boltzmann constant, and electron charge. The Seebeck coefficient is inversely proportional to the density of free electrons and therefore has a typically low value of 10^{-5} volt/°K for metals. Hence for metals

$$Z\bar{T} = \frac{S_m^2\bar{T}}{k_m\rho_m} = \frac{S_m^2}{2.45 \times 10^{-8}} = \frac{10^{-10}}{2.45 \times 10^{-8}}$$
$$\approx 4 \times 10^{-3}$$

Ordinary metals are obviously of no use for thermoelectric applications, and insulators are of no use because of their high resistivity. The semiconductor, however, is of interest for a number of reasons:

1. Relatively large Seebeck coefficients.
2. The variability of the *doping level* permits the production of materials with optimum properties. Since the Seebeck coefficient decreases while the electrical and thermal conductivities increase with the free-charge carrier density, it is possible to dope the semiconductor to a level at which the figure of merit is maximized. For most materials this corresponds to a doping level of $10^{25}/m^3$, and a Seebeck coefficient of about $\pm 200 \times 10^6$ volts/°K.
3. Heat is conducted through a material by means of two separate processes: crystal lattice vibration, and movement of electrons. In most semiconductors, due to the relatively low density of charge carriers, lattice vibration is the dominant conduction process,\and the coefficient in the Wiedemann-Franz relationship is reduced by about 25 percent of that for metals. Consequently $Z\bar{T}$ is increased by optimization of the doping level and the effective elimination of heat conduction by electron motion. As a result, it is possible to produce materials with $Z\bar{T}$ of about unity.

The development of semiconductor materials for thermoelectric uses was influenced by the fact that the rate of heat conduction due to lattice vibration tends to decrease with rising atomic weight. As a result semiconductor materials with large atomic weights, such as bismuth telluride Bi_2Te_3 and lead telluride $PbTe$ are used. Further reduction in the value of the lattice conductivity may be achieved by randomizing the crystal lattice. This is achieved by the use of semiconductor solid solutions, such as Bi_2Te_3-Bi_2Se_3 and Bi_2Te_3-$SbTe_3$. Despite the use of solid solutions and semiconductor materials of high atomic weight, it has not been possible to achieve values of $Z\bar{T}$ much greater than unity.

For example, lead telluride, which has been used extensively for small-scale generators, has a maximum value of only 0.9 for $Z\bar{T}$, which is far from the competitive value of about 6. In fact, if the lattice conductivity could be reduced so that it equals the electron conductivity, the maximum possible value of $Z\bar{T}$ is only 1.3. Therefore, unless new materials can be found in which the lattice conductivity is considerably less than the electron conductivity, it is impossible to attain values of $Z\bar{T}$ which would make thermoelectric conversion competitive with the large-capacity conventional system.*

As a result of extensive material research, the value of lattice conductivity for a mixed crystal of 0.4 PbTe–0.6 AgSbTe₂ has been reduced below that of the electron conductivity and a value of $Z\bar{T} = 1.8$ achieved at operating temperatures up to 900°K.† For refrigeration bismuth telluride alloys are found preferable, but at room temperatures have $Z\bar{T}$ values of

---

* D. A. Wright. "New Ways in Thermoelectricity." *Brit. J. Appl. Phys.* **15**: 217–227. 1964.

† H. Fleischmann, O. G. Folberth, and H. Pfister. *Z. Naturf.* **14a**: 999. 1959.

about unity.   The thermoelectric properties of some materials are given in Appendix D as a function of temperature.

Due to the foregoing consideration, the use of thermoelectric converters has been restricted to certain cases where their unique characteristics can be utilized to advantage.   The SNAP 10A nuclear reactor–thermoelectric converter system, successfully launched into a 700-nautical-mile orbit on April 3, 1965, is a good example.   The NaK-cooled nuclear reactor which provides the heat is described in Subarticle 13–1.3.   Figure 5–9 shows a schematic of the system, while Fig. 5–10 shows a cutaway representation of the satellite.

The liquid metal is pumped from the reactor to a circular inlet header on top of a truncated conical structure.   From there the metal flows through forty tubes, arranged about the surface of the structure, to a circular outlet header from which it returns to the reactor.   Cylindrical pellets of n- and p-type SiGe are alternately spaced along the length of each tube.   The pellets are electrically insulated from the tube, which is the heat source, by means of thin alumina disks.   The thermoelectric elements are connected in series-parallel arrangements giving a rated output of 580 watts at 28.5 volts into a matched load of 1.6 ohm.

The pellets are connected by copper straps at the hot junctions and by aluminum straps, which act as radiators, at the cold junctions.   Each aluminum radiator platelet is electrically insulated from the adjacent platelets by a clearance gap.   In order to increase both thermal and electrical conductivity, all material interfaces from the NaK tube through the aluminum radiator are metallurgically bonded.   The total radiator surface area is 5.8 m².

SiGe was selected in preference to PbTe, despite its lower figure of merit, because:

1. SiGe is stable at above 1250°K, whereas PbTe sublimes at temperature above 700°K and would require an encapsulant.
2. Stable low-resistance electrical contacts can be made to SiGe by metallurgical bonding.
3. Mechanical properties of SiGe are less restrictive.

An electromagnetic pump is used to circulate the fluid.   The operation of the pump is based on the MHD concept described in Chapter 8.   Since large currents (700 amp) are required to operate the pump, a number of the thermoelectric converters are connected in parallel and "shorted" directly through the pump throat, while the magnetic field is provided by a permanent magnet.   Table 5–1 gives some details of the SNAP 10A converter performance.

In summary, it appears that both thermoelectric generation and refrigeration are best suited to small-capacity applications, particularly when the characteristic advantages may be availed of.

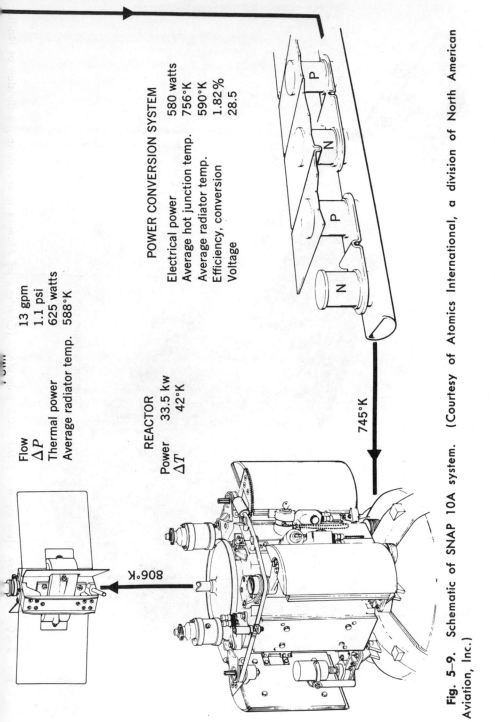

Flow　　　　　　　　　　 13 gpm
ΔP　　　　　　　　　 1.1 psi
Thermal power　　　　 625 watts
Average radiator temp.　 588°K

POWER CONVERSION SYSTEM

Electrical power　　　　　　 580 watts
Average hot junction temp.　 756°K
Average radiator temp.　　　 590°K
Efficiency, conversion　　　 1.82%
Voltage　　　　　　　　　　 28.5

REACTOR

Power　 33.5 kw
ΔT　　 42°K

745°K

806°K

Fig. 5–9. Schematic of SNAP 10A system. (Courtesy of Atomics International, a division of North American Aviation, Inc.)

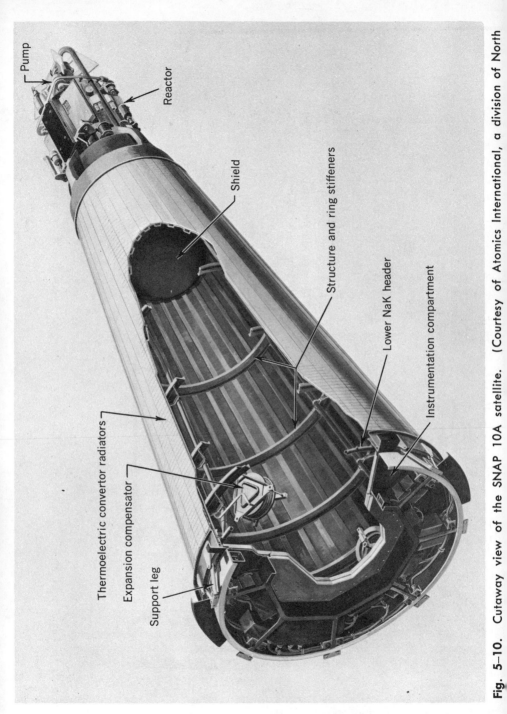

Pump

Reactor

Shield

Structure and ring stiffeners

Lower NaK header

Instrumentation compartment

Thermoelectric convertor radiators

Expansion compensator

Support leg

Fig. 5–10. Cutaway view of the SNAP 10A satellite. (Courtesy of Atomics International, a division of North

174

TABLE 5–1
SNAP 10A Thermoelectric Converter Performance*

Thermoelectric material	SiGe alloy
Figure of merit	$0.58 \times 10^{-3}/°K$
Average source temperature	775°K
Average radiator base temperature	588°K
ΔT total (ΔT_c)	187°K
ΔT thermoelectric material (ΔT)	170°K
Series thermal efficiency $(\Delta T/\Delta T_c)$	90 percent
Thermoelectric material resistance	1.41 ohms
Converter resistance	1.6 ohms
Heat radiated	33 kw
Heat through thermoelectric material	30 kw
Shunt heat loss	3 kw
Carnot efficiency	24 percent
Overall efficiency	1.63 percent
Electrical output power	540 watts
Total thermoelectric couples	1440
Open-circuit voltage/couple	0.084 volt
Converter open-circuit voltage (720 in series)	61 volts
Converter working voltage	28.5 volts
Current	19 amp
Percentage of theoretical power density	58 percent

* By permission of Atomics International.

PROBLEMS

5–1. The Peltier coefficients for two thermoelectric materials A and B within the temperature range from 400°K to 700°K may be approximated as a function of temperature by

$$\Pi_{ab} = [400T + 0.333T(T - 400) - 2 \times 10^{-4}T(T - 400)^2] \times 10^{-6} \quad \text{volts}$$

Find the value of the Peltier coefficient, the Seebeck coefficient, and the difference between the Thomson coefficients at 550°K.

5–2. If the absolute value of the Seebeck coefficient of material B in Prob. 1–1 is approximated by

$$S_b = [-200 + 0.1(T - 400)] \times 10^{-6} \text{ volts/°K}$$

within the temperature range from 400°K to 700°K, determine expressions for the absolute Seebeck, Peltier, and Thomson coefficients as a function of temperature. Evaluate each of the absolute coefficients at 550°K.

5–3. In practice it is convenient to use average values for the thermoelectric coefficients within the temperature range of operation. Find the average value of the Seebeck coefficient for the materials in Prob. 5–1 when the hot junction and cold junction temperatures are 650°K and 400°K, respectively.

5-4. A thermoelectric generator operates between 450°K and 800°K. The average value of the Seebeck coefficient may be taken as 407 × 10⁻⁶ volts/°K and

$$r_g = 2.9 \times 10^{-3} \text{ ohm} \qquad K = 21 \times 10^{-3} \text{ watts/°K}$$

a. What is the value of the open-circuit voltage?

b. Under conditions of maximum power, what are the output voltage and efficiency?

c. If the terminals are short-circuited, what are the current and the input power?

5-5. A thermoelectric generator is to be designed for use in space in conjunction with a nuclear reactor which is cooled by a liquid metal in the form of a mixture of sodium and potassium. The liquid metal circulates through a system of pipes and is then returned to the reactor. Thermoelectric elements are attached to the pipes which provide a hot junction temperature of 728°K. Radiators are attached at the cold junction and heat is given off at a temperature of 588°K. The thermoelectric materials used have the following properties:

p-type AgSbTe₂ n-type 0.75 PbTe–0.25 SnTe

$$\bar{S}_a = 242 \times 10^{-6} \text{ volt/°K} \qquad \bar{S}_b = -120 \times 10^{-6} \text{ volt/°K}$$
$$\bar{Z}_a = 1.92 \times 10^{-3}/°K \qquad \bar{Z}_b = 1.15 \times 10^{-3}/°K$$
$$\bar{\rho}_a = 4.1 \times 10^{-5} \text{ ohm-m} \qquad \bar{\rho}_b = 1.0 \times 10^{-5} \text{ ohm-m}$$
$$A_a = 0.8 \times 10^{-4} \text{ m}^2 \qquad l_b = 1.0 \times 10^{-2} \text{ m}$$
$$l_a = 0.8 \times 10^{-2} \text{ m}$$

Find the number of thermoelectric generators required to supply an output power of 500 watts if the geometry is optimized and the load is adjusted so that operation is at maximum thermal efficiency. Find the thermal efficiency and the output voltage from the power system if all the generators are connected in series. What is the relative efficiency when compared with the Carnot efficiency?

5-6. A thermoelectric generator operates between 600 and 900°K and consists of a number of individual generators connected in series. The total output voltage is 63 volts. The following data apply:

p-type material n-type material

$\bar{S}_a = 220 \times 10^{-6} \text{ volts/°K}$ $\bar{S}_b = -130 \times 10^{-6} \text{ volts/°K}$
$\bar{Z}_a = 2 \times 10^{-3}/°K$ $\bar{Z}_b = 1.3 \times 10^{-3}/°K$
$\bar{\rho}_a = 3.8 \times 10^{-5} \text{ ohm-m}$ $\bar{\rho}_b = 1.2 \times 10^{-5} \text{ ohm-m}$
maximum permissible current density   maximum permissible current density
$= 15 \times 10^4 \text{ amp/m}^2$ $= 17.2 \times 10^4 \text{ amp/m}^2$

a. Under conditions of optimized geometry, and operation at maximum efficiency, find the cross-sectional areas of materials A and B. Check that the current density does not exceed the maximum permissible value.

b. Find the maximum efficiency and compare it with the Carnot efficiency.

c. How many generators are required in series to provide the required output voltage?

5-7. Repeat Prob. 5-6 for conditions of maximum output power per unit volume.

5-8. Using the same materials as in Prob. 5-6, and operating between the same temperatures, find the cross-sectional areas of the thermoelectric materials required if both elements are to be 0.5 cm in length, a full-load output voltage of 50 volts at 15 amp is required, all elements are connected in series, operation is under optimized geometry, and the voltage regulation of the power supply is to be 10 percent.

5-9. A thermoelectric refrigerator is utilized in maintaining an electrical circuit, which dissipates 54.5 watts, at a temperature of 15°C below room temperature (27°C). A number of thermoelectric units are employed, each having an internal resistance of 7.1×10^{-3} ohm, and a thermal conductance of 17×10^{-3} watts/°K. The Seebeck coefficients of the n- and p-type materials used are -175×10^{-6} volts/°K and 200×10^{-6} volts/°K, respectively. Heat is rejected from the refrigerator at room temperature. Find the number of thermoelectric units required when operating at the maximum pumping rate. If the supply to the electrical circuit is disconnected, find the steady-state temperature within the refrigerator.

6

Photoelectric Conversion

Photoelectric energy conversion is concerned with the direct production of electricity from electromagnetic radiation. The light flux meter is the most common example of such a converter; in this case sunlight, with a frequency of about 5×10^{14} cps, constitutes the radiation. However, sources of radiation with much higher frequencies, such as gamma rays, emitted from radioactive materials, may also be used.

Unlike other direct converters, such as the thermoelectric, thermionic, and magnetohydrodynamic, the efficiency of the photoelectric converter is not governed by the upper limit associated with a Carnot heat cycle. Consequently, high efficiencies are theoretically possible. Due to the fact that solar energy is availed of, photoelectric converters are particularly well suited for space use when small quantities of power are required for unlimited periods.

6–1. RADIATION AND THE PHOTON

One of the basic concepts of modern physics is the duality of matter, or the idea that a beam of radiation may be considered as a stream of particles, called *photons*, each having an energy

$$E = h\nu \tag{6–1}$$

where the Planck constant $h = 6.625 \times 10^{-34}$ joule-sec, and ν is the frequency of the radiation in cycles per second. Since

$$\nu = \frac{c}{\lambda} \tag{6–2}$$

where c is the speed of light (2.998×10^8 m/sec) and λ is the wavelength,

Eq. 6–1 may be written as

$$E = \frac{hc}{\lambda} = \frac{1.986 \times 10^{-25}}{\lambda} \text{ joule}$$

or

$$E = \frac{1.24 \times 10^{-6}}{\lambda} \text{ ev} \qquad (6\text{–}3)$$

since 1 electron volt (ev) = 1.602×10^{-19} joule.

In general, the wavelength is expressed in angstroms (Å), where

$$1 \text{ Å} = 10^{-10} \text{ m}$$

The *intensity* of a beam of radiation, Φ, is expressed in watts per square meter, and

$$\boxed{\Phi = EN} \qquad (6\text{–}4)$$

or

$$\Phi = h\nu N \text{ watts/m}^2 \qquad (6\text{–}5)$$

where N is the *photon flux*, the number of photons crossing unit area perpendicular to the light beam per second.

Example 6–1. If the average intensity and photon energy of the sunlight at an altitude of 150 miles above the surface of the earth is 1330 watts/m² and 1.49 ev respectively, compare the surface areas required to receive a power of 6650 watts from the sun, and from a 0.95 Å gamma-radiation source if the photon flux is the same in both cases.

For sunlight, the required surface area A_s = 6650/1330 = 5 m². Since the photon flux from the gamma source (N_γ) is the same as from the sun,

$$N_\gamma = \frac{\Phi_s}{E_s} = \frac{1330}{1.49 \times 1.602 \times 10^{-19}}$$
$$= 5.57 \times 10^{21} \text{ photons/m}^2\text{-sec}$$

From Eq. 6–3, the photon energy of a 0.95 Å wavelength gamma beam is

$$E_\gamma = \frac{1.24 \times 10^{-6}}{0.95 \times 10^{-10}} = 1.302 \times 10^4 \text{ ev}$$

From Eq. 6–4

$$\Phi_\gamma = E_\gamma N_\gamma = 1.302 \times 10^4 \times 5.57 \times 10^{21} \times 1.602 \times 10^{-19} \text{ watts/m}^2$$
$$= 1.162 \times 10^7 \text{ watts/m}^2$$

Therefore for a power of 6650 watts the area required is

$$\frac{6650}{1.162 \times 10^7} \times 10^4 = 5.71 \text{ cm}^2$$

and so the area required is almost 9000 times less than for the case of solar radiation.

6-2. THE PHOTOVOLTAIC EFFECT

The discovery of the *photovoltaic effect,* or the generation of a voltage by radiation, is attributed to Adams and Day, who observed the effect in selenium in 1876.   In 1919 Coblenz discovered that a voltage is developed between the illuminated and non-illuminated regions of some semiconducting crystals, notably cuprous oxide.   The important discovery of the photovoltaic effect at a *p-n* junction of two semiconductors was made by

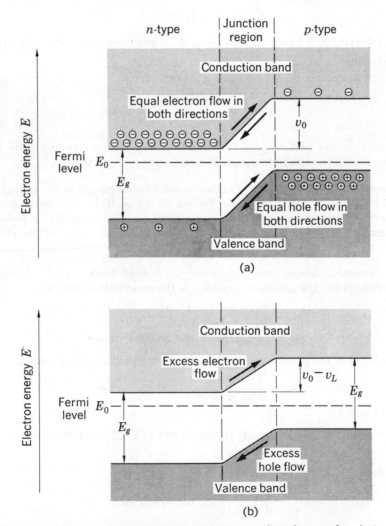

Fig. 6-1. Energy level diagram at an *n-p* junction under (a) equilibrium conditions; (b) forward bias conditions.

Ohl in 1941. It is this junction effect which is of interest when considering photoelectric energy conversion.

Figure 6–1a shows the energy-level diagram under equilibrium conditions at the junction between an n- and a p-type material. The important point to note is the fact that for equilibrium the two Fermi levels line up and the potential profile is such at the junction that electrons in the n-type material are restrained from flowing into the p-type material, but are

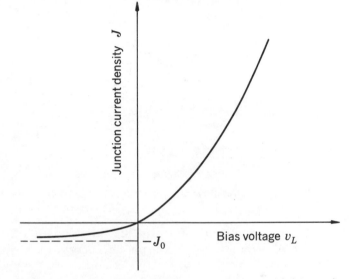

Fig. 6–2. Variation of junction current density with bias voltage.

encouraged to flow in the opposite direction. As a result, the rate of electron flow from the high-density region is equal to the rate of flow from the low-density region and therefore the net electron current across the junction is zero. A similar situation exists in the case of hole flow. The potential difference v_0, which develops across the junction in order to maintain a net zero current, is due to the difference in charge carrier concentration at each side. In the case of electron flow, there are many free electrons at the n side while there are very few at the p side. The junction potential which develops retards electron flow from the region of high free-electron density but encourages flow from the region of low free-electron density.

If a forward bias voltage is applied so that the junction potential is reduced by v_L as in Fig. 6–1b, then the flow of majority carriers is increased and the net current density across the junction (from the Boltzmann equation) is

$$J = J_0[\exp (ev_L/kT) - 1] \qquad (6\text{--}6)$$

where k is the Boltzmann constant, T the absolute temperature, and J_0 is the *reverse saturation current*, or the reverse current which flows when a large reverse bias is applied and conduction is due to minority carriers only. Figure 6–2 shows the variation of the current density across the junction as a function of the applied bias voltage v_L.

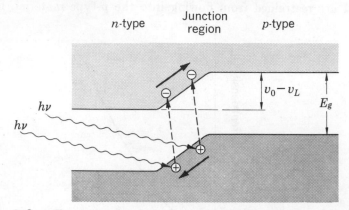

Fig. 6–3.   Charge carrier flow due to irradiation of a p-n junction.

An effect similar to applying a forward bias is produced when a p-n junction is subjected to radiation. If the photon energy $h\nu$ is greater than the energy eE_g which is required to excite electrons from the valence to the conduction band, then those excited electrons in the conduction band, and the holes in the valence band, which are close to the junction, move across under the influence of the existing electric field as shown in Fig. 6–3. As a result the junction potential is changed by an amount v_L as given by Eq. 6–6, where J is now the junction current density caused by the change in voltage across the junction.

6–3. THE PHOTOELECTRIC ENERGY CONVERTER

Figure 6–4 shows the equivalent circuit of a photoelectric energy converter. Due to the nature of the device, it is represented by a current source which provides a current J_s equal to the current density generated by the photovoltaic effect. The non-linear resistance r_g represents the junction resistance per unit area. Under short-circuited conditions, all of the generated current flows through the load; however, when a finite load is present a current J is diverted through the internal junction resistance r_g, so that

$$J_L = J_s - J \tag{6–7}$$

Since the current J depends on v_L as given by Eq. 6–6:

$$J_L = J_s - J_0[\exp(ev_L/kT) - 1] \qquad (6\text{–}8)$$

and as discussed $J_L = J_s$, for $v_L = 0$. Figure 6–5 shows a typical output characteristic of a photoelectric converter.

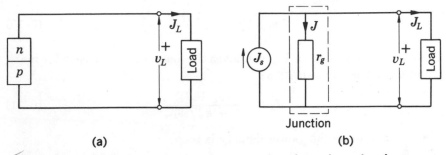

(a)   (b)

Fig. 6–4. Equivalent circuit of a p-n junction photoelectric energy converter.

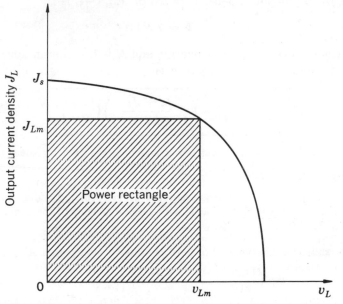

Fig. 6–5. Output characteristic of a photoelectric converter, showing the power rectangle, whose area is proportional to the power delivered to the load.

The output power density is

$$P = v_L J_L$$

Therefore from Eq. 6–8

$$P = v_L J_s - v_L J_0[\exp(ev_L/kT) - 1] \tag{6-9}$$

The load voltage v_{Lm} for maximum output power density is found by taking the derivative of Eq. 6–9, and setting the result equal to zero, giving

$$\exp(ev_{Lm}/kT) = \frac{1 + J_s/J_0}{1 + ev_{Lm}/kT} \tag{6-10}$$

Substituting Eq. 6–10 in Eq. 6–8 gives the load current density for maximum output power density as

$$J_{Lm} = \frac{(J_s + J_0)}{1 + kT/ev_{Lm}} \tag{6-11}$$

The maximum output power density is then

$$P_m = \frac{(J_s + J_0)v_{Lm}}{1 + kT/ev_{Lm}} \approx \frac{J_s v_{Lm}}{1 + kT/ev_{Lm}} \tag{6-12}$$

where v_{Lm} is determined from Eq. 6–10.

Since the input power density, based on Eq. 6–4, is

$$\Phi = \bar{E}N$$

where $\bar{E}$ is the average photon energy, and N is the photon flux, the converter efficiency at maximum power is

$$\boxed{\eta_{mp} = \frac{P_m}{\Phi} = \left(\frac{J_s + J_0}{1 + kT/ev_{Lm}}\right)\left(\frac{v_{Lm}}{\bar{E}N}\right)} \tag{6-13}$$

Example 6–2. A 20-watt solar power source is required for space use. The saturation current density J_0 and the short-circuit current density J_s of the silicon cells used are 7.1×10^{-9} amp/m² and 139 amp/m², respectively. Find the active cell surface area which is required when operating under conditions of maximum power at 300°K. What is the overall efficiency of the converter if the solar radiation intensity is 1290 watts/m²?

A trial-and-error solution of Eq. 6–10 permits the evaluation of v_{Lm}.

$$\exp\left(\frac{11,600}{300} v_{Lm}\right) = \frac{1 + (13.9 \times 10^{10})/7.1}{1 + \frac{11,600}{300} v_{Lm}}$$

from which

$$v_{Lm} = 0.535 \text{ volt}$$

Equation 6–12 gives the maximum power density as

$$P_m = \frac{(139 + 7.1 \times 10^{-9}) \times 0.535}{1 + \left(\dfrac{300}{11,600 \times 0.535}\right)}$$
$$= 71.0 \text{ watts/m}^2$$

Therefore, for a maximum power output of 20 watts, the cell-surface area that should be exposed to the sun is

$$A = \tfrac{20}{71} = 0.281 \text{ m}^2$$

The overall efficiency is

$$\eta_{mp} = \frac{P_m}{\Phi} \times 100 = \frac{71 \times 100}{1290}$$
$$= 5.5 \text{ percent}$$

6–4. DESIGN CONSIDERATIONS

In the preceding section the determination of both the saturation current density and the short-circuit current density was not considered. From Eq. 6–10 it is apparent that the output voltage at maximum power may be increased by making J_0 as small as possible, and from Eq. 6–11 the output current density at maximum power may be increased by making J_s as large as possible. Consequently, in the design of a photoelectric converter, it is desirable to make J_0 small and J_s large.

The reverse saturation current J_0 is that which flows when a large reverse-bias voltage is applied across the p-n junction. It is therefore caused by the flow of holes from the n to the p side, and by the flow of electrons from the p to the n side. In other words, J_0 is caused by the flow of the minority carriers across the junction. Therefore

$$J_0 = p_n e u_p + n_p e u_n \tag{6–14}$$

where p_n and n_p are the hole and electron densities in the n and p regions, and u_p and u_n are their mean diffusion velocities across the junction, respectively. Since the ratio of diffusion coefficient D to diffusion length L gives the mean diffusion velocity, Eq. 6–14 may be written as

$$J_0 = p_n e \frac{D_p}{L_p} + n_p e \frac{D_n}{L_n} \tag{6–15}$$

To reduce J_0 it is usual to place a heavily doped p region in contact with a moderately doped n region so that conduction is mainly due to the flow of holes from the n to the p side. As a result, Eq. 6–15 may be approximated by

$$J_0 \approx p_n e \frac{D_p}{L_p} \tag{6–16}$$

Therefore it appears important to maintain the density of minority carriers in the n region at a low level.   Since the generation of minority carriers increases rapidly with temperature, it is therefore important to operate photoelectric converters at as low an ambient temperature as possible.

The short-circuit current density J_s is that produced by the photoelectric effect.   Therefore J_s is proportional to N, the number of photons per unit area per second reaching the surface of the converter.   If a fraction k_1 of the incoming photons reach the junction zone and a fraction k_2 have sufficient energy to generate a minority carrier and cause it to cross the junction, then

$$J_s = k_1 k_2 eN \qquad (6\text{--}17)$$

Consequently, J_s may be increased by making k_1 as large as possible. This is achieved by making the thickness of material through which the incoming photons pass in order to reach the junction as small as possible. The cross-section of a cell designed with this in mind is shown in Fig. 6–6.

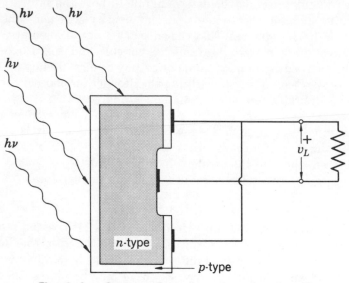

Fig. 6–6.   Cross-section of a photoelectric cell.

A thin layer (10^{-4} cm) of p-type material is diffused into the surface of an n-type base.   As a result of the geometric form, a large junction area close to the surface is achieved.   Since the p-type layer is thin, a significant fraction of the incoming photons generate charge carriers within the junction region.   The thickness of the p-type layer must be determined as a compromise between the resistance introduced when the thickness is small and charge carrier recombination when the thickness is large.   This resistance may be reduced by making more than one contact to the p-type region.

For a given source of radiation, the value of k_2 may be increased by the use of low energy gap materials. However, since this decreases v_{Lm}, a compromise must be made.

In discussing the efficiency of a photoelectric converter an important consideration is the frequency spectrum of the source. If an infrared source at 1.145 microns is considered, such that a photon has just sufficient energy (1.1 ev) to liberate an electron from silicon, then efficiencies of about 50 percent could be expected. This figure is arrived at when the process of recovering the energy imparted to the electron-hole pair is considered, since the junction voltage is only about half of the energy gap voltage. In general, however, the source photons have energies greater and less than 1.1 ev. The photons with energies less than 1.1 ev are completely wasted, as is the energy in excess of 1.1 ev in the case of more energetic electrons. Consequently only about 45 percent of the energy from a solar source may be utilized in a silicon photoelectric converter. As a result a theoretical maximum efficiency of about 23 percent is usually assumed. When reflection, photon penetration, and premature recombination are accounted for, the overall practical efficiency is usually about 10 percent, although cells with outputs of up to 150 watts/m² from sunlight have been reported. This corresponds to an efficiency of about 14 percent.

6-5. MATERIALS AND FABRICATION

Numerous materials have been considered and tested. When, as in most cases, a solar radiation source is used, an analysis of the spectrum indicates that a material with an energy gap of about 1.3 ev is preferable. Such a choice represents a compromise between the complete wasting of low-energy photons and the wasting of photon energies in excess of 1.3 ev. Since silicon has an energy gap of about 1.1 ev, it has been extensively used. Gallium arsenide, with an energy gap of 1.35 ev, has been used, but efficiencies greater than those of silicon have not been obtained. However, for space use it appears to be more resistant to the effects of photon and electron irradiation. Irradiation tests indicate that n-on-p-base cells can tolerate greater integrated fluxes than p-on-n-base cells.

In discussing the fabrication techniques for photoelectric cells, J. J. Loferski writes the following:

Historically, the first photovoltaic cells were made from selenium or cuprous oxide. In both cases, the material was polycrystalline. In neither case did solar energy conversion efficiencies exceed 1 percent and, consequently, the application of such cells was restricted to photographic exposure meters, laboratory photometers, etc. It was only with the advent of single crystal cells made from silicon, cadmium sulfide and gallium arsenide that the solar energy conversion efficiency increased by a factor of ten or more. Efficiencies of the order of 10 percent have encouraged exploitation of this method of energy conversion, but the high cost associated with fabrication of single crystal cells have limited their utilization to situations, like space vehicles, where cost is not a factor.

However, it has long been realized that in these single crystal cells the actual energy conversion occurs in a relatively small volume of the crystal (about 50μ below the illuminated surface in silicon, 5μ in GaAs) and that most of the $\sim400\mu$ cell thickness is "dead weight." These considerations have lead to a re-examination of polycrystalline photovoltaic cells and have prompted attempts to fabricate cells from sintered layers of CdS, thin films of CdS. Of these various attempts, only the latter led to efficiencies which were nearly in the "practical" range. The best of these cells were made by evaporating about 70μ of CdS onto a transparent conducting SnO_2 coating attached to a glass substrate. The SnO_2 coating served as one contact to the cell. The exposed surface of the cell was then electroplated with copper and the structure was baked at 275°C for about 10 seconds. Silver paint was used to form an electrical contact to the copper coated surface. When such a cell was illuminated through the SnO_2 coated glass, the solar energy conversion efficiency was reported to be as high as 3.5 percent. This figure should be compared to the 4 to 6 percent efficiency commonly encountered in single crystal CdS cells. (An efficiency of about 6 percent was reported for evaporated CdS photovoltaic cells prepared in slightly different fashion in a fragmentary account in the Soviet literature.)

Another important development related to thin film photovoltaic cells is the successful growth of single crystals of CdSe and CdTe by vacuum deposition onto alkali substrates. No report of photovoltaic action in such CdSe films has been published to date. In the CdTe, however, it was found that a high voltage photovoltaic effect was all that could be detected.

Thus it appears that an intensification of research on thin film photovoltaic cells should eventually lead to fabrication of cells with efficiencies approaching those of single crystal cells.*

6–6. CONCLUSION

The typical junction photoelectric energy converter has a low individual power output, and consequently many cells must be interconnected to attain useful power outputs. Usually, cells are interconnected in a series-parallel matrix, so that failure of a single cell does not lead to complete failure of the power supply. In space, open-circuit failure may be caused by mechanical vibration or contact deterioration due to heating. Radiation damage is also of concern when operating in or near the radiation belts. This problem may be partially solved by shielding the cell from beta radiation for example, with sapphire covers. However, it is more difficult to provide adequate shielding when operating in regions of high-energy photon radiation. Short-circuit failure due to micrometeorite damage may also be a problem.

* J. J. Loferski. "Recent Research on Photovoltaic Solar Energy Converters." *Proc. IEEE* **51**: 667–674. 1963.

Despite the foregoing problems, photoelectric junction converters have many advantages.   They are ideally suited to applications where a small amount of power is required over an extended period, as in the case of a communication satellite for example.   Due to the fact that the efficiency is not governed by the Carnot cycle, temperatures are not a limiting factor. The converters are simple and lightweight.

Although almost exclusive consideration is at present given to the solar radiation source, a radioactive source offers the advantage of uninterupted supply.   Alpha, beta, or gamma radiation when applied to a p-n junction produces hole-electron pairs just as photons do.   However, gamma rays tend to penetrate the material without yielding much of their energy, while alpha particles tend to damage the material lattice.   Beta particles are best suited, provided a radiation source is selected which emits beta particles having maximum energies less than the radiation damage threshold energy.   If a source of gamma radiation is available it could be indirectly utilized, since the gamma irradiation of certain materials causes beta emission, which in turn may be used to generate the electron-hole pairs.

PROBLEMS

6-1. Give the photon energy in electron volts of

   a. 600 Å orange light.
   b. 4500 Å blue light.
   c. 50 Å X-rays.
   d. 0.0005 Å cosmic rays.

6-2. Calculate the photon flux of the four types of radiation described in Prob. 6-1 if the radiation intensity in all cases is 30 watts/m^2.

6-3. The photon flux at a radius of 2 m from an isotropic, 30 Å X-ray source is 5.65×10^{16} photons/m^2-sec.   Calculate the total power radiated by the source.

6-4. A solar-powered photoelectric power source is required to provide a home with 400 kw-hr of electricity per month in a region where an average of 125 hr of sunshine per month, with an average intensity of 530 watts/m^2, are received. Calculate the exposed surface area of the photoelectric energy converter if the overall efficiency is 6.5 percent.   What is the minimum capacity of the storage batteries required to provide supply during a period of 8 days without sunshine?

6-5. The saturation and short-circuit current densities for a solar cell in a radiation intensity of 920 watts/m^2 are 5.1×10^{-9} and 150 amp/m^2, respectively. At a temperature of 280°K and under conditions of maximum power, find the minimum effective surface area required to provide an output power of 35 watts if 12 percent of the generated power is internally dissipated by contact and circuit resistance.   Find the overall efficiency at maximum power.

6-6. Find the open-circuit cell voltage of the energy converter described in Prob. 6-5.

6–7. A radiation source emits photons whose energies vary over a wide range. The photon flux is measured as a function of frequency and it is found that

$$dN = A\nu \exp(-b\nu)\, d\nu$$

where dN is the number of photons with frequencies between ν and $\nu + d\nu$ and A and b are constants. If this source irradiates a junction photoelectric converter whose energy gap is E_g and it is assumed that all photons with energies $\geq E_g$ cause unit charge to cross the junction, find the value of E_g which maximizes $J_s E_g$.

6–8. Find the percentage of the incident photons which are utilized under the optimized conditions described in Prob. 6–7.

6–9. A silicon photoelectric power source capable of developing a maximum power of 100 watts is to be designed for use in a 1.38-ev radiation flux of 1100 watts/m². The p-type silicon is lightly doped with 3×10^{23} acceptor atoms per cubic meter. At the operating temperature of 305°K it may be assumed that 60% of the acceptor atoms liberate their holes. The diffusion coefficient and diffusion length for electrons in the p-type region are 1.08×10^{-3} m²/sec and 1.1×10^{-4} m, respectively, and the energy gap for silicon is 1.12 ev. The probabilities of an incoming photon reaching the junction zone, and of subsequently causing a minority carrier to cross the junction are 0.8 and 0.4, respectively. If the source is assembled so that it consists of a number of parallel groups, each containing 100 cells in series, find

a. The total number of cells required, if each has an effective area of 1.2 cm².

b. The total output voltage and current at maximum power.

c. The percentage voltage regulation of the source between maximum power and no load.

d. The efficiency at maximum power.

7

Thermionic Conversion

The basic principle of the thermionic conversion process may be traced back to 1883, when Thomas Edison first disclosed the phenomenon of thermionic emission; however, it was not until 1915 that Schlicter proposed its use for the generation of electricity. Although Langmuir studied extensively the emission characteristics of cesium-coated tungsten surfaces during the twenties, the subject lay dormant until Hatsopolos in 1956 and V. C. Wilson in 1957 reported on their work in the field of thermionic energy conversion. Since then extensive thermionic research has been undertaken, mainly with the objective of developing an energy converter capable of utilizing the high-temperature capability of the nuclear reactor and converting this heat directly into electricity. The thermionic converter is of particular interest for use in conjunction with a nuclear reactor in space. Since the converter heat rejection temperature may be as high as 1000°K, and the rate of heat rejection varies as T^4, only a small lightweight radiator is required. The thermionic converter, like most other direct converters, has no moving parts. Also, the development of a compact, silent, thermionic nuclear power plant should be of particular interest for submarine propulsion.

7-1. OPERATION OF THE THERMIONIC ENERGY CONVERTER

Since 1956 numerous thermionic converter designs and configurations have been proposed; however, all of them depend on the fact that when a material is heated it emits electrons (a process which is similar to the liberation of steam particles when water is heated). If the stream of emitted electrons is collected at another suitable electrode (the *collector*), then the flow of electrons constitutes an electric current which may be passed through an external load, as shown in Fig. 7–1. Consequently, part of the thermal energy supplied to liberate electrons from the emitter is converted directly into electrical energy. The space between the emitter and collector is usually filled with a vapor or gas at a low pressure (of the order of 1 mm Hg).

While the operation of such a converter appears to be very simple, and indeed is easy to achieve on a small scale, a number of problems arise in practice when suitably large power densities are required. One of the most important is the limit imposed on maximum current density due

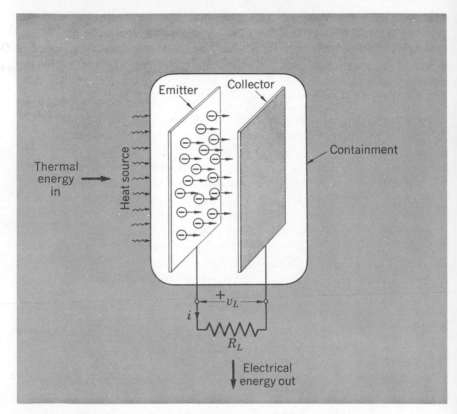

Fig. 7–1.   Schematic of a basic thermionic converter.

to the *space-charge effect*, which is caused by the electrons themselves as they leave the emitter. The emitted electrons, due to their negative charge, deter the movement of other electrons towards the collecting electrode. Various methods are used to overcome this space-charge effect, and thermionic converters are classified according to the means employed for space-charge compensation.

The formation of the space-charge potential barrier may be prevented in at least two ways: the spacing between the emitter and collector may be reduced to a small value, of the order of microns, or positive ions may be introduced into the cloud of electrons in front of the emitter. The first approach led to the development of the close-spaced vacuum converter, which proved unsatisfactory for large-scale operation due to the extremely close tolerances required. The second method has resulted in the development of both the cesium and the auxiliary discharge thermionic converters.

7-2. THERMIONIC EMISSION

Since all thermionic converters are basically dependent on the emission of electrons from a hot surface, it is appropriate to consider the thermionic emission process.

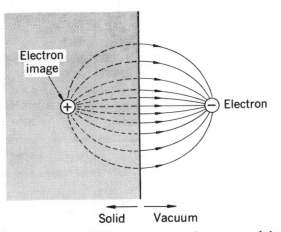

Solid   Vacuum

Fig. 7-2. Electrostatic field between an electron and its image near the surface of a metal.

The valence electrons of a metal move freely within the atomic lattice; however, at room temperatures few electrons are able to escape from the surface of the metal. The nature of the force which prevents electron emission may be attributed to an electrostatic image force. Consider Fig. 7-2, which represents an electron attempting to move from a metal surface. Once the electron leaves the surface, a net positive charge remains, and therefore there is mutual attraction between the electron, which is attempting to move from the surface, and the net positive charge which it leaves behind. If the electron has not sufficient kinetic energy to overcome this retarding electrostatic force, then it returns to the surface of the metal. Since the electrons within a metal obtain their kinetic energy as a result of thermal agitation, few electrons have sufficient kinetic energy to overcome the electrostatic forces when the metal is cold. However, as the metal is heated, more and more electrons attain energies sufficient to surmount the electrostatic barrier and leave the surface.   Consequently the rate at which electrons are thermionically emitted is strongly dependent on temperature.

The barrier which prevents emission may be represented as the energy barrier in Fig. 7–3.   The Fermi energy level represents the mean energy

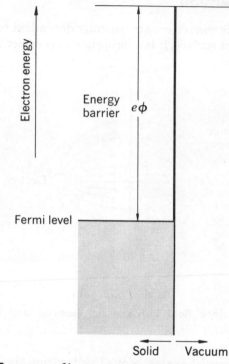

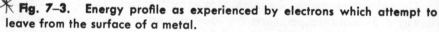

✕ Fig. 7–3.   Energy profile as experienced by electrons which attempt to leave from the surface of a metal.

level of the electrons within the metal.   Those electrons which attempt to leave the surface with energies in excess of $e\phi$, where ϕ is measured in volts and called the material *work function*, overcome the electrostatic forces and escape.   All others are returned to the metal.   As seen from Table 7–1, the effective height of the energy barrier varies from about 1.89 ev for cesium to 5.32 ev for platinum.   Surfaces with particularly low work functions may be produced by using a combination of materials.   For example work functions below one volt have been obtained by using a thin coating of cesium on a silver oxide base.

The rate at which electrons are liberated from the surface of a metal is given by the Richardson-Dushman electron current density equation:

$$J_0 = \mathcal{Q}T^2 \exp\left(-\frac{e\phi}{kT}\right) \qquad (7\text{-}1)$$

where $\mathcal{Q}$ is a universal constant with a value of $1.2 \times 10^6 \text{ amp/m}^2\text{-}°K^2$. As expected, the rate of electron emission increases rapidly with temperature and decreases exponentially as the work function of the material

TABLE 7-1
Thermionic Emission Properties of Some Materials

Material	ϕ (volts)	$\mathcal{Q}$ (amp/m^2-°K^2) $\times 10^{-6}$
Cs	1.89	0.5
Mo	4.2	0.55
Ni	4.61	0.3
Pt	5.32	0.32
Ta	4.19	0.55
W	4.52	0.6
W + Cs	1.5	0.03
W + Ba	1.6	0.015
W + Th	2.7	0.04
BaO	1.5	0.001
SrO	2.2	1.0

increases. Consequently, when large emission current densities are required, a material with a low work function should be selected and operated at as high a temperature as is practicable.

Although the value of $\mathcal{Q}$ is in theory a universal constant, in practice it is found that the value of the constant differs considerably for different materials. This is due to the assumptions made in the original derivation of Eq. 7-1, such as homogeneous surface and a work function independent of temperature. However, Eq. 7-1 serves as a basis for formulation of the empirical equations, and should only be considered as such.

Example 7-1. Compare the maximum possible output currents from a converter when it has (a) a tungsten- and (b) a cesium-coated tungsten emitter, whose effective surface areas are both 5 cm^2 and operated at a temperature of 2200°K.

(a) Using Eq. 7-1 and the appropriate values from Table 7-1, the maximum possible current for tungsten is

$$i_m = AJ_0 = 5 \times 10^{-4} \times 0.6 \times 10^6 (2200)^2 \exp\left(\frac{-11,600 \times 4.52}{2200}\right)$$

$$= 0.067 \text{ amp}$$

(b) For a cesium-coated emitter, the maximum current is

$$i_m = AJ_0 = 5 \times 10^{-4} \times 0.03 \times 10^6 \times (2200)^2 \exp\left(\frac{-11,600 \times 1.5}{2200}\right)$$

$$= 26,500 \text{ amp}$$

This example serves to demonstrate the importance of the emitter-material work function.

7-3. THE VACUUM CONVERTER

Although the vacuum converter has been shown to have severe practical limitations, due to the close spacing required between the emitter and

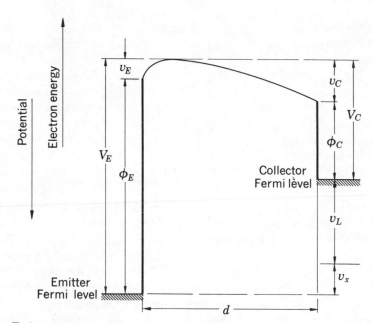

Fig. 7-4. Interelectrode potential profile of a vacuum thermionic converter.

collector, the following analysis of the device permits an insight into thermionic conversion in general and may be applied, with slight modification, to most other thermionic converters.

Figure 7-4 shows a typical potential profile between the emitter and collector of a vacuum converter, where ϕ_E and ϕ_C are the work functions of the emitter and collector, respectively. Those electrons which receive sufficient thermal energy at the hot emitter to overcome the surface barrier enter the interelectrode space. However, due to the presence of other electrons in this region, they tend to be repelled and returned again to the emitter. The potential profile indicates that only those electrons which succeed in surmounting the surface barrier ϕ_E, and in addition the space charge barrier, v_E may reach the collector electrode. Therefore the effective emitter work function, as seen by electrons which attempt to leave it, is $V_E = \phi_E + v_E$, and consequently based on Eq. 7–1 the net current density leaving the emitter is given by

$$J_E = \alpha T_E^2 \exp\left(-\frac{eV_E}{kT_E}\right) \tag{7-2}$$

Those electrons which succeed in traveling from the emitter and surmounting the potential peak are then under the influence of an accelerating potential towards the collector. Upon impact with the collector each liberates an energy $e(v_C + \phi_C) \equiv eV_C$ in the form of heat as it drops to the collector Fermi level. As purposely shown in Fig. 7–4, the collector work function is considerably smaller than the emitter work function, so that when an external load is connected between the emitter and collector there is a net potential difference, $v_L + v_x$ between the two electrodes. Each electron liberates an energy $e(v_L + v_x)$ in passing through the external circuit and returning to the emitter Fermi level, where v_x is the voltage drop across the external leads and v_L is the voltage drop across the load.

By the very nature of the potential profile the output voltage v_L is approximately equal to the difference in work function of the emitter and collector. As seen from Table 7–1, an output voltage of not much more than a few volts can be expected. Consequently, for operation at acceptable power densities, large current densities ($\sim 10^6$ amp/m^2) and high emitter temperatures (1200 to 2200°K) must be anticipated. As a result, the selection of the emitter work function must be a compromise between selecting a large value, so that v_L may be large, and selecting a small value, so that the emitted current density may be large. The current density could of course be increased independently by increasing the emitter temperature, but, apart from materials problems, the loss of heat by radiation from the emitter increases as T^4, and an upper limit is quickly reached. Consequently, the optimum design of a thermionic converter is seen to be based on a compromise between a number of competing parameters. Much of the following analysis follows that of Ingold.*

It is assumed that the converter under consideration consists of two large planar electrodes separated by an interelectrode evacuated space d. Emitter and collector surfaces are assumed to be equal in area, and uniform and homogeneous at temperatures T_E and T_C, respectively, such that the

---

* John H. Ingold. "Calculation of the Maximum Efficiency of the Thermionic Converter." *J. Appl. Phys.* **32**: 769–772. 1961.

current from the collector is negligible in comparison to that from the emitter.

The efficiency of the converter is defined as the ratio of useful electrical power output per unit emitter area to the thermal power input per unit emitter area. The useful power output density is

$$P_0 = v_L J_E \tag{7-3}$$

Under steady-state conditions the thermal power input to the emitter equals the rate at which it dissipates energy. Power loss at the emitter is mainly due to

1. The rate at which potential and kinetic energy is imparted to the electrons which leave the emitter P_e.
2. Heat radiation P_r.
3. Heat conduction through the electrical conductor P_x.

All of these power losses are expressed in terms of per unit emitter area.

The potential energy imparted to each electron which surmounts the emitter potential barrier is eV_E, while the average total kinetic energy of each electron, in terms of the emitter temperature, is $2kT_E$, where k is the Boltzmann constant. Therefore for a net emitter current density of J_E,

$$P_e = J_E \left(V_E + \frac{2kT_E}{e} \right)$$

or

$$P_e = J_E \left(V_C + v_L + v_x + \frac{2kT_E}{e} \right) \tag{7-4}$$

The radiation loss is assumed to take place between emitter and collector, so that

$$P_r = \epsilon\sigma(T_E{}^4 - T_C{}^4) \tag{7-5}$$

where ϵ is the effective emissivity, and σ, the Stefan-Boltzmann constant, has the value 5.67×10^{-8} watts/m²-°K⁴. For radiation between infinite, plane-parallel electrodes,

$$\epsilon = (1/\epsilon_E + 1/\epsilon_C - 1)^{-1} \tag{7-6}$$

where ϵ_E and ϵ_C are the emitter and collector emissivities, respectively.

Assuming the electrical emitter connection consists of a conductor of thermal conductivity k_x, resistivity ρ_x, length l, cross-sectional area A_x and resistance R_x, connected to a load at ambient temperature T_0, the heat conducted away from unit emitter area is

$$P_x = \frac{1}{A_E} \left[\frac{k_x A_x}{l} (T_E - T_0) - \frac{1}{2} (J_E A_E)^2 \frac{\rho_x l}{A_x} \right] \tag{7-7}$$

where, as in the case of the thermoelectric converter (Art. 5-3) half of the

Joule heat, which is dissipated in the conductor, is assumed to flow to each end. Equation 7–7 may be simplified by applying the Wideman-Franz law:

$$\rho_x k_x = \frac{\pi^2}{3}\left(\frac{k}{e}\right)^2 \bar{T} \tag{7-8}$$

and

$$R_x = \frac{\rho_x l}{A_x}$$

where $\bar{T} \equiv \frac{1}{2}(T_E + T_0)$ is the average conductor temperature, so that

$$P_x = \frac{\pi^2}{6}\left(\frac{k}{e}\right)^2 \frac{(T_E{}^2 - T_0{}^2)}{A_E R_x} - \frac{1}{2}J_E{}^2 A_E R_x \tag{7-9}$$

The efficiency is

$$\eta = \frac{P_0}{P_e + P_r + P_x}$$

and so from Eqs. 7–3, 7–4, and 7–9,

$$\eta = \frac{v_L J_E}{J_E\left(v_L + V_C + v_x + \dfrac{2kT_E}{e}\right) + P_r + \dfrac{\pi^2}{6}\left(\dfrac{k}{e}\right)^2 \dfrac{(T_E{}^2 - T_0{}^2)}{A_E R_x} - \dfrac{1}{2}J_E{}^2 A_E R_x} \tag{7-10}$$

In order to optimize the efficiency it is convenient to rearrange the terms in Eq. 7–10 by dividing the numerator and denominator by $J_E k T_E/e$, assuming that $T_0{}^2$ is negligible compared to $T_E{}^2$, recognizing that

$$v_x = J_E A_E R_x$$

and substituting

$$\psi_i \equiv \frac{V_i e}{T_E k} \tag{7-11}$$

so that

$$\eta = \frac{\psi_L}{\psi_L + \psi_C + \dfrac{1}{2}\psi_x + 2 + \dfrac{P_r e}{J_E k T_E} + \dfrac{\pi^2}{3\psi_x}} \tag{7-12}$$

In optimizing Eq. 7–12 it is again convenient to find the conditions necessary to minimize $1/\eta$ by setting $\partial(1/\eta)/\partial\psi_x = 0$, and $\partial(1/\eta)/\partial\psi_L = 0$. Since, based on Eq. 7–2,

$$J_E = \alpha T_E{}^2 \exp\left(-\psi_L - \psi_C - \psi_x\right) \tag{7-13}$$

and so

$$\frac{\partial J_E}{\partial\psi_x} = \frac{\partial J_E}{\partial\psi_L} = -J_E$$

The optimized values are

$$\psi_x = \pi / \sqrt{\tfrac{3}{2} + 3\Gamma} \qquad (7\text{-}14)$$

and

$$\psi_L = \frac{\psi_C + 2 + \Gamma + \psi_x(1 + \Gamma)}{\Gamma} \qquad (7\text{-}15)$$

where

$$\Gamma \equiv \frac{P_r e}{J_E k T_E} \qquad (7\text{-}16)$$

Equations 7-14 and 7-15 are not explicit solutions for the optimum values of ψ_x and ψ_L because J_E depends exponentially on the two parameters. However, the value Γ_0 for maximum efficiency may be found by substituting Eq. 7-14 and Eq. 7-15 in Eq. 7-13 and taking the logarithm of each side, giving

$$\Gamma_0 = \frac{\psi_C + 2 + \pi \sqrt{(1 + 2\Gamma_0)\tfrac{2}{3}}}{\ln\left(\dfrac{\alpha T_E{}^3 k}{P_r e}\right) + \ln \Gamma_0 - \psi_C - 1} \qquad (7\text{-}17)$$

Upon substituting Eq. 7-14 and Eq. 7-15 in Eq. 7-12 and simplifying the result, the maximum efficiency in terms of Γ_0 is

$$\eta_0 = \frac{1}{1 + \Gamma_0} \qquad (7\text{-}18)$$

The optimized value of the resistance R_{x0} for the emitter connector may be found in terms of Γ_0 from Eq. 7-14 and Eq. 7-16. Since

$$R_x = \frac{v_x}{J_E A_E} = \frac{\psi_x T_E k}{J_E A_E e}$$

then

$$R_{x0} = \frac{\pi \Gamma_0}{P_r A_E \sqrt{\tfrac{3}{2} + 3\Gamma_0}} \left(\frac{k T_E}{e}\right)^2 \qquad (7\text{-}19)$$

Similarly, Eq. 7-15 and Eq. 7-16 give the optimum load resistance as

$$R_{L0} = \frac{1}{P_r A_E} \left(\frac{k T_E}{e}\right)^2 \left[2 + \psi_C + \Gamma_0 + \frac{\pi(1 + \Gamma_0)}{\sqrt{\tfrac{3}{2} + 3\Gamma_0}}\right] \qquad (7\text{-}20)$$

Therefore for operation at maximum efficiency the emitter lead resistance, the load resistance, and the current density should be as given by Eqs. 7-19, 7-20, and 7-17, respectively.

Example 7-2.   A nuclear-powered thermionic converter is required to provide a continuous power output of 5 kw for an orbiting space laboratory. The emitter is directly heated to 1800°K and the collector radiates heat into space at 600°K. Each thermionic unit delivers an output current of 200 amp and has a planar emitter and collector with equal areas whose emissivities are 0.255 and 0.7, respectively. The emitter is connected to the load by a 3-cm-long copper conductor. If the voltage difference between the collector Fermi level and the interelectrode potential minimum* is taken as 1.8 volts, the emitter constant $Ⅾ =$ 120 $\times$ 10^4 amp/m^2-°K^2, and the resistivity of copper is 1.72 $\times$ 10^{-8} ohm-m, find, for operation at maximum efficiency,

   (a) The individual emitter area.
   (b) The diameter of the emitter lead.
   (c) The converter efficiency.
   (d) The unit load resistance.
   (e) The number of units required.
   (f) The output voltage and current if the individual units are connected in two parallel groups, each containing the same number of units in series.
   (g) The output power of the reactor.

The optimum current density is obtained from an iterative solution of Eq. 7-17. The necessary terms are first evaluated.

From Eq. 7-5 and Eq. 7-6 for planar electrodes,

$$P_r = (1/\epsilon_E + 1/\epsilon_C - 1)^{-1}\sigma(T_E^4 - T_C^4)$$
$$= (1/0.255 + 1/0.7 - 1)^{-1} \times 5.67 \times 10^{-8} \times (1.8^4 - 0.6^4) \times 10^{12}$$
$$= 13.6 \times 10^4 \text{ watts/m}^2$$

From Eq. 7-16,

$$\Gamma = \frac{13.6 \times 10^4 \times 11,600}{J_E \times 1,800} = \frac{8.74 \times 10^5}{J_E}$$

From Eq. 7-11,

$$\psi_C = \frac{1.8 \times 11,600}{1,800} = 11.6$$

and

$$\ln\left(\frac{Ⅾ T_E^3 k}{P_r e}\right) = \ln\left(\frac{120 \times 10^4 \times (1.8)^3 \times 10^9}{13.6 \times 10^4 \times 11,600}\right) = 15.3$$

Equation 7-17 may now be expressed in terms of the current density for maximum efficiency, as

$$\frac{8.74 \times 10^5}{J_{E0}} = \frac{11.6 + 2 + \pi \sqrt{(1 + 2 \times 8.74 \times 10^5/J_{E0})(\frac{2}{3})}}{15.3 + \ln(8.74 \times 10^5) - \ln J_{E0} - 11.6 - 1}$$

and this equation may be put in the form

$$0.46 \times 10^6 = 0.64 \times 10^5 \ln(J_{E0} \times 10^{-4}) + J_{E0} + 0.19 \sqrt{J_{E0}^2 + 17.48 \times 10^5 J_{E0}}$$

_____
* Since electrons are negatively charged, the highest point in the interelectrode potential profile corresponds to the potential minimum.

from which a trial solution yields

$$J_{E0} = 16.95 \times 10^4 \text{ amp/m}^2$$

and hence $\Gamma_0 = 5.17$.

(a) Since each unit is to deliver a current of 200 amp, the optimum emitter area is

$$A_E = \frac{200}{J_{E0}} = \frac{200 \times 10^{-4}}{16.95} = 11.8 \times 10^{-4} \text{ m}^2$$

(b) From Eq. 7–19 the emitter lead resistance is

$$R_{x0} = \frac{\pi \times 5.17}{13.6 \times 10^4 \times 11.8 \times 10^{-4} \sqrt{\frac{3}{2} + 3 \times 5.17}} \left(\frac{1,800}{11,600}\right)^2 = 6.1 \times 10^{-4} \text{ ohm}$$

Therefore

$$A_x = \frac{\rho l_x}{R_{x0}} = \frac{1.72 \times 10^{-8} \times 3 \times 10^{-2}}{6.1 \times 10^{-4}} = 0.00848 \times 10^{-4} \text{ m}^2$$

and so the diameter of the emitter lead should be 1.04 mm.

(c) Equation 7–18 gives the overall efficiency as

$$\eta_0 = \frac{100}{1 + 5.17} = 16.2 \text{ percent}$$

(d) Equation 7–20 gives the unit load resistance as

$$R_{L0} = \frac{1}{13.6 \times 10^4 \times 11.8 \times 10^{-4}} \left(\frac{1,800}{11,600}\right)^2$$
$$\left[2 + 11.6 + 5.17 + \frac{\pi(1 + 5.17)}{\sqrt{\frac{3}{2} + 3 \times 5.17}} \right]$$

$$= 35.3 \times 10^{-4} \text{ ohm}$$

(e) The power output from each unit is

$$i_{E0}^2 R_{L0} = 200^2 \times 35.3 \times 10^{-4} = 141 \text{ watts}$$

Since a total output of 5000 watts is required,

$$\text{number of units} = \tfrac{5000}{141} = 35.5$$

or 36, to the next larger number.

(f) The output voltage of each unit is

$$v_L = i_{E0} R_{L0} = 200 \times 35.3 \times 10^{-4} = 0.706 \text{ volt}$$

and hence if 18 units are connected in series, their combined voltage is $18 \times 0.706 = 12.7$ volts. If two groups of 18 are connected in parallel then the total output current is $200 \times 2 = 400$ amp.

(g) Since the converter output with 36 units is 5.08 kw, and the efficiency of conversion is 16.2 percent, the power output of the reactor must be $5.08/0.162 = 31.4$ kw.

In the preceding example the voltage between the collector Fermi level and the interelectrode potential minimum was specified. The position of the potential minimum was not specified; in fact it may occur at either of the electrodes, or in the interelectrode space, as illustrated in Fig. 7–5.

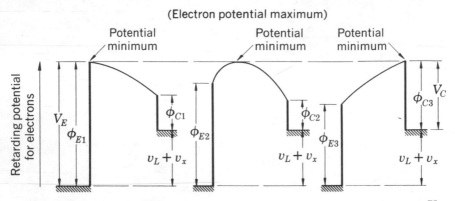

Fig. 7–5. Interelectrode potential profiles in which the values of V_E, V_C, v_L, and v_x are the same.

Obviously, selection of the electrode materials must be governed by the work function required, and hence a knowledge of the interelectrode potential profile is necessary so that ϕ_E and ϕ_C may be determined.

In the vacuum converter the interelectrode potential is governed by Poisson's equation. For an infinite planar diode this is

$$\frac{d^2V(x)}{dx^2} + \frac{e}{\epsilon_0}\,n(x) = 0 \qquad (7\text{–}21)$$

Langmuir* presents a solution to this equation in terms of a dimensionless quantity γ representing the potential in the interelectrode space, and a dimensionless quantity ξ representing the distance from the electron potential minimum to the electrodes, as shown in Fig. 7–6.

The actual interelectrode potential $V(x)$ with respect to that at the minimum $V(0) = 0$, is related to the dimensionless quantity γ by

$$\gamma = \frac{eV(x)}{kT_E} = \frac{11{,}600}{T_E}\,V(x) \qquad (7\text{–}22)$$

and the actual distance x from the potential minimum is related to ξ by

$$\xi = \frac{J_E^{1/2}}{T_E^{3/4}}\,m^{1/4}e^{1/2}\left(\frac{\pi}{2k}\right)^{3/4} x \qquad (7\text{–}23)$$

* I. Langmuir. "Effect of Space Charge and Initial Velocities on the Potential Distribution and Thermionic Current Between Parallel Plane Electrodes." *Phys. Rev.* **21**: 426. 1923.

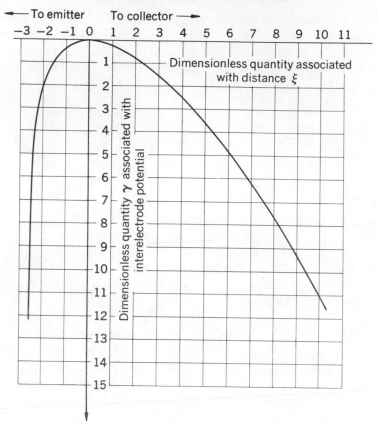

Fig. 7–6. Normalized solution to Eq. 7–21.

or

$$\xi = 9.18 \times 10^5 \frac{J_E^{1/2}}{T_E^{3/4}} x \qquad (7\text{–}24)$$

where x is expressed in centimeters, J_E in amperes per square centimeter, and T_E in °K.

Example 7–3. In the case of Example 7–2, find the required interelectrode spacing if materials with work functions of 2.198 and 1.3 volts are selected for the emitter and collector respectively.

The origin of the x and $V(x)$ coordinates is selected to coincide with the potential minimum, so that the emitter is located at $x = -x_E$ and the collector is located at $x = x_C$ as shown in Fig. 7–7. Since the work functions are specified and $v_L + v_x = 0.828$ volts,

$$v_E = 0.43 \text{ volts} \qquad v_C = 0.5 \text{ volts}$$

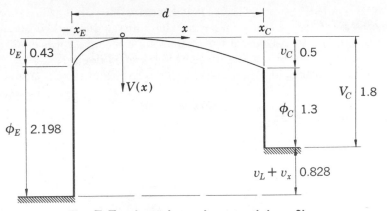

Fig. 7–7. Interelectrode potential profile.

The interelectrode spacing $d = |x_E| + |x_C|$ may be calculated using the normalized curve in Fig. 7–6.   From Eq. 7–22,

$$\gamma = \frac{11,600}{1,800} \, V(x) = 6.46 \, V(x)$$

and therefore when $V(x) = v_E = 0.43$ volts,

$$\gamma_E = 6.46 \times 0.43 = 2.77$$

Therefore from Fig. 7–6, for $\gamma_E = 2.77$, $\xi_E = -2.195$.   From Eq. 7-24,

$$\xi = 9.18 \times 10^5 \times \frac{(16.95 \times 10^4)^{1/2}}{(1800)^{3/4}} \, x = 13.4 \times 10^5 x$$

Therefore

$$x_E = \frac{\xi_E}{13.4 \times 10^5} = \frac{-2.195}{13.4 \times 10^5} = -0.162 \times 10^{-5} \text{ cm}$$

Similarly

$$\gamma_C = 6.46 \times 0.5 = 3.23 \qquad \text{and} \qquad \xi_C = 4.68$$

Therefore

$$x_C = \frac{4.08}{13.4 \times 10^5} = 0.35 \times 10^{-5} \text{ cm}$$

and so

$$d = (0.162 + 0.35) \times 10^{-5} = 0.512 \times 10^{-5} \text{ cm}$$

It is apparent that close interelectrode spacing is required in the vacuum converter, and a potential minimum occurs close to the emitter surface.

7–4. THE GAS-FILLED CONVERTER

In order to achieve acceptable power output from the vacuum converter it is necessary to use extremly small interelectrode spacing.   The problem of course is not in achieving such a small spacing initially but in achieving the necessary flatness and stability of the emitter during the operating life of the converter.   General use of the vacuum converter is considered unlikely and emphasis is being placed on gas filled devices.

Rather than using closely spaced electrodes to reduce the electron space-charge effect, gas-filled converters are designed so that positive ions are continuously generated and mingle with the electrons in front of the emitter.   If the positive ion density is sufficient to neutralize the electro-static field of the electrons, then, once an electron is liberated at the

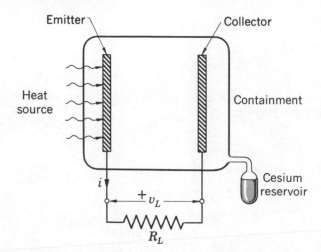

Fig. 7–8. Schematic representation of a cesium thermionic converter.

emitter, it experiences no retarding electrostatic field; consequently, all electrons are free to move to the collector and considerably larger current densities are obtained than in the equivalent vacuum converter.   Acceptable electrode spacing may now of course be used.

7–4.1. The Cesium Converter.   The cesium converter has received by far the greatest attention since the renewal of interest in thermionic energy conversion.   It consists of emitter and collector enclosed in a container filled with cesium vapor, as in Fig. 7–8.   The density of gaseous cesium atoms is controlled by regulation of the cesium reservoir temperature.

The presence of the cesium serves two purposes.   The primary purpose is the supply of positive ions for electron space-charge compensation, but in addition the cesium vapor condenses on the cool collector and imparts to it a desirably low work function close to that of cesium.   The generation of the cesium ions within the converter may be caused by *contact* (*resonance*) *ionization* and by *volume ionization*.

Contact ionization occurs when an atom contacts a hot material whose work function is greater than the ionization potential of the atom. Under such circumstances an outer-shell electron becomes more closely bound to the material surface than to its atom. When the surface is sufficiently hot the positive ion and electron are emitted. Consequently when cesium, with an ionization potential of 3.9 volts, comes in contact with a hot tungsten emitter, whose work function is 4.52 volts, contact ionization occurs, and positive ions are continuously produced at the emitter surface.

It might at first be thought that for complete neutralization of the electron space charge the ion current density leaving the emitter should equal the electron current density; however, it is the densities of ions and electrons which must be equal for space-charge neutralization. Since current density is

$$J = ne\bar{u} \tag{7-25}$$

where n, e, and $\bar{u}$ are the particle density, charge, and mean velocity, respectively, the ratio of electron to ion current for space charge neutralization is therefore

$$\frac{J_E}{J_i} = \frac{n_e e \bar{u}_e}{n_i e \bar{u}_i} = \frac{\bar{u}_e}{\bar{u}_i} \tag{7-26}$$

If the electrons and ions are in thermal equilibrium, so that they have the same kinetic energies, then

$$\tfrac{1}{2} m_e \bar{u}_e{}^2 = \tfrac{1}{2} m_i \bar{u}_i{}^2 \tag{7-27}$$

so that

$$\frac{\bar{u}_e}{\bar{u}_i} = \sqrt{\frac{m_i}{m_e}} \tag{7-28}$$

and therefore from Eq. 7-26 and Eq. 7-28

$$\boxed{\frac{J_E}{J_i} = \sqrt{\frac{m_i}{m_e}}} \tag{7-29}$$

In the case of cesium $\sqrt{m_i/m_e} = 492$, so that if one ion leaves the emitter for each 492 electrons which do so, then complete space-charge neutralization is achieved, and so electrons when leaving the emitter experience no external retarding electrostatic field.

In the cesium converter the degree of space-charge neutralization is called the *ion richness ratio* and defined as

$$\beta = \frac{492 J_i}{J_E} \tag{7-30}$$

So for incomplete neutralization $\beta < 1$, and when excess ions are provided $\beta > 1$.

The rate of arrival of neutral cesium atoms at the emitter is dependent on the cesium gas pressure, and consequently on the cesium reservoir temperature. For the most effective production of ions it has been found that the emitter temperature should be at least 3.6 times the cesium reservoir temperature.

At low pressure (10^{-4} mm Hg), when the mean free path of the particles is large compared to the electrode spacing, most of the electrons move from the emitter to the collector without collision, and consequently impact ionization of the cesium is negligible. Therefore under such conditions essentially all of the positive ions must be generated by contact at the emitter. In order to increase the output current the rate of ion production for neutralization must be increased. This calls for raising the cesium reservoir temperature to increase the pressure and arrival rate of cesium atoms at the emitter. The emitter temperature must also be increased. In practice, high emitter temperatures, above 1900°K, are required for acceptable power densities. In most cases these temperatures are unacceptable, and this mode of operation, the so-called *unignited mode*, where volume ionization is negligible, is not attractive for energy conversion.

If the cesium pressure is increased so that the mean free path of the electrons is small compared to the electrode spacing, the electrons have multiple collisions as they drift towards the collector. Under such circumstances a *plasma* is said to exist between the electrodes. A plasma consists of a mixture of electrons, positive ions and neutral particles, having an overall neutral charge, i.e., equal positive and negative charge per unit volume. The plasma is almost field-free, apart from a small potential gradient across it, necessary to maintain charge flow when the plasma is conducting. There is usually a narrow gap, called the *sheath* between the plasma and each electrode, which contains either electrons or ions, and so large potential gradients can occur in this region, as indicated in Fig. 7–9. Due to the probability of significant voltage drops across each sheath, the mean potential of the plasma may differ considerably from that of either electrode. The magnitude and sign of the voltage drop across each sheath is not only dependent on the magnitude of the ion richness ratio β but on the current flow through the plasma. The sheaths may be considered as devices which encourage or discourage charged particle flow of a particular sign from the plasma, and adjust to satisfy the boundary conditions imposed on the plasma.

In examining the operation of the high-pressure ($\sim$1 mm Hg) cesium converter it is important to consider the output current-voltage characteristic of both the unignited and the high-pressure or ignited mode shown in Fig. 7–10. Certain regions are exaggerated in order to present all the major regions. In practice, under certain conditions of space-charge neutralization, some of the features may not be observed.

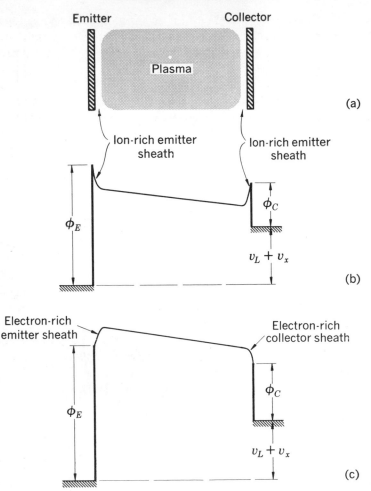

Emitter   Collector

Plasma

(a)

Ion-rich emitter sheath   Ion-rich emitter sheath

ϕ_E ϕ_C

$v_L + v_x$

(b)

Electron-rich emitter sheath   Electron-rich collector sheath

ϕ_E ϕ_C

$v_L + v_x$

(c)

Fig. 7–9. (a) Schematic of plasma and sheath in interelectrode region. (b) Potential profile when space charge is completely neutralized $(\beta \geq 1)$. (c) Potential profile when space charge is partially neutralized $(\beta < 1)$.

The output characteristic is seen to consist of two parts corresponding to the unignited and ignited modes. The discontinuity is only observed at low values of β and *electrode-spacing–pressure* product pd (mill-torr). The unignited mode characteristic is drawn on an expanded scale, and at the usual emitter temperatures of less than 1800°K the output current is insignificant compared to that of the ignited mode.

Examination of the deep penetration region is achieved by applying a reverse bias voltage to the diode. The small current which flows is due

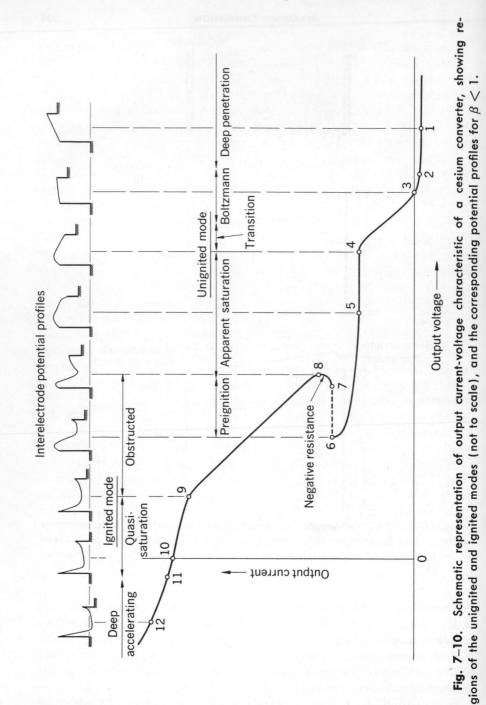

Fig. 7–10. Schematic representation of output current-voltage characteristic of a cesium converter, showing regions of the unignited and ignited modes (not to scale), and the corresponding potential profiles for $\beta < 1$.

to back electron emission from the collector, and ions from the emitter. Point 3 corresponds to open circuit voltage, and the profile is such that the number of electrons which reach the collector is equal to the number emitted, due to collector back emission.

As load is applied, the output current increases until a limit is reached due to space-charge limitation ($\beta < 1$, as in the potential profile), or due to collection of all the electrons that are emitted ($\beta > 1$).

Further loading results in the transition from the unignited to the ignited mode. Region 7–8 is called the *negative resistance region*. A spherical violet-pink glow discharge, or "ball of fire," forms at a point close to the emitter and spreads to cover the total emitter region as the current increases. The negative slope of the characteristic results from the changing cross-sectional area of the discharge. The potential profile shows the presence of what is called a *double sheath* at the emitter, with a large accelerating potential for electrons once they cross this sheath. These electrons have sufficient energy to cause volume ionization of the cesium atoms, which are in turn accelerated towards the emitter and reduce the height of the electron-rich double sheath, thus permitting the liberation of additional electrons. Operation in this, the *obstructed region*, is desirable, since usually the product of output voltage and current is a maximum here. As more current is drawn and more ions are generated a point is reached, 9, at which the emitter electron space-charge is completely neutralized and the double sheath disappears.

Operation at lower voltages is then said to be in the *quasi-saturation region*. The current continues to increase, though at a considerably reduced rate, until the converter is short-circuited (10). The additional current flow in the quasi-saturation region is attributed to (a) the fact that as the emitter sheath grows the ion current generation, and flow to the emitter, increases, (b) the electron back emission current from the plasma decreases with the sheath growth, and (c) the increasing ion current causes high electrostatic fields at the emitter and results in additional electron emission due to an anomalous Schottky effect.

The ignited mode of operation is the only means of obtaining adequate power densities in a cesium converter at the desirable emitter temperatures below 1800°K. However, the unignited mode is much better understood than the ignited mode. Despite the great amount of research work which has been conducted, the ionization mechanisms of the ignited mode are not completely understood. For this reason it is difficult to develop a satisfactory theoretical model for the cesium converter operating in the ignited mode. However, Fig. 7–11 shows some typical results, obtained from the experimental converter in Fig. 7–12. It is apparent why operation in the obstructed region is desirable. There, current densities above 50 amp/cm² are obtained at approximately 0.5 volt, resulting in output power densities

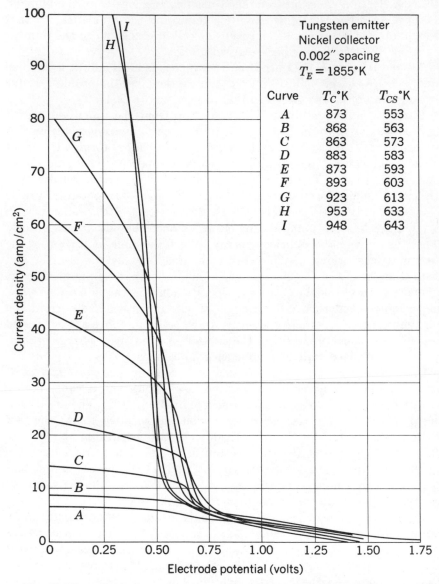

Curve	T_C°K	T_{CS}°K
A	873	553
B	868	563
C	863	573
D	883	583
E	873	593
F	893	603
G	923	613
H	953	633
I	948	643

Tungsten emitter
Nickel collector
0.002″ spacing
$T_E = 1855$°K

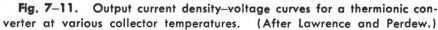

Fig. 7–11. Output current density–voltage curves for a thermionic converter at various collector temperatures. (After Lawrence and Perdew.)

greater than 20 watts/cm². Other experimenters* have reported output current densities of 100 amp/cm² at 0.75 volt and estimated efficiencies of above 22 percent.

It is also found experimentally that there is an optimum electrode spacing. This is not surprising, since when the electrodes are too close together the electrons have insufficient opportunity to cause ionization

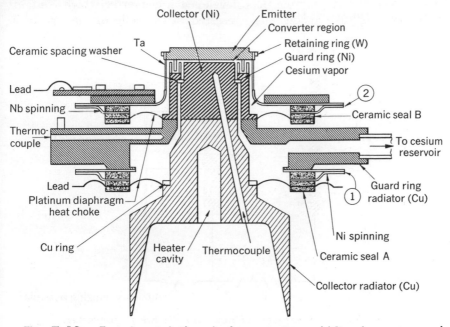

Fig. 7–12. Experimental thermionic converter. (After Lawrence and Perdew.)

while traveling from the emitter to collector, whereas, when the electrode spacing is large the internal resistance becomes excessive. A spacing of about 0.05 mm is usually found to be optimum.

7-4.2. The Auxiliary Discharge Converter. In addition to those converters already considered there are many other types. Most of these are being developed in order to achieve some desirable characteristic not easily attainable with the cesium system. For example, the auxiliary discharge converter† has been developed to permit low-temperature ($T_E \sim$

---

* V. C. Wilson, H. F. Webster, and J. Lawrence. "Rapporteur Paper on Converter Performance from the International Conference on Thermionic Electrical Power Generation, London, England." *Thermionic Specialist Conference Report.* San Diego, Calif. 1965.

† Edward M. Walsh. "Thermionic Energy Conversion." *Nuclear News* (American Nuclear Society) **7**: 48–50. September, 1964.

1500°K) operation using either fossil- or nuclear-fueled heat sources. These converters are also filled with inert gas, such as argon, neon, or xenon (at 1 to 4 mm Hg), and so the corrosion problems associated with cesium are eliminated.

Ions are produced in the auxiliary discharge converter by applying a voltage, greater than the ionization potential of the gas, to a third electrode. Gabor, for example, has developed a converter which contains a "spark-plug"-like arrangement inserted in the collector, as shown in

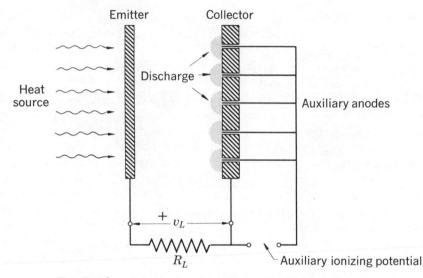

Fig. 7–13. Schematic of auxiliary discharge converter.

Fig. 7–13. A continuous auxiliary discharge is not necessary. It has been found that the ion lifetime is lengthened by reflection at the emitter, and so sufficient ions are produced if an auxiliary discharge is "fired" at about 500-μsec intervals.

The main disadvantage of this type of converter is the complexity introduced by the auxiliary discharge system. However, since ion production is independent of the electrode work functions, it is possible to use low work function materials, and consequently achieve the desired output power density at relatively low temperatures. This is most important since the temperatures required for the operation of cesium converters cannot be easily attained with conventional heat sources, and there are significant materials problems when the high temperatures provided by nuclear power sources are utilized. The power used in producing ions for space-charge neutralization is found to be considerably less than in the cesium converter, and also due to significantly lower radiation losses from the relatively cool emitter, the possible overall efficiencies are high. Fabrication is simplified and the problems of electrode surface instability reduced by the relatively large (~1 mm) electrode spacing which may be used. However, one major problem remains to be solved, and this is the development of suitable long-life low work function collector and emitter materials.

7–5. THERMIONIC NUCLEAR REACTORS

In general, the development of thermionic converters has been based on the assumption that the high emitter temperatures required would be supplied by a nuclear power source, whether for use in space or on the ground. It is appropriate therefore to examine the integration of a nuclear reactor and a thermionic conversion system.

The thermionic converter may be designed for use outside the core of the reactor, or incorporated within the core itself. In the former case a high-temperature coolant loop transfers heat from the reactor to the emitters. Heat is rejected by the collectors either by radiation into space or to a secondary coolant loop. The temperature of the coolant would therefore have to be at a temperature of at least 1500°K, indicating the use of a liquid metal such as lithium. However, since the converters are connected in series, each emitter must be isolated electrically from the coolant. Consequently, a material capable of acting both as an electrical insulator and as a thermal conductor at temperatures above 1500°K is required. Such a material is not available, nor is it likely to be developed in the foreseeable future.

If the converters are an integral part of the fuel element, then the design resembles that of an ordinary reactor core with cylindrical fuel elements. However, each fuel element consists of a number of converters connected in series, rather like the batteries in a flashlight, as shown in Fig. 7–14. Since existing high-temperature nuclear fuels do not absorb cesium, or exhibit the surface stability required, due to close electrode spacing, the fuel must be enclosed with a suitable cylindrical casing which acts as the emitter electrode. Surrounding the emitter are the concentric annular regions of cesium vapor, the collector, insulation, and an outer thin-walled tube which aligns and supports all the converters in the fuel rod. The emitter of each converter is electrically connected and mechanically cantilevered from the collector of the next converter. All converters in a fuel element are in vapor communication. Note also that all electrical insulators in this design are on the collector, or low-temperature, side of the converters.

The fuel elements in the reactor are electrically connected in parallel-series combinations. The reactor is cooled either by means of a liquid-

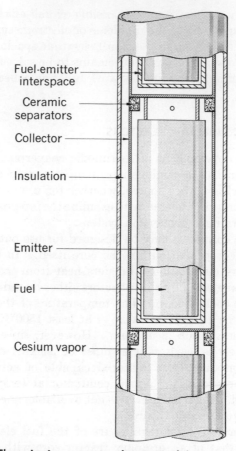

Fuel-emitter interspace

Ceramic separators

Collector

Insulation

Emitter

Fuel

Cesium vapor

Fig. 7–14. Thermionic converter integrated into a nuclear reactor fuel element. (By permission, from Elias P. Gyftopoulos.)

metal loop if the system is designed for space or submarine propulsion, or by any other coolant if the application does not require a high heat rejection temperature.

The critical size of a thermionic reactor must of course be considerably larger than the equivalent conventional reactor, due to the reduction of the thermal utilization factor caused by the introduction of the additional non-fissile materials in the fuel rods. The reactor size may be maintained within the desired limits by using more highly enriched fuel.

7–6. HEAT PIPES

For acceptable efficiencies, thermionic converters must be operated at high power densities, with output powers of as much as 50 watts/cm².

Many possible heat sources are not capable of delivering sufficient heat flux. A radio-isotope heat source is one example, and a fossil-fuel burner can only provide the desired heat flux at the sacrifice of efficiency. These limitations can be overcome by use of heat pipes to concentrate the flux.

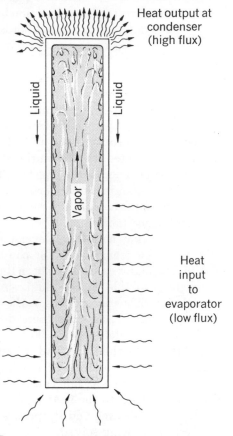

Heat output at condenser (high flux)

Liquid

Liquid

Vapor

Heat input to evaporator (low flux)

Fig. 7–15. Schematic of a heat-pipe flux-concentrator.

The operation of a heat pipe is based on the fact that large quantities of heat can be transferred, with a very small drop in temperature by evaporation of a liquid, transport of the vapor through a duct, and condensation back to the liquid phase subsequently. For continuous operation the condensate must be returned to the evaporator. The heat pipe uses capillary action to supply the return force.

Figure 7–15 shows a schematic of a cylindrical heat pipe. The inside wall of the pipe is lined with a capillary, or wick, structure, which is saturated with the working fluid. The wick structure may take many forms, ranging from several layers of wire mesh, to rectangular grooves cut in the inside wall of the tube.

When heat is applied to one section of the tube the working fluid evaporates from the surface of the wick, and moves to the other section where it condenses and yields its latent heat of vaporization. The condensed liquid is drawn back towards the heated section by capillary action. Although the capillary force is not very great, neither is the mass circulation rate. For example, 20 kw of heat may be transferred by a circulation rate of 1 g of lithium per second.

Output power densities of 100 to 400 watts/cm² are possible* and flux concentrations of 1:12 have been reported.† Therefore heat sources, which generate sufficiently high temperatures, but whose maximum heat-flux density is too low, by even more than one order of magnitude, may still satisfactorily drive a thermionic converter. In addition, operation of the heat pipe is not significantly affected by gravitational forces, and since only small temperature drops occur across the pipe ($\sim$5°K at temperatures above 1750°K), it is possible to separate the converter from the heat source. The heat pipe may also be used for cooling the collector and permits the development of lightweight space radiators.

The main problems confronting heat-pipe development are those of material compatibility and mass transport. For converter applications liquid metals are used, and in many cases it has been found that the wick, or wall structure, is slightly soluble in the fluid. As a result, small amounts of the structural materials are dissolved in the condenser section, carried along to the evaporator section, and there deposited when the fluid is evaporated. However, a lifetime of 4300 hr at 1400°K using a NbZr-99 structure and lithium as the fluid, and a lifetime of 335 hr at 2200°K using a tungsten structure and silver as the fluid, have been obtained. In the latter case failure was not caused by mass transport, but by leakage of WF_6 and/or H_2 into the heat pipe. Research interest has only recently developed in this area and it appears that the material problems are well on the way to being solved.

PROBLEMS

7-1. Compare the radiator areas required for a thermionic and a thermoelectric converter, both of which reject by radiation the same quantity of heat into space, but at 900°K and 600°K, respectively.

7-2. To what temperature should the following materials be heated in order

* W. A. Ranken, and J. E. Kemme. "Survey of Los Alamos and Euratom Heat-Pipe Investigations." *Thermionic Conversion Specialist Conference Report*, pp. 335–36, San Diego, Calif. 1965.
† W. B. Hall. "Heat-Pipe Experiments," pp. 337–40, *ibid*.

to provide a temperature-limited current of 200 amp, if each has an effective area of 5 cm²?

   a. 1.5 ev barium oxide.
   b. Thoriated tungsten.
   c. Platinum.

7–3. Four thermionic converters are operating under space-charge-limited conditions. All converters operate at an emitter temperature of 1600°K and conditions are such that the electron-retarding interelectrode potential with respect to the emitter surface is 0.3 volt. Find the space-charge-limited current density when the emitters are of

   a. Strontium oxide.
   b. Cesiated tungsten.
   c. Thoriated tungsten.
   d. Molybdenum.

7–4. A thermionic converter is to be designed to deliver an output current of 72 amp when the space charge limiting potential is 0.1 volt. The solar heat source provides an emitter temperature of 1600°K. Find an emitter material which would provide the desired current, if the effective emitter area is to be 5×10^{-4} m². As an initial approximation use the theoretical value of $\alpha = 1.2 \times 10^{6}$ amp/m²-°K². Neglect interelectrode loss.

7–5. Find the output voltage of a high-temperature thermionic converter unit with a tungsten emitter and a thoriated tungsten collector, if the interelectrode potential minimum is at 0.48 volt and 0.6 volt with respect to the potential of the emitter and collector surfaces, respectively. The output current of 40 amp passes through a 0.22-cm-diameter, 3-cm-long emitter lead, whose resistivity is 4×10^{-7} ohm-m. The resistance of the collector lead is negligible.

7–6. Find the open-circuit voltage of a vacuum thermionic converter with a SrO emitter at 1500°K and a BaO collector at 600°K.

7–7. Derive Eq. 7–14 and Eq. 7–15.

7–8. Derive Eq. 7–17.

7–9. A thermionic reactor is required to supply a continuous electrical output of 9 kw for a small lunar laboratory. The reactor is operated to provide an emitter temperature of 1850°K and heat is radiated into space at a collector temperature 700°K. The output current of each thermionic unit is 220 amp and the emitter and collector may be assumed to be of equal area and planer with emissivities of 0.2 and 0.65, respectively. The emitter lead is a 5-cm-long rod of resistivity 3×10^{-8} ohm-m. The voltage difference between the collector Fermi level and the interelectrode potential minimum is to be 1.6 volts. The emitter constant α is 120×10^{4} amp/m²-°K². Find, for operation at maximum efficiency,

   a. The area of each electrode.
   b. The emitter lead dimensions.
   c. The efficiency of the converter.
   d. The number of units required.

7-10. A thermionic vacuum converter is designed to operate at emitter and collector temperatures of 1800°K and 600°K respectively. If the effective interelectrode emissivity is 0.25, find the minimum interelectrode current density required to achieve an efficiency of 25 percent.

7-11. A planar vacuum converter with emitter and collector work functions of 2.3 ev and 1.0 ev, respectively, is operated at an electrode current density of 12×10^4 amp/m^2 and an emitter temperature of 1850°K. Taking $\mathcal{C} = 120 \times 10^4$ amp/m^2-°K^2, find the distance of the potential minimum from the emitter.

7-12. If the converter described in Prob. 7-11 has an interelectrode spacing of (a) 0.6×10^{-3} cm and (b) 10^{-3} cm, find the output voltage. Neglect the electrode lead voltage drop.

7-13. Find the ratio of electron to ion currents necessary at the emitter of a gas-filled thermionic converter to provide complete space charge neutralization when the filling is

a. Argon.
b. Neon.
c. Cesium vapor.
d. Potassium vapor.

7-14. An ion richness ratio of 0.7 is achieved in a cesium converter operating in the unignited mode. Find the effective production rate of ions at the emitter when $J_E = 14 \times 10^4$ amp/m^2.

7-15. A gas-filled converter has emitter and collector work functions of 2.1 ev and 1.3 ev, respectively. When operating at an electrode current density of 55×10^4 amp/m^2, thin ion rich sheaths of 0.7 volts and 0.6 volts exist at the emitter and collector respectively. If the interelectrode spacing is 2×10^{-5} m and the plasma resistivity is 1.82×10^{-2} ohm-m, find the output voltage. Neglect the voltage drop in the leads.

7-16. From experimental results it is found that the output current density of a cesium converter, operating in the obstructed mode, may be expressed as a function of output voltage by

$$J_E = (80 - 27v_L - 20v_L{}^2)10^4 \text{ amp/m}^2, \quad 0 \le v_L \le 1.0$$

Find the output current density, power density, and voltage at maximum power.

8

Fluiddynamic Converters

The converters considered in this chapter are the magnetohydrodynamic (MHD) and the electrogasdynamic (EGD) systems. Unlike other direct converters, the energy input is in the form of a high-velocity, high-temperature fluid, part of whose energy is converted into electricity within the converter. Both systems are well suited to large-scale application and converters with main-power station capacity are under consideration. The principles involved in the operation of MHD generators may also be applied to the design of electromagnetic pumps and ion rockets for long range space propulsion.

8-1. BASIC PRINCIPLES OF MAGNETOHYDRODYNAMIC CONVERSION

The generation of electricity in the MHD converter is based upon the Faraday effect; that is, a voltage is generated across a conductor which is caused to move through a magnetic field. In the MHD converter the conductor is a fluid and a pressure difference causes it to flow through the magnetic field. Figure 8-1 shows the essential features.

Fluid is forced to flow at velocity $\mathbf{U}$ normal to a magnetic field of flux density $\mathbf{B}$. As a result, a potential gradient

$$\boxed{\mathbf{E} = \mathbf{U} \times \mathbf{B}} \qquad (8\text{-}1)$$

is induced across the fluid. Since $\mathbf{U}$ and $\mathbf{B}$ are shown in the positive y and z directions, respectively, the potential gradient is in the positive x direction, and so in this case

$$E = UB$$

Assuming the flux density and velocity are constant and uniform, a voltage

$$e_g = Ed = UBd \qquad (8\text{-}2)$$

221

is induced across a channel of width d.   If electrodes are placed as shown, a current JA circulates through an external load R_L, where A is the area of each electrode.   If the conductivity of the fluid is assumed constant at

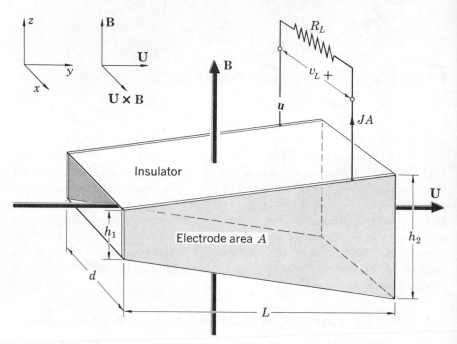

Fig. 8–1.   Schematic of magnetohydrodynamic converter.

σ, then the load voltage

$$v_L = e_g - JA \frac{d}{\sigma A}$$

$$= UBd - \frac{Jd}{\sigma} \tag{8–3}$$

The MHD converter may therefore be represented by an internal voltage

$$e_g = UBd \tag{8–4}$$

in series with an internal resistance $d/\sigma A$ delivering a current AJ as shown in Fig. 8–2.

The output to internal voltage ratio is termed the *loading factor*, and is denoted by

$$K = \frac{v_L}{UBd} \tag{8–5}$$

From Eq. 8–3 and Eq. 8–5 the current density is

$$J = UB\sigma(1 - K) \tag{8–6}$$

The specific power output, or the power output per unit volume Ad between the electrodes, is

$$P_0 = \frac{v_L i}{Ad} = \frac{KUBdJA}{Ad} = KUBJ$$

Substituting for J from Eq. 8–6 gives

$$P_0 = \sigma U^2 B^2 K(1 - K) \tag{8–7}$$

Upon differentiating Eq. 8–7 with respect to K and setting equal to zero, it is seen that for maximum power output $K = \frac{1}{2}$. This result of course

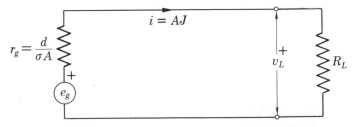

Fig. 8–2.   Equivalent circuit of the basic MHD generator.

could have been arrived at from the principle of maximum power transfer, which specifies that load resistance should equal the internal resistance of the source, in which case $v_L = \frac{1}{2}UBd$, and $K = \frac{1}{2}$. The maximum specific power output is

$$P_{0m} = \tfrac{1}{4}\sigma U^2 B^2 \tag{8–8}$$

In this idealized converter the only power loss considered is specific power loss due to Joule heating of the fluid and is given by

$$P_J = \frac{i^2 r_g}{Ad} = \frac{J^2 A^2 d}{Ad\sigma A} = \frac{J^2}{\sigma}$$

and from Eq. 8–6

$$P_J = \sigma U^2 B^2 (1 - K)^2 \tag{8–9}$$

The fractional efficiency of an ideal MHD converter is therefore

$$\eta = \frac{P_0}{P_0 + P_J} = \frac{1}{1 + P_J/P_0} \tag{8–10}$$

and from Eq. 8–7 and Eq. 8–9

$$\eta = \frac{1}{1 + \dfrac{1 - K}{K}} = K \tag{8–11}$$

Therefore in the ideal converter the efficiency is equal to the loading factor, and consequently at maximum power the efficiency is 50 percent. Figure 8–3 shows the performance characteristics of an ideal converter.

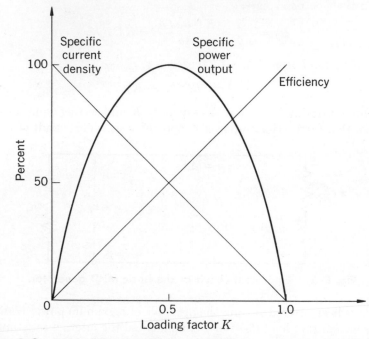

Fig. 8–3. Variation of efficiency, specific power output, and specific current density as a function of the converter loading factor for an ideal MHD converter.

The foregoing analysis of the ideal converter yields characteristics which are of course significantly different from those obtained in practice, or when the many loss factors associated with the system are taken into consideration. However the results of this simple analysis serve as a standard of comparison for actual converter performance, and of course serve also as a means for making initial crude design estimates.

Example 8–1. The design of a MHD converter using a gas as the working fluid is based on the following:

$$A = 0.2 \text{ m}^2$$
$$d = 0.22 \text{ m}$$
$$\sigma = 42 \text{ mho/m}$$
$$U = 1800 \text{ m/sec}$$
$$B = 1.1 \text{ weber/m}^2$$

Find

   (a) The output voltage, power, and efficiency at a loading factor of 0.7.
   (b) The maximum power output.
   (c) The current at maximum power output.
   (d) The short-circuit current.
   (e) The open-circuit voltage.

   (a) From Eq. 8–5, the output voltage is

$$v_L = KUBd = 0.7 \times 1800 \times 1.1 \times 0.22$$
$$= 305 \text{ volts}$$

From Eq. 8–7, the total output power is

$$P_L = AdP_0 = Ad\sigma U^2B^2K(1 - K)$$
$$= 0.2 \times 0.22 \times 42(1800)^2(1.1)^2 \times 0.7(1 - 0.7)$$
$$= 1.515 \times 10^6 \text{ watts}$$

From Eq. 8–11 the fractional efficiency is equal to K, so the efficiency is 70 percent.

   (b) From Eq. 8–8, the maximum power output is

$$P_{Lm} = AdP_{0m} = \tfrac{1}{4}Ad\sigma U^2B^2$$
$$= 0.25 \times 0.2 \times 0.22 \times 42(1800)^2(1.1)^2$$
$$= 1.8 \times 10^6 \text{ watts}$$

   (c) From Eq. 8–6, the current at maximum power output is

$$i_{mp} = AJ_{mp} = AUB\sigma(1 - K_{mp})$$
$$= 0.2 \times 1800 \times 1.1 \times 42(1 - 0.5)$$
$$= 8300 \text{ amp}$$

   (d) From Eq. 8–6, it is seen that the short-circuit current is twice that at maximum power, therefore

$$i_{sc} = 8300 \times 2 = 16,600 \text{ amp}$$

   (e) At open circuit, $K = 1$, and so from Eq. 8–5

$$v_{Loc} = UBd = 1800 \times 1.1 \times 0.22 = 435 \text{ volts}$$

Although the above results are based on theory developed from an ideal converter, they serve to demonstrate the large power-handling capability of the MHD converter, and give some idea of the voltage, current, and dimension magnitudes encountered in practice, when a gas is used as the working fluid. Liquid metals are used as the working fluid in some converters, in which case higher current densities, lower output voltages, and lower velocities are typical.

8-2. THE BASIC LAWS OF MHD

   The accurate design of a MHD converter is a formidable task, and the evolution of a reliable and competitive system requires a thorough understanding of a complex problem involving the interaction of electro-magnetics, fluid mechanics, and heat transfer. Although it is certainly outside the scope of this text to cover the subject in the necessary detail required for a large-scale engineering development effort, the six governing equations which will now be developed are the basis of all MHD design.

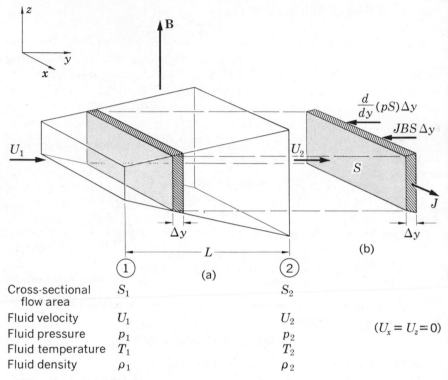

	①	②	
Cross-sectional flow area	S_1	S_2	
Fluid velocity	U_1	U_2	$(U_x = U_z = 0)$
Fluid pressure	p_1	p_2	
Fluid temperature	T_1	T_2	
Fluid density	ρ_1	ρ_2	

Fig. 8–4. Schematic of (a) MHD fluid duct; (b) differential volume from within the duct.

The basic dependent variables are

    B   Magnetic field.
    E   Electric field.
    J   Current density.
    U   Velocity.
   p, ρ, T Thermodynamic state variables (pressure, density, temperature) which in general are represented by fifteen scalar quantities.

Figure 8–4 is a schematic of a variable flow area MHD fluid duct in which the inlet and outlet state variables are as shown. The basic laws of MHD conversion are derived from the general equations of fluid mechanics, suitably modified for electromagnetic effects, and from the appropriate forms of the Maxwell equations for a moving, deformable medium.

8–2.1. Conservation of Mass. Under steady-state conditions the rate at which mass enters the duct should be equal to the rate at which it emerges; therefore

$$m = S_1 U_1 \rho_1 = S_2 U_2 \rho_2 \qquad (8\text{--}12)$$

8–2.2. Conservation of Momentum. From Newton's second law, the rate at which a body changes momentum is equal to the total force acting on it. The working fluid in passing through the duct is subjected to two types of force: surface force and body force. The surface force is composed of normal pressure and viscous shear, while the body forces are gravitational, electrostatic, and the Lorentz force $\mathbf{J} \times \mathbf{B}$. The main forces for a gas are caused by the pressure difference, which moves the fluid through the duct, and the Lorentz force, which slows the fluid down, and in so doing removes energy.

The mass flow rate into the differential volume in Fig. 8–4b is $SU\rho$ at a velocity U. Therefore the momentum flow rate into the volume is $SU^2\rho$, and so the rate of change of momentum within the volume is

$$-\frac{d}{dy}(S\dot{U}^2\rho)\,\Delta y \qquad (8\text{--}13)$$

where the negative sign indicates that the fluid experiences a force in the negative y direction if the fluid gains momentum in moving through the duct.

The net pressure force acting on the elemental volume is

$$-S\frac{dp}{dy}\,\Delta y$$

where the negative sign indicates that the pressure force would be in the negative y direction should the pressure gradient be positive. Therefore the net pressure and Lorentz force on the volume $S\,\Delta y$ in the positive y direction is

$$-S\frac{dp}{dy}\,\Delta y - JB(S\,\Delta y) \qquad (8\text{--}14)$$

Equating Eq. 8–13 and Eq. 8–14 gives

$$-\frac{d}{dy}(SU^2\rho)\,\Delta y = -S\frac{dp}{dy}\,\Delta y - JB(S\,\Delta y)$$

or

$$\frac{m}{S}\frac{dU}{dy} = \frac{dp}{dy} + JB \qquad (8\text{--}15)$$

8–2.3. Conservation of Energy. The first law of thermodynamics requires that under steady-state adiabatic conditions the energy supplied to the differential volume must be equal to the change in fluid energy as it passes through the volume.

The current, in passing through the fluid, causes Joule heating, which adds energy at a rate J^2/σ per unit volume. The fluid may also carry with it electrostatic and electromagnetic energy, but this is ignored here. The fluid energy per unit mass is the sum of its enthalpy H and its kinetic energy $\frac{1}{2}U^2$. Therefore the rate at which energy enters the differential volume is

$$m(H + \tfrac{1}{2}U^2) = SU\rho(H + \tfrac{1}{2}U^2)$$

and so the net change in fluid energy in flowing through the volume is

$$\frac{d}{dy}\left[SU\rho\left(H + \frac{1}{2}U^2\right)\right]\Delta y$$

Therefore

$$\frac{d}{dy}\left[SU\rho\left(H + \frac{1}{2}U^2\right)\right]\Delta y = \frac{J^2}{\sigma}S\,\Delta y$$

or

$$\boxed{\frac{d}{dy}\left[U\rho\left(H + \frac{1}{2}U^2\right)\right] = \frac{J^2}{\sigma}} \tag{8–16}$$

8–2.4. The Governing Electrical Equations. The electrical equations are based on Ohm's law, Faraday's law, and Ampere's law and are in general

$$\boxed{\mathbf{J} = \sigma[\mathbf{E} + \mathbf{U} \times \mathbf{B} - \beta(\mathbf{J} \times \mathbf{B})]} \tag{8–17}$$

$$\boxed{\nabla \times \mathbf{E} = -\frac{\partial \mathbf{B}}{\partial t}} \tag{8–18}$$

and

$$\boxed{\nabla \times \mathbf{B} = \mu\mu_0\mathbf{J}} \tag{8–19}$$

where the last term in Eq. 8–17 accounts for the Hall effect and β is the *Hall constant,* both of which will be discussed later. In Eq. 8–19 μ_0 is the permeability of free space ($4\pi \times 10^{-7}$ henry/m) and μ is the relative permeability of the fluid.

Example 8–2. A MHD converter is to be designed for use with combustion gas which is seeded with 1 percent potassium to increase its average conductivity to 31 mho/m. The magnetic field is uniform and of density 1.6 weber/m². The duct is to be designed for a constant gas velocity of 850 m/sec, at a loading factor of 0.6, inlet pressure $p_1 = 2.7$ atm, and an exhaust pressure $p_2 = 0.7$ atm. The width of the duct is to remain constant at $d = 0.3$ m, and the height at inlet

$h_1 = 0.1$ m. Determine the length of the duct and the height h_2 at the outlet. What is the output current, voltage, and power?

Since the design is for constant velocity, Eq. 8–15 becomes

$$\frac{dp}{dy} = -JB$$

and substituting for J from Eq. 8–6 gives

$$\frac{dp}{dy} = -UB^2\sigma(1 - K) \tag{8–20}$$

Upon integrating Eq. 8–20 the length of duct required for a pressure change of Δp is

$$L = \frac{\Delta P}{UB^2\sigma(1 - K)} = \frac{(2.7 - 0.7) \times 1.01 \times 10^5}{850 \times (1.6)^2 \times 31 \times (1 - 0.6)} = 7.5 \text{ m}$$

Since $U_1 = U_2$, Eq. 8–12 gives the outlet area as

$$S_2 = S_1 \left(\frac{\rho_1}{\rho_2}\right) \tag{8–21}$$

and since the equation of state for the gas is

$$p = \Re\rho T \tag{8–22}$$

where $\Re$ is the gas constant, Eq. 8–21 becomes

$$S_2 = S_1 \left(\frac{p_1}{p_2}\right)\left(\frac{T_2}{T_1}\right) \tag{8–23}$$

The relationship between temperature and pressure for the modified adiabatic expansion is

$$\frac{T_2}{T_1} = \left(\frac{p_2}{p_1}\right)^{K(\gamma-1)/\gamma} \tag{8–24}$$

where $\gamma = 1.2$, and is the ratio of the specific heats, and K is the loading factor. Under open-circuit conditions $K = 1$, and the gas expands adiabatically. However, when $0 \leq K \leq 1$, the load current heats up the gas in flowing through it and as a result T_2 is greater than in the adiabatic case. Substituting Eq. 8–24 in Eq. 8–23 gives

$$S_2 = S_1 \left(\frac{p_2}{p_1}\right)^{[K(\gamma-1)/\gamma]-1}$$
$$= 0.03 \left(\frac{0.7}{2.7}\right)^{[0.6(1.2-1)/(1.2)]-1} \tag{8–25}$$
$$= 0.101 \text{ m}^2$$

Therefore

$$h_2 = \frac{S_2}{d} = \frac{0.101}{0.3} = 0.337 \text{ m}$$

The electrode area is

$$A = L \left(\frac{h_1 + h_2}{2}\right) = 7.5 \left(\frac{0.1 + 0.337}{2}\right)$$
$$= 1.64 \text{ m}^2$$

Neglecting the Hall effect, Eq. 8–6 gives the current density as

$$J = 850 \times 1.6 \times 31(1 - 0.6)$$
$$= 16.9 \times 10^3 \text{ amp/m}^2$$

and

$$i = JA = 16.9 \times 10^3 \times 1.64$$
$$= 27.7 \times 10^3 \text{ amp}$$

From Eq. 8–5 the output voltage is

$$v_L = 850 \times 1.6 \times 0.3 \times 0.6$$
$$= 245 \text{ volts}$$

The total output power is

$$v_L i = 245 \times 27.7 \times 10^3$$
$$= 6.8 \times 10^6 \text{ watts}$$

8–3. MHD LOSS MECHANISMS

The foregoing analysis has neglected many important loss mechanisms which must be taken into account when analysing the MHD converter. The principal losses are

1. Hall effect loss.
2. End loss.
3. Heat transfer and fluiddynamic loss.
4. Electrode loss.

Each of these phenomena has been the subject of detailed papers and their coverage in this section will only be of a general nature.

8–3.1. Hall Effects. When electrons move through a magnetic field they experience the Lorentz force, which is normal to both the direction of motion and to the magnetic field, and expressed by

$$\mathbf{F} = e\mathbf{u}_e \times \mathbf{B} \qquad (8\text{–}26)$$

where e is the charge on the particle in coulombs and $\mathbf{u}_e$ is the electron velocity. Consequently, rather than moving in a straight path between the electrodes, the electrons move in a curved path and so tend to flow preferentially to one end of the collecting electrode. As a result an electric field builds up in the axial direction. However, the electrodes act as a short circuit to this field and so large short-circuit currents flow axially in the electrodes and dissipate power.

The obvious solution to this problem has been the use of segmented electrodes as shown in Fig. 8–5. The use of sufficient segments reduces the Hall effect loss to an acceptable level. Since each pair of electrodes must be isolated, each must be loaded independently. Such an arrangement of course causes inconvenience. In practice each set of electrodes

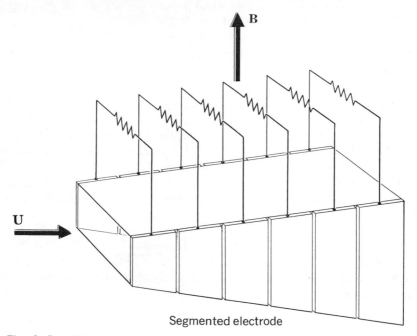

Segmented electrode

Fig. 8–5. Schematic of magnetohydrodynamic converter with segmented electrodes.

feeds a separate inverter which converts the individual power contributions into alternating current, where all is combined to provide a single a-c power source.

Correction for the Hall effect is important in gases when the radius of the curved electron path is not large compared to the average distance an electron travels between collisions. The radius of the path r is determined by the balance of centrifugal and magnetic force:

$$\frac{m_e u_e^2}{r} = e u_e B$$

yielding

$$r = \frac{m_e u_e}{eB} \tag{8–27}$$

where m_e is the electron mass.

8–3.2. End Loss. A shunt path between the electrodes is provided by the fluid at the upstream and downstream sides of the electrodes. The shunt currents at both ends of the generator may introduce significant losses, particularly when the fluid conductivity is high.

Sutton[†] has examined these losses and shown that the ratio of the actual power density P_a to the ideal power density P_0 as previously considered is given by

$$\frac{P_a}{P_0} = 1 - \frac{1}{A^*}\left(\frac{K}{1-K}\right) \tag{8-28}$$

where

$$A^* = \frac{\pi}{2\ln 2}\frac{L_E}{d} \tag{8-29}$$

L_E is the electrode length and L_E/d is called the electrode aspect ratio. Therefore end losses may be reduced by making the electrode aspect ratio large.

The efficiency of the ideal converter was shown to equal K, and since the actual output power with end losses is given by Eq. 8–28, the actual efficiency with end losses is

$$\eta_a = K\left[1 - \frac{1}{A^*}\left(\frac{K}{1-K}\right)\right] \tag{8-30}$$

Therefore both the actual output power and efficiency become zero when

$$1 - \frac{1}{A^*}\left(\frac{K_z}{1-K_z}\right) = 0$$

or when

$$K_z = \frac{A^*}{1+A^*} \tag{8-31}$$

At loading factors greater than the value in Eq. 8–31 the converter ceases to act as a generator, and operates as a pump.

Upon differentiating Eq. 8–30 with respect to K and equating to zero, it is found that the maximum efficiency occurs at a loading factor of

$$K_{\eta m} = 1 - \frac{1}{\sqrt{1+A^*}} \tag{8-32}$$

From Eq. 8–7 and Eq. 8–28

$$P_a = \sigma U^2 B^2 K\left(1 - K - \frac{K}{A^*}\right) \tag{8-33}$$

Upon differentiating Eq. 8–33 with respect to K and setting the result

† G. W. Sutton and A. Sherman. *Engineering Magnetohydrodynamics.* McGraw-Hill Book Co., Inc. 1965. New York.

equal to zero, the loading factor for maximum power is

$$K_{pm} = \frac{A^*}{2(A^* + 1)} \qquad (8\text{-}34)$$

A comparison between the characteristics of the ideal converter and that in which end losses are significant is given in Fig. 8–6. Maximum efficiency is achieved for $K < K_z$, while maximum power output occurs for a value of $K < 0.5$.

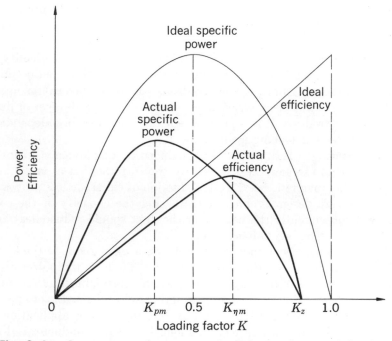

Fig. 8–6. Comparison of power and efficiency characteristics for ideal and actual system with end losses.

For a given aspect ratio the end losses may be reduced in two ways. Insulating vanes may be placed in the duct at the inlet and outlet. A single vane placed in midstream, parallel to the flow, at the inlet and outlet would, for example, double the aspect ratio. The most successful results are achieved, however, by using magnetic pole faces which are longer than the length of the electrodes, so that the magnetic field extends beyond the ends of both electrodes.

8–3.3. Heat Transfer and Fluiddynamic Loss. Since the fluid flow is in general turbulent, heat transfer calculations are based on empirical relationships. However, insufficient material is available for study of heat transfer through turbulent boundary layers under electromagnetic conditions. Under these conditions it is believed that the heat transfer rate may be increased significantly.

Heat transfer loss is significant in the small-capacity converter, but as the volume-to-surface area ratio is increased, this loss should not be of great significance.

Very little data is available on the fluiddynamic loss due to skin friction under turbulent conditions when electromagnetic effects are included. Consequently calculations have been based on conventional relationships. De Groff* estimates that the fluiddynamic loss is from 10 to 12 percent of the maximum power output for a duct L/d ratio of 10 and a Reynold's number of 10^5.

8-3.4. Electrode Loss. Due to the fact that the fluid in the vicinity of the duct walls is usually at a low temperature, its electrical conductivity is low. Therefore significant voltage drops (up to 13 percent of open-circuit voltages) have been experienced across the thin cool layer of fluid next to the electrodes. However, findings vary considerably, depending on the measurement technique adopted.

8-3.5. Summary. Hall effect loss is reduced by employing segmented electrodes. End loss may be reduced by the introduction of vanes and extension of the magnetic field, while reduction of electrode loss proves to be a more severe design problem. Increasing the capacity of the converter, and consequently the volume of the duct should reduce heat and friction loss to secondary importance.

It should be noted that consideration has not been given to the losses associated with producing the magnetic field. To date, the power dissipated in the field coils of the magnet has been an appreciable fraction of the generator output. However, superconducting field coils, with zero power dissipation, are under development but the engineering application is complicated. The performance of long lengths of superconductor is difficult to predict; also, due to the large energy stored per unit weight of coil, means must be developed to protect the coil against catastrophic failure when non-superconducting regions appear.

8-4. PLASMA MHD CONVERTER SYSTEMS

Virtually the entire effort to date in the field of magnetohydrodynamics has been devoted to the plasma (or gas) MHD cycle. Ideally, it would be desirable to operate the system at an inlet temperature of about 3000°K and an ambient outlet temperature. If power could be converted over such a wide temperature range, then the Carnot efficiency would approach

---

* Harold M. De Groff. "Thermodynamics of MHD." NASA Report N65-16192. Purdue University. 1964.

90 percent. Unfortunately, the conductivity of the gas decreases rapidly with temperature, and in fact gases at temperatures below 2000°K have unacceptably low conductivities. Even at peak combustion temperatures of ~3000°K the normal combustion gases have a conductivity far too low for practical MHD conversion. To overcome this problem, a material with a low ionization potential is added to the gas. The addition of 1 percent potassium by volume, for example, increases the gas conductivity to 1 mho/m at 2200°K and to almost 90 mho/m at 3000°K.

Several methods have been proposed for extending the lower temperature range. One is to increase the conductivity by the addition of nonthermal ions (non-equilibrium ionization) generated by various means, such as the formation of a glow discharge, or subjecting the gas to radiation. Passing a continuous series of shock waves down the duct has been suggested, since there is an extremely high temperature region, and consequently a high conductivity region, behind the shock front. There are many practical problems associated with these schemes and although the technical feasability of non-equilibrium ionization in closed cycle systems is largely accepted there is little experimental evidence for the flexibility of high specific power operation at plasma temperatures below 1800°K. At present it seems more realistic to utilize the relatively high temperature gas which leaves the MHD converter as the heat source for a conventional steam power plant. The MHD plant would therefore act as a topping cycle and could, typically, increase the overall plant efficiency from the current value of about 40 percent to as much as 55 percent. A possible arrangement of such a plant is shown schematically in Fig. 8-7.

The system is open-cycle, in that the MHD working fluid is not recirculated. The intake air is compressed and passed through a regenerator, where its temperature is raised to ensure the high combustion temperatures necessary in the MHD converter. Economic operation requires recovery of the seed material before the gases are rejected from the system. When the fuel is coal, and this appears to be the most economical energy source, the recovery problem is complicated by the high ash content of the gases. Since the molten ash is also likely to coat the inside of the converter and short-circuit the electrodes the problems of burning coal are many. Oil or gas as the fuel should present less difficult problems.

If the gas-cooled nuclear reactor could be used as the heat source in a closed loop with the MHD converter, there would be no seed recovery or coating problems. A gas such as helium seeded with cesium could be used as the fluid. However, gas outlet temperatures from existing reactors are not sufficiently high. But experiments on the Dragon reactor have shown that gas outlet temperatures of 1130°K can be achieved, while individual fuel elements have been tested at 2200°K. Such tests indicate that a reactor outlet gas temperature of 1800°K could be achieved without

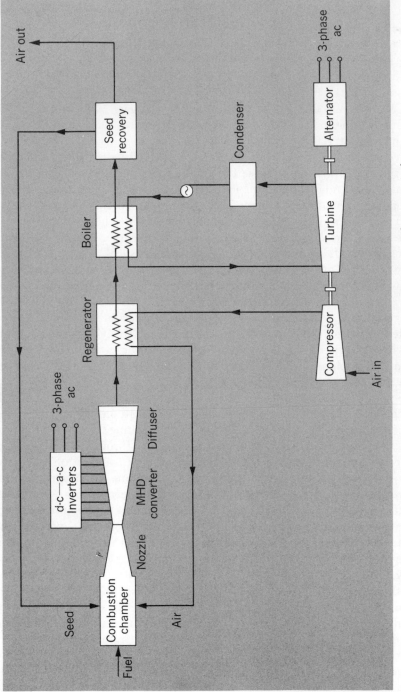

Fig. 8—7. Schematic of a binary MHD-steam open-cycle power plant.

ext... technological development, and with a considerable effort in fuel element development a temperature on the order of 2100°K might be reached. In addition, however, it appears necessary to determine if the conflicting needs for high gas pressure in the reactor and low gas pressure in the converter can be reconciled. Low gas pressures imply much larger reactor systems.

8-5. LIQUID-METAL MHD CONVERTERS

The development of a MHD converter, which uses a liquid metal, at temperatures below 1400°K, as the working fluid, indicates the feasibility

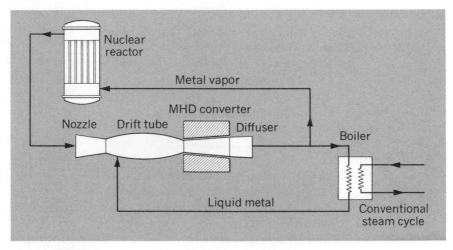

Fig. 8–8. Schematic diagram of the Prem two-phase cycle.

of coupling it directly to a liquid-metal cooled nuclear reactor. Since the fluid is then an excellent conductor minimum temperature limits are not governed by acceptable conductivity levels, but rather by the maximum safe operating temperature of the reactor.

8-5.1. Basic Cycle. The basic steps in the various liquid-metal MHD cycles proposed so far are the same. One proposed by Prem* is especially suited for large power stations and is shown schematically in Fig. 8–8. It consists of two loops. One loop contains the nuclear reactor which partially vaporizes the fluid. The thermal energy of the resulting two-phase fluid is converted to kinetic energy by expanding the fluid through a supersonic nozzle into what is called the *drift tube*. Here atomized liquid

*L. L. Prem and W. E. Parkins. "New Method of MHD Power Conversion Employing a Fluid Metal." Paper No. 63. *International Symposium on MHD Electric Power Generation.* Paris, France, July, 1964.

from the second loop is injected into the two-phase high-veloci___.m. The injected liquid is accelerated (just as fine dust particle___ ___en introduced into a wind tunnel) and at the same time the vapor present in the flow condenses on the cooler fluid.   Therefore the fluid stream enters the MHD converter predominantly as a liquid having a high velocity of about 150 m/sec.   Within the converter a major part of the kinetic energy of the fluid is converted into electrical energy.   A portion of the emergent liquid passes through a heat exchanger where the waste heat of the liquid metal cycle is rejected, the remainder is circulated again through the reactor loop.

Potassium and cesium have both been considered as the working fluids, but predicted efficiencies of the unoptimized cycle for a reactor outlet temperature of 1390°K are 5.5 and 6 percent, respectively.   However, if two immiscible liquids such as cesium and lithium are used, efficiencies above 12 percent can be expected.

Other cycles are under investigation but all are basically similar to the one described.   When the liquid-metal MHD converter is used as the topping cycle for a modern supercritical steam plant operating at about 4000 psi, 850°K, and an efficiency of 45 percent, the overall attainable cycle efficiency is between 55 and 60 percent.   The liquid-metal cycle is assumed to operate between 1550°K and 880°K.

8–5.2. Comparison of Plasma and Liquid-Metal MHD Cycles.   The principal disadvantages of the liquid-metal converter when compared with the plasma converter are associated with the design of a suitable system capable of operating with a high-temperature liquid and vaporized metal which reaches duct velocities of 150 m/sec.   Due to the high conductivity of the metal, the induced voltages are in general low ($\sim$10 volts) and consequently current densities of at least an order of magnitude greater than in the plasma converter are encountered.   However, one important advantage of the liquid-metal converter is the fact that a-c power may be generated directly.   If three-phase stator windings are placed about the duct, as in Fig. 8–9, so that they produce a magnetic field which moves in the y direction, then the flow of molten metal past the coils is exactly analogous to the movement of the squirrel-cage rotor in the linear induction motor.   If the fluid is moving at a speed U greater than the speed U_f of the field produced by the three-phase stator windings, then, due to the relative slip $s = (U_f - U)/U_f$, electric power is fed into the windings. Transformers may then be used to step up the voltage for transmission.

The converter could of course be readily turned into a pump by making the field velocity greater than that of the fluid, in which case the slip would become positive, and motor, rather than generator action would result.

Initial calculations for a liquid-metal MHD, a-c induction converter indicate that the end loss would be large. However, a method has been found for minimizing these losses by adding compensating poles to cancel the flux changes at zero slip and thus achieve, in a one-flux-wavelength generator, substantially the "infinite length" efficiency.

Due to the low magnetic Reynolds number of the gas in present plasma converters ($\sim 10^{-2}$), similar direct a-c generation conversion does not appear feasible. As a result, relatively expensive d-c to a-c inverters must be used.

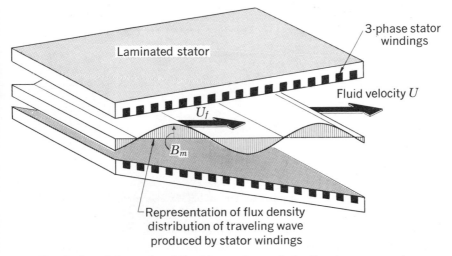

Fig. 8–9. Schematic of liquid metal, a-c induction type converter.

Apart from the fact that the upper temperature requirements of the liquid-metal converter are considerably lower than in the case of the plasma converter, permitting the use of nuclear power, the power density achieved in a liquid-metal converter is approximately an order of magnitude higher than that attainable from the plasma converter. The size of the equivalent liquid-metal converter is therefore much smaller, and so the cost of the magnet or coil is substantially less than for a plasma converter. The magnet cost is a major item in a MHD plant.

8–6. ELECTROGASDYNAMIC CONVERSION

The electrogasdynamic (EGD) converter generates electric power by causing a supply of unipolar ions to flow against an opposing induced electric field. Figure 8–10 represents a typical converter stage, as developed by Gourdine Systems, Inc. Fuel is burned under pressure with air in a combustion chamber and the combustion gas, or hot gas from a nuclear reactor, allowed to flow through the EGD converter duct. At the entrance to the duct, unipolar ions are generated in the gas by any convenient method. The Gourdine converter uses a discharge from a corona electrode which causes low ionization levels of the order of 10^{17} ions/m³. The auxiliary power required to generate these ions is reported to be about 5 percent of the generated power.

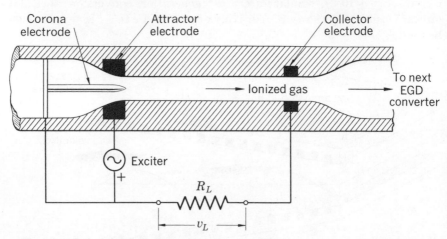

Fig. 8–10. Schematic cross-section of EGD converter. (Adapted, by permission of Foster Wheeler Corporation.)

The ionized gas particles are carried down the duct with the other neutral gas atoms. Shortly after the converter is activated the accumulation of positive ions at one end of the duct causes a large potential difference along it, which tends to prevent the flow of additional positive ions, and consequently the flow of gas through the duct. If a collector electrode is connected as shown through a load, then the potential developed across the tube may be availed of as an electric power source. Thus the energy of the gas is converted directly to electrical energy.

8–7. BASIC ANALYSIS OF THE EGD CONVERTER

In this simplified analysis of an EGD converter, heat transfer through the walls of the duct is neglected. The main losses which affect the efficiency are due to friction, turbulence and change in velocity, and losses associated with ion slip. Tests show that frictional losses are dominant, and in fact effectively control the converter efficiency. To a close estimate, the converter efficiency may then be written as

$$\eta = \frac{\Delta p_e}{\Delta p_e + \Delta p_f} \tag{8–35}$$

where Δp_e is the pressure drop in the duct due to electric body forces and Δp_f is the pressure drop due to friction at the walls of the duct. The friction pressure drop is

$$\Delta p_f = C_f \rho \, \frac{U^2 L}{2d} \tag{8-36}$$

where C_f is the coefficient of friction, ρ the gas density, U the gas velocity, L the duct length, and d the duct diameter, as shown in Fig. 8–11.

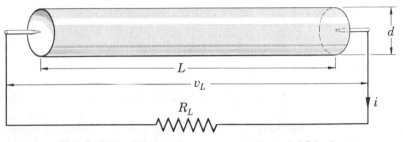

Fig. 8–11. Schematic representation of EGD duct.

Assuming an average positive ion charge density of n_p within the duct and a constant axial electric field E_x, then the electrostatic force on the ions per unit volume is $E_x n_p e$ and so the total electrostatic force acting on the ions within the duct is $E_x n_p e L \pi d^2 / 4$. Therefore the pressure drop is

$$\Delta p_e = E_x n_p e L \tag{8-37}$$

The space charge in the tube causes a radial field E_r. The field at the wall of the duct may be determined from the fact that the total electric flux issuing from unit length of tube is equal to the total charge per unit length. Therefore since the flux density is

$$D = \epsilon_0 E \tag{8-38}$$

where ϵ_0 is the permittivity of free space (8.85×10^{-12} coulomb/newton-m²), it follows that

$$\epsilon_0 E_r \pi d = e n_p \pi d^2 / 4$$

or

$$e n_p = \epsilon_0 E_r 4 / d \tag{8-39}$$

Maximum Δp_e is reached when both E_r and E_x have their maximum values, i.e., the breakdown potential of the gas E_b. Therefore, setting $E_r = E_x = E_b$ and substituting Eq. 8–39 in Eq. 8–37 gives the maximum value of Δp_e as

$$\Delta p_{em} = 4\epsilon_0 E_b^2 L / d \tag{8-40}$$

Upon substituting Eq. 8–40 and Eq. 8–36 in Eq. 8–35, the maximum efficiency is found to be

$$\eta_m = \frac{1}{1 + C_f \rho U^2 / (8\epsilon_0 E_b{}^2)} \qquad (8\text{–}41)$$

The output current is equal to the rate of charge flow through the duct:

$$i = n_p e U \pi d^2 / 4 \qquad (8\text{–}42)$$

where the ion density is, in accord with Eq. 8–39,

$$i = \pi \epsilon_0 E_r U d \qquad (8\text{–}43)$$

The maximum power density is

$$P_{0m} = \frac{i_m v_L}{L \pi d^2 / 4} = 4 \epsilon_0 U E_b{}^2 / d \qquad (8\text{–}44)$$

Example 8–3. A test EGD duct is to be designed to generate a maximum voltage of 150,000 volts, direct-current, using a gas with an average density of 1.0 kg/m³ and a duct velocity of 105 m/sec and a maximum permissible potential gradient of 3×10^6 volts/m. If the effective coefficient of friction is 0.02 and a duct of 1.0-cm diameter is selected, find

    (a) The maximum efficiency of conversion.
    (b) The average ion density in the duct.
    (c) The maximum current.
    (d) The effective duct length.
    (e) The maximum power developed.

(a) From Eq. 8–41, the maximum efficiency of conversion is

$$\eta_m = \left[1 + \frac{0.02 \times 1 \times (105)^2}{8 \times 8.85 \times 10^{-12} \times 9 \times 10^{12}} \right]^{-1} = 74 \text{ percent}$$

(b) From Eq. 8–39, the average ion density in the duct is

$$n_p = \frac{8.85 \times 10^{-12} \times 3 \times 10^6 \times 4}{1.6 \times 10^{-19} \times 10^{-2}} = 6.62 \times 10^{16} \text{ ions/m}^3$$

(c) From Eq. 8–42, the current is

$$i_m = 6.62 \times 10^{16} \times 1.6 \times 10^{-19} \times 105 \times \pi \times 10^{-4} \times 0.25 = 87 \times 10^{-6} \text{ amp}$$

(d) Since a voltage of 150,000 volts is required and a potential gradient of 3×10^6 volts/m is permissible, the duct length is

$$L = \frac{v_L}{E_b} = \frac{1.5 \times 10^5}{3 \times 10^6} = 5 \times 10^{-2} \text{ m}$$

(e) The maximum power developed is

$$P_m = i_m E_b L = 87 \times 10^{-6} \times 3 \times 10^6 \times 5 \times 10^{-2} = 13.02 \text{ watts}$$

It is apparent from Example 8–3 that the output power per duct is in general not large.   In practice several hundred ducts would be operated in both series and parallel combinations.   Output voltages from an EGD duct are high ($\sim$200,000 volts) and consequently appropriate insulation must be provided between the electrodes.   A duct material such as beryllium oxide appears suitable and research is underway to preserve the high duct resistivity despite the use of ash-bearing combustion gases.   Tests

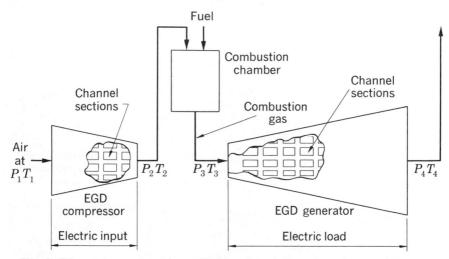

Fig. 8–12.   Schematic of an EGD fossil-fueled power plant.   (Courtesy of Foster Wheeler Corporation.)

indicate that any conducting deposition on the tube wall is rapidly burnt off as all the other stages feed current through it.

An inherent feature of the EGD converter is the small amount of power which is extracted per converter, making it necessary to use many stages. However, since there are no significant minimum temperature limits the gas may be permitted to expand through numerous stages until it is near atmospheric pressure and near normal stack temperatures, after which it is discharged to the atmosphere.

Figure 8–12 represents an EGD fossil-fueled power plant.   The EGD compressor functions like the converter, but in reverse.   That is, the electric field is used to propel the gas and compress it.   Of course, a conventional mechanical compressor could be used equally as well.

Operation of the EGD converter in conjunction with the gas-cooled reactor appears to be particularly appropriate.   Figure 8–13 shows a schematic of a closed-loop helium-cooled system.   An important fact, which may favor use of the EGD converter, in preference to the MHD converter, is that the high gas pressures (600 psi) used to increase heat transfer within the nuclear reactor are also required to reduce ion mobility and increase the breakdown voltage in the EGD system, whereas high gas pressures are not desirable in the MHD system.

One of the significant advantages of the EGD plant, when compared with an equivalent MHD plant, is the absence of any conventional steam

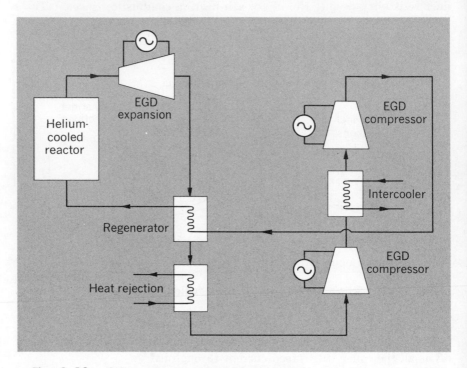

Fig. 8–13. Schematic of a closed-loop helium-cooled system. (Courtesy of Foster Wheeler Corporation.)

plant as a bottoming cycle. The EGD system promises to be self-sufficient and able to extract energy from the gas until standard stack conditions are reached. Consequently large quantities of cooling water, required by the binary MHD-steam plant, are not needed for operation of the EGD system, so that location in arid regions is not a major problem.

Since high electrical gas conductivity is not a requirement, the need for extra-high-temperature operation and the injection and recovery of seed material is not encountered. However, ion mobilities in the EGD converter gas must be low. The presence of ash in the gas is found to reduce significantly the mobility. Increasing the gas pressure also reduces the ion mobility and in addition increases the breakdown voltage of the gas. This is important since large interelectrode voltages are desirable so that the specific power output may be high. The efficiency of the converter is particularly dependent on low friction loss. Since the cross-sectional area of each duct is small ($\sim$0.5 cm²), the surface-to-volume

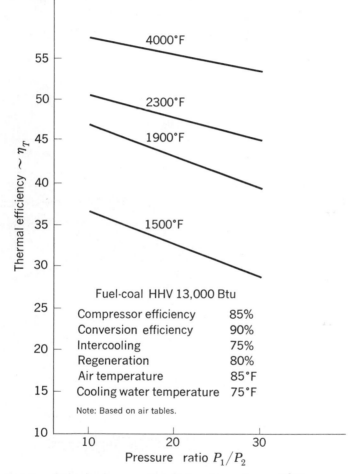

Fig. 8–14. Estimated overall efficiencies of an EGD power system. (Courtesy of Foster Wheeler Corporation.)

ratio is high and severe skin-friction losses may be encountered if particular attention is not given to the aerodynamics of the duct.

As seen in Fig. 8–14, overall plant efficiencies of about 55 percent are predicted at an inlet temperature of 4000°F ($\sim$2500°K), while overall efficiencies of above 35 percent are predicted at 1500°F ($\sim$1000°K), which is within the operating temperature range of the gas-cooled nuclear reactor.

The direct generation of high-voltage alternating current may be achieved by applying an alternating voltage across the corona discharge region and so regulating the rate of ion production and consequently the charge flow to the collector electrode.

Although development of the EGD system is yet in its infancy, it appears to offer many attractive features.   There are important difficulties which must be faced in attempting to develop a large-scale EGD power plant. For example, electrodes must be designed which can operate for lengthy periods in the presence of ash-bearing combustion gas.   Reliable high-voltage insulation for both the duct and terminal leads must be developed.

PROBLEMS

8-1. A fluid moves at velocity $\mathbf{U} = 10^3(1.2\mathbf{i} + 0.3\mathbf{j} + 0.2\mathbf{k})$ m/sec through a magnetic field of flux density $\mathbf{B} = 0.1\mathbf{i} + 1.0\mathbf{j} + 0.2\mathbf{k}$ weber/m^2.

  a. Find the magnitude of the maximum potential gradient induced in the field.
  b. Find the potential induced across 0.5 m of fluid in the $\mathbf{k}$ direction.

8-2. In the initial design of a MHD plasma converter the following parameter values are proposed

$$B = 1.3 \text{ weber/m}^2$$
$$U = 2000 \text{ m/sec}$$
$$A = 0.3 \text{ m}^2$$
$$d = 0.2 \text{ m}$$
$$\sigma = 39 \text{ mho/m}$$

If the fluid velocity is assumed to be normal to the direction of the magnetic flux find, for an output voltage of 300 volts,

  a. The loading factor.
  b. The current density in the plasma.
  c. The power output.
  d. The efficiency.

8-3. For the proposed converter of Prob. 8-2, find the maximum power output, the short-circuit current, and the open-circuit voltage.

8-4. A fluid enters a duct with velocity U_1 in the y direction, density ρ_1, and cross-sectional area of flow S_1.   It is required that the fluid velocity should decrease along the duct as

$$U(y) = U_1 - U_0(1 - e^{-y/L_1})$$

where y is the distance of travel along the duct, U_0 and L_1 are constants.   Find the required cross sectional area of the duct as a function of y if the fluid is assumed to expand linearily such that $\rho(y) = \rho_1 + \beta y$.

8-5. If the fluid flow conditions described in Prob. 8-4 result from passing the fluid through a magnetic field which varies in the y direction, so that

$$B(y) = B_0 \sin \frac{\pi y}{L}$$

where B_0 is the maximum flux density and L is the length of duct within the magnetic field, and the fluid pressure within the duct varies as

$$p(y) = p_1 - p_0(1 - e^{-y/L_2})$$

where p_0 and L_2 are constants and p_1 is the inlet pressure, find the induced current density as a function of y.

8-6. A seeded gas with average conductivity of 35 mho/m passes at a constant velocity of 900 m/sec through a uniform magnetic field of 1.3 weber/m^2 density. At a loading factor of 0.65, an inlet pressure p_1 of 2.5 atm and an exhaust pressure p_2 of 0.8 atm. The width of the duct remains constant at 0.42 m and the height at inlet $h_1 = 0.13$ m. Find the length of the duct and the height h_2 at the outlet. Find the ideal output current, voltage, and power ($\gamma = 1.2$).

8-7. If the system described in Prob. 8-6 were designed for a constant pressure throughout the duct, what should be the length of the duct if the gas density remains constant at 0.155 kg/m^3 and the outlet velocity is 300 m/sec, while the inlet velocity is 900 m/sec?

8-8. How much power is dissipated due to end losses in the system described in Prob. 8-6?

8-9. Taking into account end losses, what is the required loading factor for operating the system described in Prob. 8-6 at (a) maximum efficiency, and (b) maximum power? Find the power developed in each case.

8-10. An MHD converter, using liquid sodium as the working fluid, is to be designed to develop a total power of 3.93 megawatts when operating at a loading factor of 0.6. The duct inlet is of square cross-section of side lengths 0.1 m. The width of the duct is to remain constant at 0.1 m, while the height varies to permit the fluid to flow at constant pressure. The average velocity of the fluid is to be 200 m/sec. Assuming linearity and a uniform flux density of 0.13 weber/m^2, and an aspect ratio of 4, and accounting for end losses, find the actual power developed per unit volume, the dimensions of the duct, and the difference in inlet and outlet velocities. Assume

average electrical conductivity of the fluid = 6.88 × 10^6 mho/m
density of the fluid = 780 kg/m^3

8 11. The output voltage per stage of an EGD converter is to be 130,000 volts D–C. A gas with an average density of 1.3 kg/m^3, a maximum permissible potential gradient of 2.8 × 10^6 volts/m and a velocity of 90 m/sec is used. The effective coefficient of friction is 0.018 when a duct of 0.8 cm diameter is used. Find

a. The effective length of the duct.
b. The number of ions in the duct.

   c. The maximum efficiency of the converter.

   d. The maximum current.

   e. The maximum power density.

8–12. If an EGD converter is designed so that the maximum radial potential gradient is half the axial potential gradient derive an expression for the maximum efficiency and power output.

8–13. What is the total pressure difference between the gas at the inlet and outlet of the converter described in Prob. 8–11 under maximum output conditions?

8–14. A duct of an EGD converter is operated so that the maximum radial field is equal to the axial field. The gas velocity is increased to 200 m/sec until electrostatic breakdown of the gas occurs. If the duct diameter is 0.6 cm and the current prior to breakdown is 95×10^{-6} amp what is the maximum potential gradient occurring within the gas?

9
Fuel Cells

Fuel cells convert chemical to electrical energy isothermally and directly. In the conventional fossil-fueled (coal, oil, and gas) power plant, chemical energy is converted into thermal energy in the boiler, then into mechanical energy in the turbine, and finally into electrical energy in the alternator. The development of the fuel cell, therefore, promises to eliminate the intermediate energy states and also the associated energy conversion equipment. Since most of the electrical energy produced today is obtained by the liberation of chemical energy from fossil fuels, the development of a direct and simple method is certainly significant. Since the fuel cell is not subject to the limitations of the Carnot cycle, it has prospects of attaining considerably better conversion efficiencies than systems employing thermal cycles. Although the use of fuel cells for central-station energy conversion is not yet justified, fuel cell systems are a practical reality and, for example, have been used on board the Gemini space craft, not only for provision of the necessary electrical energy, but also for the capability of supplying drinking water for the astronauts.

9–1. THE BASIC FUEL CELL

In 1802 Sir Humphrey Davy suggested the idea of a fuel cell, and in 1839 the first laboratory unit was used by Sir William Grove to demonstrate that the electrolysis of water could be reversed. Between 1900 and 1930 considerable attention was given to the development of a fuel cell system. However, the concurrent rapid advance in the development of the internal combustion engine discouraged further fuel cell study until the postwar period, when its possible application as an auxiliary electric power supply for space craft revitalized the field. In turn, this application has focused new attention on the fuel cell as a large-capacity energy converter. Possible applications are diverse: military, central station, or even power for off-the-road vehicles. Consequently, fuel cell systems may be classified as: small special-purpose or space-craft systems, which may use costly fuels in order to operate under the best possible conditions; and larger-capacity systems where the use of cheap, impure, and less reactive fossil fuels is dictated by economic considerations.

The most highly developed fuel cell is the hydrogen-oxygen cell. This type of cell was extensively developed by General Electric for use in the Gemini space craft and is considered here as an example. In the cell the well-known process of the electrolysis of water is reversed. Instead of breaking water down into its components, by passing an electric current through it, water is formed by permitting hydrogen and oxygen to combine in a controlled chemical reaction that liberates energy in the form of electricity and heat.

Figure 9–1a is a schematic of the basic hydrogen-oxygen fuel cell. Hydrogen and oxygen as fuel and oxidant, respectively, are fed into two compartments which are separated by an ion-exchange membrane (a sheet of polymer plastic). Two catalytic electrodes (electrodes which also act as catalysts) bonded to each side of the membrane are connected to the electrical load. The hydrogen, after passing through the porous anode, splits into positive hydrogen ions and electrons at the ion exchange membrane as shown in Fig. 9–1b. Therefore the anode reaction is

$$2H_2 \rightarrow 4H^+ + 4e \qquad (9\text{--}1)$$

The hydrogen ions pass through the membrane, while the electrons pass through the external load circuit, and both meet and combine with oxygen to form water at the cathode. The cathode reaction is therefore

$$4H^+ + 4e + O_2 \rightarrow 2H_2O \qquad (9\text{--}2)$$

The overall reaction for the hydrogen-oxygen fuel cell may be written as

$$2H_2 + O_2 \rightarrow 2H_2O \qquad (9\text{--}3)$$

The by-product (water) is removed from the cell by a wick structure and fed to a common collection point. This water has been made available to the astronauts in the Gemini space craft.

Fuels other than hydrogen, such as propane or octane, as well as methyl alcohol and ammonia, may be used directly in certain fuel cell systems. The numerous other types of fuel cells all depend on the basic feature of fuel and oxidant separated by an ion transport region. For example, the high-temperature cells, designed to use the gases produced by the combustion of fossil fuels, employ solid mixed oxides, or fused carbonates, as the ion transport material, while the fuel is CO and H_2, and the oxidant is air and CO_2.

Anode	$2H_2$			$\longrightarrow$	$4H^+$	$+$	$4e$
Cathode	$4H^+$	$+$	$4e$	$+$ O $\longrightarrow$	$2H_2O$		
Overall	$2H_2$	$+$	O_2	$\longrightarrow$	$2H_2O$		

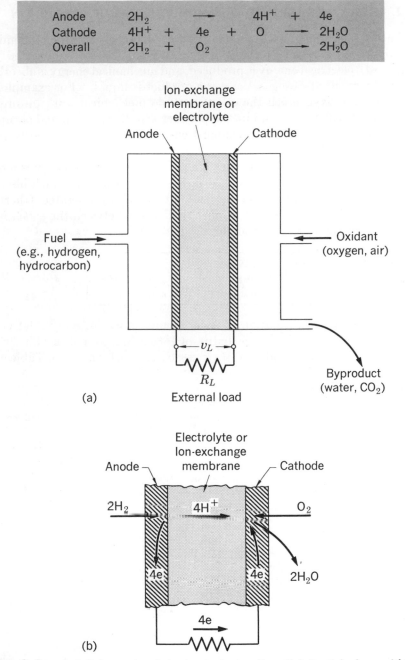

Fig. 9–1. (a) Schematic of the basic fuel cell. (b) Particle flow within the fuel cell.

9–2. ENERGY RELEASE IN THE CONTINUOUS CHEMICAL REACTION

The process taking place in a fuel cell is a controlled continuous chemical reaction. As a result of this reaction thermal energy is liberated (or absorbed), electrical energy is produced, and mechanical energy is absorbed when the reactants are gases and the product is liquid. For example, in the hydrogen-oxygen cell the gas sources do mechanical work in forcing the reactants into the cell, but the product is in liquid form and occupies negligible volume, and so mechanical energy must be continuously provided to the cell.

When a chemical reaction takes place a net amount of energy is either liberated or absorbed. In the case of fuel cells, reactions which liberate energy are of interest. The net amount of energy liberated (thermal plus electrical) may be found from the difference between the *enthalpy of formation* of the reactants and the products, ΔH.

$$\Delta H = \sum_{\text{reactants}} \Delta H_r - \sum_{\text{products}} \Delta H_p \qquad (9\text{–}4)$$

The enthalpy of formation of a compound is its enthalpy relative to that of its elements. The enthalpy of formation, at 1 atm and 298°K (STP), of some compounds and their associated ions is listed in Table 9–1.

TABLE 9–1
Enthalpy of Formation ΔH° and Gibbs Free Energy ΔG° of Compounds and Ions
at 1 Atmosphere and 298°K (STP)

Compound or Ion	ΔH° Enthalpy of Formation (joule/kg mole) $\times 10^{-6}$	ΔG° Gibbs Free Energy (joule/kg mole) $\times 10^{-6}$
CO	−110	−137.5
CO_2	−394	−395
CH_4	−74.9	−50.8
Water	−286	−237
Steam	−241	−228
LiH	+128	+105
$NaCO_3$	−1122	−1042
CO_3^{--}	−675	−529
H^+	0	0
Li^+	−277	−293
OH^-	−230	−157

Example 9–1. A high-temperature fuel cell uses carbon monoxide as fuel and air as the oxidizer. If the cell reactions are

anode $\quad CO + CO_3^{--} \rightarrow 2CO_2 + 2e$

cathode $\quad CO_2 + \frac{1}{2}O_2 + 2e \rightarrow CO_3^{--}$

overall $\quad CO + \frac{1}{2}O_2 \rightarrow CO_2$

find, in terms of standard temperature and pressure, the enthalpy of formation per mole at each electrode and the sum of electrical and thermal energy released per mole in the overall reaction.

For the anode reaction, using values from Table 9–1, the energy liberated at STP is

$$\Delta H^\circ = [(-110 - 675) - (-2 \times 394)] \times 10^6 = 3 \times 10^6 \text{ joule/kg mole}$$

For the cathode reaction

$$\Delta H^\circ = [(-394) - (-675)] \times 10^6 = 281 \times 10^6 \text{ joule/kg mole}$$

For the overall reaction

$$\Delta H^\circ = [(-110) - (-394)] \times 10^6 = 284 \times 10^6 \text{ joule/kg mole of CO}$$

As would be expected, the sum of the energies associated with the anode and cathode reactions is equal to the energy released by the overall reaction.

9–3. STANDARD CELL POTENTIAL

It is apparent from the foregoing that the determination of the net energy released in a fuel cell reaction is a simple matter. Part of this energy is in the form of heat and the remainder is removed as electrical energy. To examine the electrical characteristic of a cell it is important to be able to divide the net energy released into its thermal and electrical parts. Obviously, it is desirable that the electrical part should be as large as possible, but an upper limit is set by the second law of thermodynamics.

Entropy is associated only with the disorderly thermal energy released. Electrical energy is orderly and has no entropy. If the chemical reaction results in an entropy change ΔS at constant temperature T, then the thermal energy released by the reaction must be at least $T \Delta S$. Consequently, for a reaction in which the enthalpy of formation is ΔH, the electrical energy released per mole is

$$W_e \lesssim \Delta H - T \Delta S \qquad (9\text{–}5)$$

If the process is completely reversible, then the equality sign applies and the electrical power output is a maximum. Equation 9–5 may be expressed in terms of the specific *Gibbs free energy*, which is defined as

$$G = H - TS \qquad (9\text{–}6)$$

so that

$$W_e \lessgtr \Delta G \qquad (9\text{–}7)$$

where

$$\Delta G = \sum_{\text{reactants}} \Delta G_r - \sum_{\text{products}} \Delta G_p \qquad (9\text{–}8)$$

Table 9–1 gives values of the Gibbs free energy for some compounds and ions at STP.

Since H and G are expressed in terms of energy per kilogram mole, W_e is the electrical energy developed when one kilogram mole of electrons passes through the external circuit. One kilogram mole of electrons is Avogadro's number (6.02×10^{26}) of electrons, which has a total charge of 96.5×10^6 coulomb. The charge associated with a kilogram mole of electrons is called a kilofaraday $\mathfrak{F}$. If n moles of electrons are associated with the reaction, and the internal cell voltage developed is e_g, the electrical energy released per kilogram mole is

$$W_e = n\mathfrak{F}e_g \qquad (9\text{–}9)$$

Therefore from Eq. 9–9 and Eq. 9–7 the internally generated voltage

$$e_g \lessgtr \frac{\Delta G}{n\mathfrak{F}} \qquad (9\text{–}10)$$

Example 9–2. Find the maximum possible value of the internally generated voltage of the hydrogen-oxygen cell at STP, where the product is in its liquid state.

From Eq. 9–3, the reaction is $2H_2 + O_2 \rightarrow 2H_2O$, so that, from Eq. 9–8,

$$\Delta G° = [(0 + 0) - (-2 \times 237)] \times 10^6 = 474 \times 10^6 \text{ joule/kg mole}$$

From Eq. 9–2, four moles of electrons are generated, so that $n = 4$. Therefore, from Eq. 9–10,

$$e_g° = \frac{474 \times 10^6}{4 \times 96.5 \times 10^6} = 1.23 \text{ volts}$$

Under operating conditions the output voltage of a fuel cell is of the order of 1 volt. Consequently for operation at an acceptable specific power, high current densities are required.

9-4. TEMPERATURE AND PRESSURE DEPENDENCE OF THE FUEL CELL

The characteristics of a fuel cell are dependent on the operating temperature and the partial pressures of the reactants and products. Consequently, for analysis of cell operation under other than standard conditions, account must be taken of the existing temperature and partial pressures.

From Eq. 9-6, the specific Gibbs free energy $G = H - TS$, and since enthalpy $H = E_i + pV$, where E_i is the internal energy, p is the pressure, and V the volume of the system under consideration, Eq. 9-6 becomes

$$G = E_i + pV - TS \qquad (9\text{-}11)$$

and putting Eq. 9-11 in differential form

$$dG = dE_i + p\,dV + V\,dp - T\,dS - S\,dT \qquad (9\text{-}12)$$

By combining the first and second laws of thermodynamics, the well-known expression for the change in internal energy

$$dE_i = T\,dS - p\,dV \qquad (9\text{-}13)$$

is obtained. Upon substituting Eq. 9-13 in Eq. 9-12

$$dG = V\,dp - S\,dT \qquad (9\text{-}14)$$

When the reactants and products are at the same equilibrium temperature, $dT = 0$ and so Eq. 9-14 becomes

$$dG = V\,dp \qquad (9\text{-}15)$$

Since

$$\frac{pV}{T} = \Re \qquad (9\text{-}16)$$

where $\Re$ is the universal gas constant (8314 joule/kg mole-°K), Eq. 9-15 becomes, upon substitution and integration,

$$G - G^\circ = \int_{p^\circ}^{p} \Re T \frac{dp}{p} = \Re T \ln \frac{p}{p^\circ} \qquad (9\text{-}17)$$

where G is the Gibbs free energy at a pressure p. If $p^\circ \equiv 1$ atm, then Eq. 9-17 becomes

$$\boxed{G - G^\circ = \Re T \ln p} \qquad (9\text{-}18)$$

Consider the general fuel cell reaction

$$aA + bB \rightarrow cC + dD \qquad (9\text{-}19)$$

in which the reactants and products are gases at temperature T and partial pressures p_A, p_B, p_C, and p_D, respectively. Then from Eqs. 9-8 and 9–18, the maximum value of the free energy liberated in the reaction under other than standard conditions is

$$\Delta G = \Delta G^\circ + a \Re T \ln p_A + b \Re T \ln p_B - c \Re T \ln p_C - d \Re T \ln p_D$$

$$= \Delta G^\circ + \Re T \ln \left(\frac{p_A^a p_B^b}{p_C^c p_D^d} \right) \tag{9-20}$$

Assuming the ideal gas laws to hold, Eqs. 9–7, 9–9, and 9–20 then give

$$n \Im e_g = n \Im e_g{}^\circ - \Re T \ln \left(\frac{p_C^c p_D^d}{p_A^a p_B^b} \right)$$

so that

$$e_g = e_g{}^\circ - \frac{\Re T}{n \Im} \ln \left(\frac{p_C^c p_D^d}{p_A^a p_B^b} \right) \tag{9-21}$$

Equation 9–21 gives an expression for the generated voltage in the fuel cell for other than standard conditions. However, it only applies when the reactants and products obey the ideal gas laws. In most cases, however, solutions in condensed phases must be considered, and with this in mind the theory has been extended. As a result, Eq. 9–21 is then written as

$$\boxed{ e_g = e_g{}^\circ - \frac{\Re T}{n \Im} \ln \left(\frac{\mathscr{C}_C^c \mathscr{C}_D^d}{\mathscr{C}_A^a \mathscr{C}_B^b} \right) } \tag{9-22}$$

where $\mathscr{C}_X$ is termed the *activity* of component X, and has a value equal to the partial pressure of component X only when the component obeys the ideal gas laws. The activity expresses the tendency of a component to escape from a solution as compared to the tendency to escape at STP. Equation 9–22 is called the *Nernst equation*.

Example 9–3. Find the internally generated voltage of the hydrogen-oxygen cell at a temperature of 32°C, when air is used as the oxidant and the product is water. The air is supplied at a pressure of 1.2 atm and the hydrogen is at a pressure of 1.1 atm.

The activity of water may be taken as unity, and since the hydrogen fuel may be assumed to act as an ideal gas the activity is equal to the partial pressure, so that $\mathscr{C}_{H_2} = 1.1$. Since the partial pressure of oxygen in air is 0.21 and the air pressure is 1.2 atm, the activity of the oxygen $\mathscr{C}_{O_2} = 1.2 \times 0.21 = 0.252$. Therefore, for the reaction of Eq. 9–3, the internally generated voltage is given by Eq. 9–21 as

$$e_g = e_g{}^\circ - \frac{\Re T}{n \Im} \ln \left(\frac{\mathscr{C}^2_{H_2O}}{\mathscr{C}^2_{H_2} \mathscr{C}_{O_2}} \right)$$

$$= 1.23 - \frac{8314 \times 305}{4 \times 96.5 \times 10^6} \ln \frac{1}{(1.1)^2 \times 0.252}$$

$$= 1.222 \text{ volts}$$

9–5. OPERATION OF THE FUEL CELL UNDER LOAD

As in the case of the simple electrochemical battery, the output voltage of the fuel cell decreases as load is applied. This decrease in voltage is mainly attributed to chemical polarization and to the internal resistance of the cell. Other effects, less important under operating conditions, such as concentration and resistance polarization, also tend to reduce the terminal voltage. Figure 9–2 shows a typical output voltage and current characteristic, or *polarization curve*, of a fuel cell. The open-circuit terminal

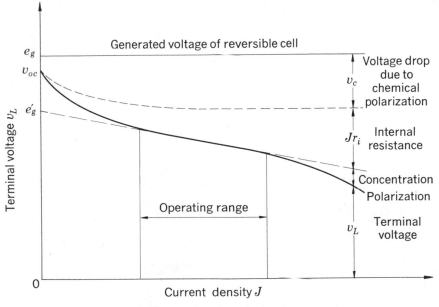

Fig. 9–2. Fuel cell polarization curve.

voltage v_{oc} is less than the value of e_g as calculated from the Nernst equation (Eq. 9–22) due to irreversible processes, and as the load current is increased the terminal voltage initially drops significantly. This loss in voltage is said to be due to *chemical polarization* and is caused by several irreversible effects at the electrodes. It is sometimes termed an *activation polarization* and may be regarded as the voltage required to cause the ions to break away from the electrode at which they are formed. The voltage drop due to chemical polarization may be expressed in terms of the *Tafel equation* as

$$v_c = \alpha + \beta \log_{10} J \qquad (9\text{–}23)$$

where α and β are constants and J is the electrode current density. The values of α and β depend on the electrode materials. β is usually about

0.1 volt/decade where J is in amperes per square meter. However, the value of α varies considerably, not only for different cells but is also sensitive to electrode surface conditions and the existing impurity concentration.

Usually the fuel cell polarization curve within the operating range is characterized by an almost linear region. There the decrease in terminal voltage is mainly due to the internal ohmic resistance r_i of the cell. This comprises the ion-exchange membrane, or electrolyte, resistance; the contact resistance between the membrane and the electrodes; and the resistance associated with the electrodes themselves. If the linear part of the polarization curve is extended to intersect the voltage axis at e'_g, then the equivalent circuit of Fig. 9–3 may be used to represent the cell when the operating range is within the linear region of the curve.

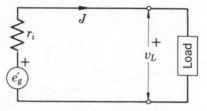

Fig. 9–3. Fuel cell equivalent circuit for use within the linear range.

At large current densities, voltage loss due to *concentration polarization* becomes significant. This loss is due to electrostatic effects and to concentration gradients within the interelectrode space. The electrostatic effects are similar to those of space charge encountered in the thermionic converter. Interelectrode density gradients develop which may cause reactant depletion in the vicinity of the electrodes. The latter effect may be reduced, when a liquid electrolyte is used, by causing the electrolyte to circulate so that adequate reactant arrival rate is achieved at the electrodes. In all cases an increase in temperature increases the ion diffusion rate and so tends to reduce the concentration polarization loss. Under typical operating conditions this loss is negligible compared to those of chemical polarization and internal resistance.

The efficiency of a simple cell η may be based on the ratio of the electrical output energy to the total energy liberated by the chemical reaction, so that

$$\eta = \frac{n \mathfrak{F} v_L}{\Delta H} \qquad (9\text{–}24)$$

Since the operation of the fuel cell is not governed by the Carnot cycle, efficiencies as high as 60 to 70 percent may be achieved without recourse to high temperatures.

Example 9–4. A fuel cell converter, operating on pure hydrogen and oxygen, is required to supply an electrical output power of 2000 watts. Each cell is to have porous titanium electrodes of 0.05-m² area separated by the ion-exchange membrane, a 0.0011-m-thick sheet of polymer plastic with an effective resistivity of 0.22 ohm-m. The hydrogen and oxygen are supplied to the cell at pressures of 24 psia and 20 psia, respectively. The water which is formed is condensed on wicks, fed from the cell, and made available to the astronauts. In order to avoid significant concentration polarization loss, the cell is to be operated at an electrode current density of 1000 amp/m². For an operating temperature of 35°C, the coefficients of the Tafel equation are experimentally found to be $\alpha = 0.006$ volt and $\beta = 0.095$ volt/decade where J is in amperes per square meter and all the loss may be associated with the oxygen electrode. Assume a contact and circuit resistance drop of 0.05 volt (1 atm = 14.7 psia). Find

    (a) The terminal voltage.
    (b) The number of cells required.
    (c) The efficiency.
    (d) The amount of thermal energy which is rejected for each kilogram mole of oxygen used.

    (a) Upon substituting the value of $e_g{}^\circ = 1.23$ volts, as found in Ex. 9–2, in Eq. 9–22,

$$e_g = 1.23 - \frac{8314 \times 308}{4 \times 96.5 \times 10^6} \ln \frac{1^2}{(1.63)^2 \times 1.36} = 1.238 \text{ volts}$$

Since it is assumed that both the hydrogen and the oxygen behave as perfect gases, the individual pressures are used in place of the activities.

From Eq. 9–23, the voltage drop due to chemical polarization is

$$v_c = 0.006 + 0.095 \log_{10} 10^3 = 0.291 \text{ volt}$$

and the voltage drop across the ion-exchange membrane is

$$0.22 \times 0.0011 \times 10^3 = 0.242 \text{ volt}$$

so that, accounting for contact and circuit resistance, the terminal voltage is

$$v_L = 1.238 - 0.291 - 0.242 - 0.05 = 0.655 \text{ volt}$$

    (b) The output power density of each cell is

$$P - Jv_L = 10^3 \times 0.655 = 655 \text{ watts/m}^2$$

and since each cell has an area of 0.05 m², the power output of each cell is $655 \times 0.05 = 32.75$ watts. In order to provide a total output of 2000 watts, $2000/32.75 = 61$ cells are required.

    (c) From Eq. 9–24,

$$\eta \approx \frac{4 \times 96.5 \times 10^6 \times 0.655 \times 100}{(0 + 0) - (-2 \times 286) \times 10^6} = 44 \text{ percent}$$

(d) The energy which is evolved in the form of heat Q_t is obtained from the difference between the total energy liberated by the reaction and the electrical output:

$$Q_t = \Delta H - n\mathcal{F}v_L$$
$$= (2 \times 286 \times 10^6) - (4 \times 96.5 \times 10^6 \times 0.655)$$
$$= 319 \times 10^6 \text{ joule/kg mole of oxygen}$$

9–6. FUEL CELL DEVELOPMENT

Two main types of fuel cell converter are under development: the low-temperature converter, typically for use in space, and the high-temperature converter for military and commercial applications. Since the requirements in the two cases differ considerably the problems encountered and the approach to their solution also differ significantly. Unlike the fuel cell converter under development for use in space, the commercial system must be capable of using basic fossil fuels such as natural gas and oil. Many different systems are under development and, rather than describing specific fuel cell converters, general system classifications are considered.

9–6.1. Low-Temperature Fuel Cells.

In general, low-temperature fuel cell converters use hydrogen as the fuel and oxygen as the oxidizer. Due to the high cost of fuel, these converters are considered suitable only for special uses, and in particular for use in space.

The Bacon cell, developed by Francis T. Bacon in 1952, and many similar cells developed since that date, employ a liquid KOH electrolyte which separates the porous electrodes as shown in Fig. 9–4a. The dominant cell reaction is

anode $2H_2 + 4OH^- \rightarrow 4H_2O + 4e$
cathode $2H_2O + O_2 + 4e \rightarrow 4OH^-$
overall $2H_2 + O_2 \rightarrow 2H_2O$

Although high current densities of as much as 8000 amp/m² can be obtained by operating at temperatures up to 500°K and pressures up to 40 atm, this type of cell has many disadvantages. Due to the fact that the electrolyte reacts with CO_2 to form $KHCO_3$ care must be taken to ensure the purity of the hydrogen and oxygen fuel. To ensure an even distribution of gas, the electrodes must have uniform porosity. Constructional flaws and other imperfections can cause accumulation of gas in the electrolyte and mixing of gases whenever small gas-pressure differences exist. Sintered metal electrodes are fragile, and porous carbon electrodes are both fragile and bulky. Owing to these disadvantages, the Bacon-type cell is unsuited for use in space.

The solid-electrolyte fuel cell, or ion-exchange membrane fuel cell, which has been described in Art. 9–1, has more acceptable features. The membrane may consist, for example, of a finely powdered sulphonated

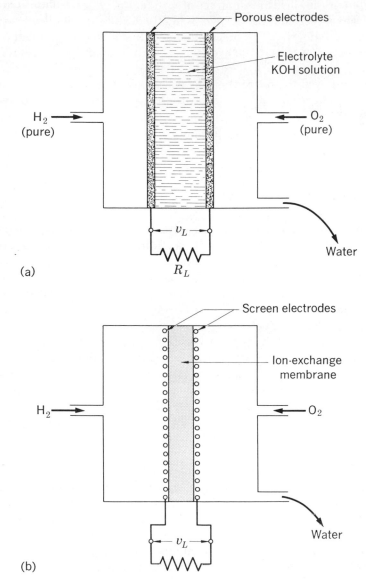

Fig. 9–4. (a) Bacon-type fuel cell employing liquid electrolyte and porous electrodes. (b) Ion-exchange membrane cell with screen electrodes.

polystyrene resin, held in a matrix of an inert polymer.   This structure acts as a gas-impervious barrier, yet is highly flexible, mechanically strong, and chemically inert.   The membrane acts like a sponge and can hold a certain amount of water; the excess can be drained away or removed by circulating the gases.   Of necessity, electrodes with discontinuous contact are employed to ensure that the gases have easy access to the membrane.   The electrodes are either in the form of screens pressed against the membrane by means of back-up plates, or in the form of perforated metal sheets.   Such structures are cheap and rugged, and *flooding* of the electrodes, encountered in the Bacon-type cell, cannot of course occur. In addition, and an important advantage in certain cases, is the fact that the membrane is immune to carbon dioxide impurities and that air, instead of oxygen, can be used if the air is permitted to flow continuously past the membrane.

The main disadvantage of the cell is the relatively high electrical resistance of the membrane.   However, the membrane, including the electrodes, is only about 3 mm in thickness but for space use the low weight and volume per unit electrode area compensate for the imposed low current density.   The cell may be damaged due to heating and drying of the membrane if excessive current densities are permitted.   For this reason a reliable overload protective system is required.

The ion-exchange fuel cell converter has proved itself successful on board the Gemini spacecraft, and it appears that this type of fuel cell will continue to be developed in preference to the liquid electrolyte type.

9–6.2. High-Temperature Fuel Cells.   In general, high-temperature fuel cells are designed to use a variety of impure and inexpensive fuels and air.   Fossil fuels can usually be broken down, either inside or outside the cell, into a mixture of hydrogen and carbon monoxide, and so the high-temperature fuel cell converter must be designed to operate with such a mixture in the presence of other impurities.

The choice of a suitable electrolyte is complicated by the fact that carbon monoxide reacts with an alkaline electrolyte, and does not produce a hydrogen ion with an acid electrolyte.   Two types of electrolyte have been found suitable: the carbonate and the mixed oxide.

Since operating temperatures of about $1200°K$ are required, aqueous electrolytes are not practicable due to their high vapor pressures at these temperatures.   Molten salts, such as sodium or potassium carbonate, have been developed for use.   In such cases lithium carbonate is usually added to lower the melting point.   The electrolyte is then impregnated into a sintered material, such as magnesium oxide, having a porosity of 40 to 50 percent.   Thus the magnesium oxide provides mechanical strength and simultaneously immobilizes the molten carbonate.   The slab of impregnated sintered material is placed between the electrodes, which are usually fabricated from powdered nickel, iron, or silver.

The operation of such a cell depends on first *cracking* the fossil fuel to produce hydrogen and carbon monoxide. This is achieved by causing the fuel to react with steam and carbon dioxide. Since both are products

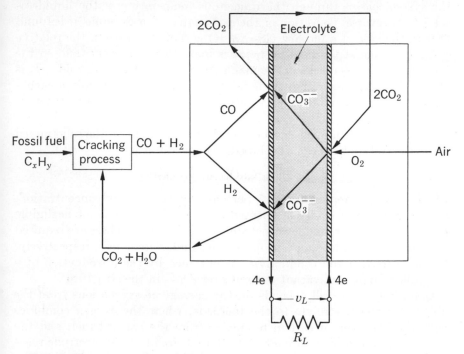

Fig. 9–5. Schematic of high-temperature fuel cell converter with a carbonate electrolyte.

of the cell reaction, it is possible to introduce the *raw* fuel into the cell; and the cracking process proceeds under the high operating cell temperature. The carbon monoxide and hydrogen products then react with carbonate ions in the electrolyte as follows:

$$CO + CO_3^{--} \rightarrow 2CO_2 + 2e$$
$$H_2 + CO_3^{--} \rightarrow CO_2 + H_2O + 2e$$

resulting in the release of electrons, carbon dioxide, and steam, as represented in Fig. 9–5. The electrons travel through the external circuit and reach the oxygen electrode, where they participate in forming carbonate ions from oxygen and carbon dioxide:

$$4e + O_2 + 2CO_2 \rightarrow 2CO_3^{--}$$

Carbonate electrolytes have been extensively developed, in most cases in conjunction with magnesium oxide as the absorbent body, but a number of problems have been encountered.   The major one is gas leakage through small stress cracks and through a gradually increasing number of open pores in the refractory magnesium oxide body.   Stress cracks arise when the system passes through the dangerous temperature of the liquid-to-solid (and reverse) transition of the carbonate.   For example, it is found that in the case of a ternary (Li–Na–K) carbonate mixture, the relative volume change at the melting point is more than 5 percent, and so the formation of stress cracks in the magnesium oxide is hard to avoid.   It is also found that magnesium oxide is slightly soluble in the molten carbonate, so that a slow but steady disintegration of the ceramic structure takes place.

With the problems of the carbonate electrolyte in mind, the solid mixed oxide electrolyte has been developed.   Typically it is

$$[ZrO_2]_{0.85}[CaO]_{0.15}[\Box o\text{-}\text{-}]_{0.15}$$

where $[\Box o\text{-}\text{-}]_{0.15}$ represents a 15 percent oxygen vacancy concentration. Such a mixture of oxides is selected to meet the demands of negligible cation conductivity, and low electronic conductivity.   These are required to prevent electrode composition changes and voltage loss, respectively. Optimum oxygen ion conductivity is obtained by the introduction of a controlled number of vacant oxygen sites $\Box o\text{-}\text{-}$ in the structure.

Operation of the cell depends on the passage of oxygen ions from the air side of the electrolyte to the fuel side, where the oxygen combines with the hydrogen or carbon monoxide from the cracked fuel, and the liberated electrons flow through the external circuit.   The electrode reactions are

$$\text{anode} \qquad O_2 + 4e \rightarrow 2O^{--}$$
$$\text{cathode} \qquad 2O^{--} + 2H_2 \rightarrow 2H_2O + 4e$$

or

$$2O^{--} + 2CO \rightarrow 2CO_2 + 4e$$

The by-products are carbon dioxide and steam, which may be used in the fossil-fuel cracking process.   The cell is represented schematically in Fig. 9–6.

Although only carbon monoxide and hydrogen have been considered as the fuel, the cell should be able to utilize any fuel which reacts chemically or electrochemically with oxygen at the temperature of operation. In 1965 Westinghouse Electric Corporation demonstrated an experimental 115-watt mixed-oxide, solid-electrolyte fuel cell converter which operates directly from coal gases.   The converter contains 400 thimble-size hollow cylindrical fuel cells and operates at a temperature of 1260°K.   The cells fit together like drainage tiles arranged in stacks of 20 inside 20 pipes. Coal gases flow through the inside of the cylinders, while heated air passes around the outside surface of the cells.   To maintain its 1260°K temperature, the converter is housed in a heated oven. However, converters of several kilowatts would generate sufficient heat to maintain the operating temperature without the aid of an external heat supply. A long-term problem seems to lie in maintaining bonding between the electrodes and the solid electrolyte.

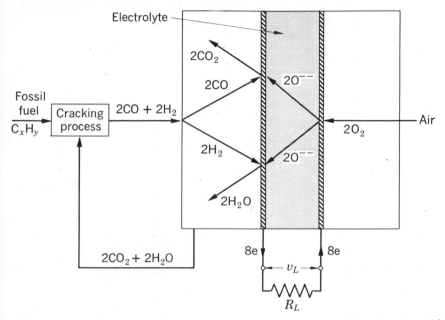

Fig. 9–6. Schematic of high-temperature fuel cell with mixed solid oxide electrolyte.

The Westinghouse fuel cell converter has also been used in reverse to recover oxygen from the waste products exhaled in breathing. Electrical power is supplied to the cell. At the operating temperature (1260°K), both carbon dioxide and water vapor decompose, releasing oxygen ions at the cathode. These ions move through the electrolyte to the anode, where they loose their electrons and become molecules of oxygen, suitable for breathing in space. Hydrogen and solid carbon are by-products of the process. The Westinghouse studies indicate that a complete oxygen-generating system, capable of supplying the needs of four men, including the fuel cells, controls, insulation, and other auxiliary equipment, would weigh about 30 kg, occupy about 0.09 m³, and require a power input of about 1000 watts.

9–6.3. Regenerative Fuel Cells. If energy, be it thermal, electrical, radioactive, etc., is supplied to the products of a fuel cell converter so that they are reconverted into their original state, and again recirculated through the cell, the system is said to be *closed-cycle regenerative*. Such a system (Fig. 9–7) may be suitable for use in space in conjunction with a nuclear reactor. The fuel cell product AB is directed to the nuclear reactor where, at the high reactor temperature, it dissociates into fuel and oxidant A and B. These are then returned to the fuel cell.

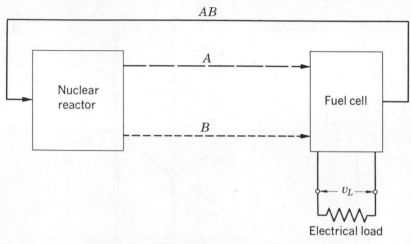

Fig. 9–7. Regenerative fuel cell system.

9–6.4. Development Requirements. Although the fuel cell has demonstrated its ability to convert chemical energy into electrical energy effectively and efficiently, there are some basic requirements which must be satisfactorily met before it achieves widespread acceptance. These may be grouped under *invariance* and *reactivity* requirements.

The invariance requirements are aimed at ensuring the long life of the cell, and specify that no side reactions should take place with the material of the cell, so that the electrolyte, electrodes, and cell members remain unchanged during the life of the cell. The invariance requirement means also that there should be no interdiffusion of fuel and oxidizer and *drowning* or *bubble-through* which can cause poisoning of catalysts and clogging of the pores in electrolytes. The invariance requirement is met by the development and use of suitable materials. However, although it may be satisfactorily met for the specialized case when pure fuels and oxidizers can be used, it is considerably more difficult when cheap impure fuels and air must be used. Various side effects appear inevitable, and means must be devised to dispose of the products of these subsidiary reactions.

The reactivity requirement specifies that all reactions should proceed fully so that discharged atoms have as low an energy as possible under the circumstances, so that the maximum amount of electrical energy is released. For example, if carbon is to be oxidized, all of it should be oxidized to carbon dioxide rather than to carbon monoxide.

Another reactivity requirement is concerned with the speed of the reaction. The maximum current density is limited by the maximum rate at which the cell reaction can take place per unit electrode area. The reaction rate can be increased by suitable electrode surface design, so that the interaction interface of gas, electrolyte, and electrode is as large as possible. This is achieved by using porous electrodes. Increased pressure, temperature, and the use of catalysts also increase the reaction rate. However, steps which are taken to increase the reaction rate are usually in conflict with the invariance requirement, so that in all cases a compromise must be made between the two requirements.

Fuel cell converters have been satisfactorily demonstrated in space for missions of relatively short duration. However, their satisfactory development for general use poses a number of difficult material and electrical problems. It is likely that fuel cell converters will first prove themselves in special military and industrial applications before the development of large central station fuel cell converter systems is attempted.

PROBLEMS

9-1. A fuel cell converter, operating on pure hydrogen and oxygen, is required to supply a power output of 750 watts. Electrodes of 0.037 m² active area are used and are separated by an ion-exchange membrane which is 0.002 m thick and has a resistivity of 0.3 ohm-m. The hydrogen and oxygen are supplied to the cell at pressures of 1.8 atm and 1.9 atm respectively, and operation is at a current density of 1200 amp/m². If the Tafel coefficients are $\alpha = 0.008$ volts and $\beta = 0.1$ volts/decade at the operating temperature of 28°C and the contact and circuit resistance voltage drop is 0.04 volts. Find

    a. The terminal voltage.
    b. The power output from each cell and the minimum number of cells required.
    c. The efficiency.
    d. The amount of thermal energy which is rejected for each kilogram mole of oxygen used.

9-2. A hydrogen-oxygen fuel cell converter with N cells, each of area A, is operated at a current density J. Determine an expression for the rate at which water is produced.

9-3. Find the rate in pints per hour at which water is produced by the converter considered in Ex. 9-4.

9-4. Find the mass of hydrogen fuel necessary to operate the fuel cell converter of Prob. 9-1 for one day.

9-5. Find the total energy released when 1 kg of methane (CH_4) is oxidized to produce water and carbon dioxide at STP.

9-6. What is the maximum possible electrical energy which would be produced when 1 kg of methane (CH_4) is oxidized to produce water and carbon dioxide at STP?

9-7. For the fuel cell converter of Ex. 9-1, find the maximum possible value of the internally generated voltage at STP.

9-8. Repeat Prob. 9-7 for an operating temperature of 1100°K and partial gas pressures of 1.5 atm, 0.19 atm, and 0.22 atm for CO, O_2, and CO_2, respectively. Assume that the gases are ideal.

9-9. Find the internally generated voltage of a hydrogen-oxygen fuel cell operating at 500°K where the hydrogen and the air are each at a pressure of 40 atm.

9-10. The terminal voltage of a certain hydrogen-oxygen fuel cell may be expressed as a function of current density in amperes per square meter within the linear operating range of the cell by $v_L = 0.94 - 3 \times 10^{-4}J$ volts. Find the current density and terminal voltage for maximum power output.

9-11. A fuel cell converter is required to supply a constant power P_L during a space mission. The polarization curve, within the operating range, may be represented by $v_L = a - bJ$. If the weight of the converter is C_1A, where C_1 is a constant and A is the total effective electrode area, find an expression for the terminal voltage and the current density if the system is designed for minimum weight.

9-12. The polarization curve of a particular hydrogen-oxygen fuel cell converter proposed for use in space is $v_L = 1.0 - 10^{-4}J$, where J is in amperes per square meter, and v_L is in volts. If the converter mass is 11 kg/m² of effective electrode area and a constant power output of 10 kilowatts is required, find, for a design of minimum mass,

   a. The current density.
   b. The terminal voltage of each cell.
   c. The mass of the converter.
   d. The efficiency.

9-13. A central station high-temperature fuel cell converter uses carbon monoxide as fuel and air as the oxidizer under the following conditions:

operating temperature	1200°K
internal resistance per square meter	2×10^{-4} ohm-m²
partial pressure of CO	0.71 atm
partial pressure of O_2	0.31 atm
partial pressure of CO_2	0.51 atm
current density	1100 amp/m²
α	0.01 volt
β	0.09 volt/decade
effective cell area	0.2 m²
effective converter output	10^4 kw

Find

   a. The terminal voltage.
   b. The number of cells required.
   c. The approximate efficiency.
   d. The rate in kg/hr at which CO and O_2 must be supplied.

Bibliography: Part II

GENERAL

ANGRIST, S. W. *Direct Energy Conversion.* Rockleigh, N.J.: Allyn & Bacon, Inc. 1965.

CHANG, S. S. L. *Energy Conversion.* Englewood Cliffs, N.J.: Prentice-Hall, Inc. 1963.

KAYE, J., and WELSH, J. A. *Direct Conversion of Heat to Electricity.* New York: John Wiley & Sons, Inc. 1960.

SUTTON, G. W. *Direct Energy Conversion.* New York: McGraw-Hill Book Co., Inc. 1966.

THERMOELECTRIC

COHEN, R. W., and ABELES, B. "Efficiency Calculations of Thermoelectric Generators with Temperature Varying Parameters." *J. Appl. Phys.*, **34**: 1687. 1963.

CORLISS, W. R., and HARVEY, D. L. *Radioisotope Power Generation.* Englewood Cliffs, N.J.: Prentice-Hall, Inc. 1964.

EGLI, P. H. *Thermoelectricity.* New York: John Wiley & Sons, Inc. 1960.

FRITTS, R. W. "Design Parameters for Optimizing the Efficiency of Thermoelectric Generators Utilizing p-Type and n-Type Lead Telluride." *Trans. AIEE*, Part I, **78**: 817. 1960.

FRITTS, R. W. "Lead Telluride Alloys and Junctions." Chap. 10, in CADOFF, I. B., and MILLER, E. (eds.). *Thermoelectric Materials and Devices.* New York: Reinhold Publishing Corp. 1960.

GOLDSMID, H. J. *Applications of Thermoelectricity.* London: Methuen & Co., Ltd. 1960.

GOLDSMID, H. J. *Thermoelectric Refrigeration.* New York: Plenum Press, Inc. 1964.

JOFFE, A. F. *Semiconductor Thermoelements and Thermoelectric Cooling.* London: Infosearch, Ltd. 1957.

MACDONALD, D. K. C. *Thermoelectricity: An Introduction to the Principles.* New York: John Wiley & Sons, Inc. 1962.

MACKAY, D. B. *Design of Space Power Plants.* Englewood Cliffs, N.J.: Prentice-Hall, Inc. 1963.

ROSI, F. D., HICKINGS, E. F., and LINDENBLAD, N. E. "Semiconducting Materials for Thermoelectric Power Generation." *RCA Review*, **22**: 82. 1961.

SCOTT, W. C., and SCHULMAN, F. "Space Electric Power." *Astronautics and Aerospace Eng.* May, 1963.

PHOTOELECTRIC

BUBE, R. H. *Photoconductivity of Solids.* New York: John Wiley & Sons, Inc. 1960.

LOFERSKI, J. J. "Recent Research on Photovoltaic Solar Energy Converters." *Proc. IEEE,* **51**: 667. 1963.

LOFERSKI, J. J. "Theoretical Considerations Governing the Choice of the Optimum Semiconductor for Photovoltaic Solar Energy Conversion." *J. Appl. Phys.,* **27**: 777. 1956.

PRINCE, M. B. "Applications of Silicon Solar Cells for Space and Terrestrial Use." *Acta Electronica,* **5**: 330. 1961.

RAPPAPORT, P. "The Photovoltaic Effect and Its Utilization." *RCA Review,* **20**: 373. 1959.

TAUC, J. "Generation of an emf in Semiconductors with Nonequilibrium Current Carrier Concentrations." *J. Appl. Phys.,* **29**: 308. 1957.

ZAREM, A. M., and ERWAY, D. C. *Introduction to the Utilization of Solar Energy.* New York: McGraw-Hill Book Co., Inc. 1963.

THERMIONIC

FOUAD, A. A., and WALSH, E. M. "Cyclic Analysis of the Gabor-Type Auxiliary Discharge Thermionic Converter." *Advanced Energy Conversion,* **5**: 71. 1965.

GABOR, D. "A New Thermionic Generator." *Nature,* **189**: 868. 1961.

GABOR, D. "The Theory of Gas Discharges with Extraneous Ion Supply." *Advanced Energy Conversion,* **3**: 307. 1963.

GYFTOPOULOS, E. P., and HATSOPOULOS, G. N. "Thermionic Nuclear Reactors." *Electrical Engineering,* p. 108. February, 1963.

INGOLD, J. H. "Calculation of the Maximum Efficiency of the Thermionic Converter." *J. Appl. Phys.,* **32**: 769. 1961.

LANGMUIR, I. "Effect of Space Charge and Initial Velocities on the Potential Distribution and Thermionic Current Between Parallel Plane Electrodes." *Physical Review,* **21**: 419. 1923.

LEWIS, H. W., and REITZ, J. R. "Thermoelectric Properties of the Plasma Diode." *J. Appl. Phys.,* **30**: 1439. 1959.

MICHAELSON, H. B. "Work Functions of the Elements." *J. Appl. Phys.,* **21**: 536. 1950.

REIMANN, A. L. *Thermionic Emission.* New York: John Wiley & Sons, Inc. 1934.

WALSH, E. M. "Application of Auxiliary Discharge to Thermionic Converters." *Northeast Electronics Research and Engineering Meeting Record,* **7**: 146. 1965.

WALSH, E. M. "Comparison of the Approach to Thermionic Energy Conversion in Europe and the United States." *Nuclear News,* **7**: 48. 1964.

WALSH, E. M., and FOUAD, A. A. "Cost of Space-Charge Neutralization in the Gabor-Type Auxiliary Discharge Thermionic Converter." *Thermionic Conversion Specialist Conf. Report*, p. 79. 1965.

FLUIDDYNAMIC

BROGAN, T. R. "MHD Power Generation." *IEEE Spectrum*, p. 58. February, 1964.

CAMBEL, A. B. *Plasma Physics and Magnetofluid Mechanics*. New York: McGraw-Hill Book Co., Inc. 1963.

COOMBE, R. A. (ed.). *Magnetohydrodynamic Generation of Electric Power*. New York: Reinhold Publishing Corp. 1964.

COWLING, T. *Magnetohydrodynamics*. New York: Interscience Publishers, Inc., 1958.

DAMAN, E. L. *Electrogasdynamic Power Generation*. Livingston, N.J.: Foster Wheeler Corp. 1966.

ELLIOTT, D. G. "DC Liquid-Metal Magnetohydrodynamic Power Generator." (Sixth Symposium on Engineering Aspects of Magnetohydrodynamics, University of Pittsburgh and Carnegie Institute of Technology.) 1965.

HARRIS, L. P., and COBINE, J. D. "The Significance of the Hall Effect for Three MHD Generator Configurations." *Trans. ASME*, ser. A, **83A**: 392. 1961.

KERREBROCK, J. L. "Magnetohydrodynamic Generators with Nonequilibrium Ionization." *AIAA J.*, **3**: 591. 1965.

PETRICK, M. "Liquid-Metal Magnetohydrodynamics." *IEEE Spectrum*, p. 137. March, 1965.

SPORN, P., and KANTROWITZ, A. "Magnetohydrodynamics . . . Future Power Process?" *Power*, **103**(11): 62. 1959.

SUTTON, G. W., and SHERMAN, A. *Engineering Magnetohydrodynamics*. New York: McGraw-Hill Book Co., Inc. 1965.

WRIGHT, J. K., *et al.* "Some Factors Influencing the Design of Open-Cycle Fossil-Fuel MHD Generators for the Electricity Supply Industry." (Symposium on Magnetoplasmadynamic Electrical Power Generation, University of Durham, England.) 1962.

FUEL CELLS

CARMAN, P. C. *Flow of Gases Through Porous Media*. New York: Academic Press, Inc. 1956.

JASINSKI, R. J., and KIRKLAND, T. "Fuel Cells: A State-of-the-Art Report." *Mech. Eng.*, p. 51. 1964.

LIEBHAFSKY, H. A., and CAIRNS, E. J. "Electrochemical Kinetics and the Fuel Cell." (General Electric Research Information Report No. 65-RL-3906C.) April, 1965.

LIEBHAFSKY, H. A., and GRUBB, W. T. "The Fuel Cell in Space." *Amer. Rocket Soc. J.*, p. 1183. September, 1961.

LIEBHAFSKY, H. A., *et al.*, in GOULD, R. F. (ed.). *Fuel Cell Systems.* (Advances in Chemistry Series, No. 47.) Washington, D.C.: American Chemical Society. 1965.

PEATTIE, C. G. "Hydrocarbon-Air Fuel Cell Systems." *IEEE Spectrum*, p. 69. June, 1966.

PEATTIE, C. G., *et al.* "Performance Data for Molten-Electrolyte Fuel Cells Operating on Several Fuels." *Proc. 1962 Pacific Energy Conversion Conf.*, *San Francisco, Calif.* August, 1962.

YOUNG, G. J. *Fuel Cells.* New York: Reinhold Publishing Corp. 1963.

III

Nuclear-Thermal Conversion

10

Introduction

The process of nuclear-to-thermal energy conversion is basically concerned with the liberation and control of the energy stored within the atomic nucleus.   The liberation of this energy in the nuclear fission reaction is dependent on the interaction of neutrons with the atomic nucleus. A brief review of nuclear structure is therefore appropriate.

10–1. THE NUCLEUS

The atom consists of a positively charged nucleus surrounded by *electrons* e as shown, for example, by the beryllium atom in Fig. 10–1a.   In the conventional chemical liberation of thermal energy, such as the burning of coal, it is the orbital electrons which are redistributed among the atoms, but the nuclear structure is unaltered.   However, in the release of nuclear energy it is the nucleons constituting the nucleus of the atom which are redistributed, and the energy released due to electron redistribution is insignificant.

The nucleus is composed of two types of primary particles, *neutrons* n and *protons* p, and both of these particles can exist outside of the atomic nucleus.   The neutron is an uncharged particle and therefore is uninfluenced by electric fields.   For this reason it has the important property of being able to penetrate the nucleus, unhindered by electrostatic fields, and cause *fission* or splitting of the nucleus.   The mass of the neutron is found to be somewhat greater than that of the hydrogen atom, and expressed in atomic mass units (amu),

$$\text{mass of neutron} = 1.008983 \text{ amu}$$

The amu is defined in terms of the O-16 atom, which has a mass of exactly 16 amu.

10–2. NUCLEAR FISSION

Nuclear fission, or the splitting of an atomic nucleus, may be brought about with some heavy elements by injecting an additional neutron into the nucleus. With this addition the nucleus becomes unstable, splitting into two main fission fragments, as well as ejecting, on the average, more than one new neutron. These new neutrons can cause further fissions and thus a chain reaction becomes possible.

Uranium is the only substance found in nature that can propagate such a chain reaction. Natural uranium contains three *isotopes*. Isotopes are atoms with the same number of protons and electrons, but different numbers of neutrons, as illustrated by the beryllium atoms in Fig. 10–1.

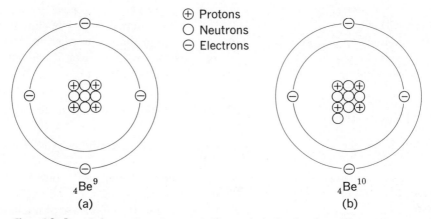

Fig. 10–1. Schematic representation of (a) the beryllium atom and (b) the radioactive beryllium isotope $_4Be^{10}$.

The notation used in describing a nucleus is $_ZX^A$, where X is the symbol of the element, Z is the charge on the nucleus, and A is the mass number, which is equal to the sum of the neutrons and protons in the nucleus. Thus uranium-235 is written $_{92}U^{235}$, where the number of *nucleons* (nucleons being either neutrons or protons) in the nucleus is 235 and the number of protons is 92.

Natural uranium contains 99.3 percent of U-238, 0.7 percent of U-235, and traces of U-234. Of the three, only U-235 is suitable for fission in conventional nuclear power reactors. In the U-235 fission process, a neutron penetrates the atom and enters the nucleus. There is a certain probability of fission occurring. Should this happen, the nucleus divides into two principal fragments and two or three (average, 2.47) neutrons are ejected. For a sustained chain reaction, at least one neutron per fission must cause a new fission. *Criticality* is said to be achieved when exactly one neutron per fission causes a new fission. This situation is represented in Fig. 10–2.

Most of the nuclear energy is released in the form of the kinetic energy of the fission fragments. The two principal fragments quickly loose their kinetic energy by impact with other atoms, and in this process the energy of fission is converted into thermal energy. The fission process is also

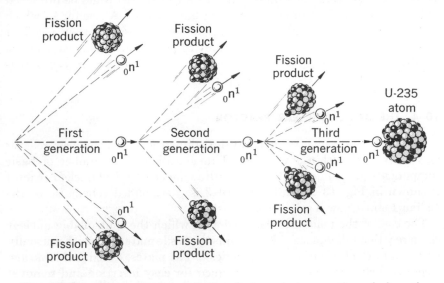

Fig. 10–2. Representation of the fission chain reaction during three generations.

accompanied by the emission of *gamma radiation*, which is electromagnetic in nature, and by the liberation of particle radiation, such as *beta* and *alpha radiation*, due mainly to the decay of the unstable fission products. It is the accumulation of newly formed fission products which accounts for the high radioactivity of materials which have been involved in a nuclear fission process. Nuclear stability of these fission products is not attained immediately and in some cases requires thousands of years for completion.

10 3. THE BREEDING PROCESS

Although natural uranium contains only 0.7 percent of U-235 it may be used as the fuel of the nuclear power reactor. The U-235 concentration may be increased considerably by processing, but usually most of the atoms present in the fuel are U-238, which do not fission readily.

However, U-238 has the important property of absorbing neutrons and, after some days, changing into a new element, plutonium, which fissions just like U-235. U-238 is called a *fertile material* because it can be converted into fissionable material. Thus a new fuel, Pu-239, is being produced from the U-238, while the U-235 is being burned up. Since about 2.5 neutrons are produced for each U-235 atom fissioned, it appears that 1.5 neutrons are not utilized in maintaining the chain reaction, and that these could be used in converting U-238 into plutonium at the same rate as the U-235 is being burned up. In this way new fuel could be produced as fast as the original uranium is being burned up. A reactor in which this is possible is called a *breeder*. In practice the design of such a reactor is difficult, since loss of more than about 19 percent of the neutrons from the desired process cannot be tolerated if the plutonium production rate is to be as great as the U-235 burn-up rate.

10–4. THE BASIC NUCLEAR REACTOR

Although the geometry and physical dimensions of a nuclear reactor may be varied within a very broad range, all have a number of basic components in common. A cutaway drawing of a typical nuclear reactor is shown in Fig. 13–2, while Fig. 10–3 is a simplified schematic of the Indian Point (New York) reactor system.

The *core* of the reactor is that region in which the controllable nuclear chain reaction takes place. It contains the fissile material, which is usually uranium in the form of rods or bundles of flat plates, called *fuel elements*. These fuel elements are usually designed for easy insertion and removal from the core. The uranium may be used with its natural 0.7 percent U-235 content, or enriched with over 90 percent U-235.

Most of the space separating the fuel elements is filled with a material called a *moderator*, such as graphite or heavy water, which tends to reduce the speed of the fast neutrons to a level where the probability of causing fission is greater. Neutrons which have been completely slowed and have an energy corresponding to the temperature of the material are called *thermal neutrons*. At room temperature, 293°K, their average energy is 0.0253 electron volt (ev), corresponding to an average speed of 2200 m/sec.

Control of the chain reaction is achieved by inserting neutron-absorbing materials, such as cadmium or boron steel, into the core. These controlling elements may be in the form of rods, which may be raised or lowered as required. Such control rods are of two types, *safety rods*, which are capable of absorbing a large quantity of neutrons and are withdrawn to start up the reactor, and *shim rods*, which then provide the fine control of the reactor during operation.

A number of shields surround the core. Usually there is a *reflector*, which may consist of about 18 in. of graphite, and serves to prevent loss of neutrons from the fission process. This is important, for although 2.47 neutrons are generated per fission, and only one neutron is required to maintain the chain reaction, there are many processes competing for the excess neutrons. In addition to leakage from the core, the neutrons are

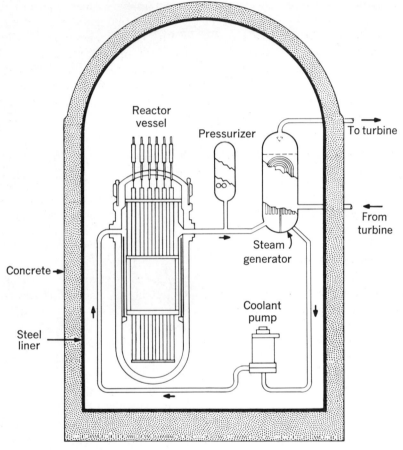

Fig. 10–3. Simplified schematic of the Indian Point reactor system. (Courtesy of Con Edison.)

subject to capture not only by the large quantity of U-238 usually present, but also by the other materials in the reactor core.

A *thermal shield* prevents excessive heating of the pressure vessel. Since the process of fission is accompanied by the emission of a number of types of radiation, such as alpha and beta particles, gamma rays, and neutrons, it is necessary to shield the reactor personnel from this radiation. *Biological shields* surround all radioactive regions. Concrete is found to be a satisfactory material in many cases and such a shield, several feet thick, is placed about the reactor, or about the reactor building.

A coolant (liquid, gas, or molten metal) is circulated through the core and removes the heat generated by the fission process. This thermal

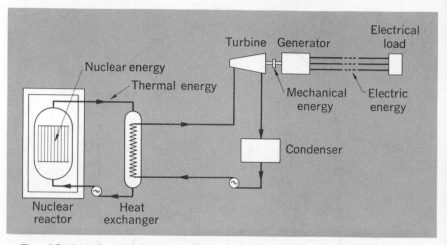

Fig. 10–4. Conventional nuclear power system for the generation of electricity.

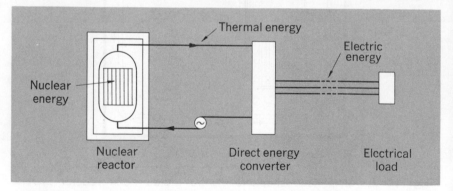

Fig. 10–5. Nuclear power system for the generation of electricity using a direct energy converter.

energy may then be utilized as required, and in the conventional system it is used for the generation of steam which drives a turbogenerator unit for the production of electricity. Figure 10–4 shows such a typical nuclear power system.

In more advanced systems some or all of the heat from the reactor would be converted directly into electricity. Devices which convert thermal energy into electric energy are called *direct energy converters*, because they eliminate the conventional boiler and turbine that convert thermal energy into mechanical energy as well as the generator that converts mechanical energy into electrical energy. Thermoelectric, magneto-hydrodynamic, and thermionic converters are examples of devices which perform the transition from thermal to electrical energy in one step. Figure 10–5 shows a nuclear power system incorporating a direct energy converter. However, in most cases a more efficient arrangement would be provided by a combination of the systems in Fig. 10–4 and Fig. 10–5.

11

The Conversion of Mass
into Energy

11–1. THE ENERGY-MASS RELATIONSHIP

Forty years before the release of nuclear energy, Einstein postulated that it is theoretically possible to convert matter into energy and to convert energy into matter. The Einstein law,

$$E = mc^2 \tag{11–1}$$

where E = energy in joules, m = mass in kilograms, and c = speed of light in vacuum (3×10^8 m/sec), is fundamental to the study of nuclear energy.

A simple calculation shows that, if it is possible to convert 1 kg of matter into energy, then, from Eq. 11–1, the energy released is

$$E = 1 \times (3 \times 10^8)^2$$
$$= 9 \times 10^{16} \text{ joules}$$

The burning of 1 kg of coal provides about 3×10^7 joules of heat. Hence 3×10^9 kg of coal would be required to supply the same quantity of energy as would be liberated by the complete conversion of 1 kg of matter into energy.

As yet there is no known way of completely converting mass into energy. However, in the process of fission about 0.1 percent of the U-235 is converted into energy, and so 1 kg of U-235 in a nuclear reactor is capable of providing as much heat as about 3000 metric tons of coal.

11–2. ATOMIC UNITS

In calculations concerned with the atomic nucleus, or small numbers of atoms, the conventional systems of units, such as the mks or fps, are too large.   As a result a system which is more convenient when dealing with small quantities of matter has been adopted.

The atomic mass unit (amu) is defined as one-sixteenth the mass of the neutral O-16 atom.   Therefore in atomic mass units an atom of oxygen has a mass of 16.000 amu.   But the O-16 atom has a mass of 26.56 $\times$ 10^{-27} kg; therefore 1 amu = 26.56 $\times$ 10^{-27}/16 = 1.66 $\times$ 10^{-27} kg.

The unit of energy adopted is the electron volt, which is equivalent to the work involved in moving an electron through an electrical potential of one volt.   In terms of mks units,

$$1 \text{ ev} = 1.602 \times 10^{-19} \text{ joule}$$

Since the energy released when one U-235 nucleus undergoes fission is about 200 $\times$ 10^6 ev, nuclear calculations are frequently based on the Mev (10^6 ev = 1 Mev).

If Einstein's energy-mass relationship of Eq. 11–1 is expressed in atomic units, the energy equivalent of 1 amu is

$$E = 1.66 \times 10^{-27}(3 \times 10^8)^2 = 1.492 \times 10^{-10} \text{ joule}$$
$$= \frac{1.492 \times 10^{-10}}{1.602 \times 10^{-13}} \qquad = 931 \text{ Mev}$$

Therefore 1 amu of mass is equivalent to 931 Mev of energy.   Table 11–1 gives convenient relationships between conventional and atomic units.

TABLE 11–1

1 Mev	= 10^6 ev		
	= 1.602	$\times$ 10^{-13}	joule
	= 4.45	$\times$ 10^{-20}	kw-hr
	= 1.52	$\times$ 10^{-16}	Btu
	= 1.18	$\times$ 10^{-13}	ft-lb
	= 5.98	$\times$ 10^{-20}	hp-hr
1 amu	= 1.66	$\times$ 10^{-27}	kg
	= 3.66	$\times$ 10^{-27}	lb

11–3. NUCLEAR REACTIONS

Nuclear reactions involve the rearrangement of the neutrons and protons which form the nucleus.   Since the number of neutrons and protons present before and after the reaction is the same, it is possible to write balanced equations for the nucleus which are similar in form to chemical equations.

Nuclear reactions may be initiated by bombarding a target nucleus with a small particle, such as a neutron, a proton, or an alpha particle, whose mass and symbols are shown in Table 11–2.   High-energy gamm radiation may also cause a nuclear reaction.   The proton symbol $_1\text{H}^1$

indicates that the particle has a mass number of unity, and carries a single positive charge. This is the same as the nucleus of the hydrogen atom. Similarly, the alpha particle is the nucleus of the helium atom, which consists of 4 nucleons, two of which are positively charged. Therefore the alpha particle consists of 2 protons and 2 neutrons bound together.

TABLE 11–2

Symbols and Mass of Common Nuclear Particles

Particle	Symbol	Mass (amu)
Neutron	$_0n^1$ or n	1.008983
Proton	$_1H^1$ or p	1.007595
Deuteron	$_1H^2$ or d	2.01420
Alpha	$_2He^4$ or α	4.00280
Electron	e, $_-e$, or β	0.00054862

Consider some nuclear reactions which may be caused by the neutron. If an $_8O^{16}$ atom is bombarded by neutrons, the following reaction may occur:

$$_8O^{16} + {}_0n^1 \rightarrow {}_8O^{17} \rightarrow {}_6C^{13} + {}_2He^4 \qquad (11\text{–}2)$$

Equation 11–2 indicates that the bombarding neutron is absorbed into the $_8O^{16}$ nucleus, forming the $_8O^{17}$ isotope. The nucleus is unstable and so it emits an alpha particle. The nucleus is then that of $_6C^{13}$. In other words, by bombarding an oxygen atom with neutrons a new atom with the properties of carbon is formed, and an alpha particle is emitted. This nuclear reaction is termed a (n,α) reaction, and frequently a shorter notation

$$O^{16}(n,\alpha)C^{13}$$

is used.

The following are other typical nuclear reactions:

$$_4Be^9 + {}_1H^1 \rightarrow {}_5B^{10} \rightarrow {}_4Be^8 + {}_1H^2 \quad \text{or} \quad Be^9(p,d)Be^8$$
$$_5B^{10} + {}_2He^4 \rightarrow {}_7N^{14} \rightarrow {}_7N^{13} + {}_0n^1 \quad \text{or} \quad B^{10}(\alpha,n)N^{13}$$
$$_{12}Mg^{25} + \gamma \rightarrow {}_{12}Mg^{25} \rightarrow {}_{11}Na^{24} + {}_1H^1 \quad \text{or} \quad Mg^{25}(\gamma,p)Na^{24}$$

In most nuclear reactions it is found that the sums of the masses involved before and after the reactions are unequal. In some cases there is a net mass increase, which means that a fraction of the energy provided to cause the reaction is converted into mass. The energy so converted is called *the Q of the reaction*. When energy is converted into mass it is said to be a *negative Q reaction*, and likewise when energy is released during the reaction it is said to be a *positive Q reaction*. Appendix A lists the atomic weight of a selected number of isotopes.

Example 11–1.   Determine the Q value for the $Be^9(p,d)Be^8$ reaction.

The reaction is

$$_4Be^9 + {_1}H^1 \rightarrow {_4}Be^8 + {_1}H^2$$

Since we are concerned with a nuclear reaction, the mass of each nucleus is obtained by subtracting the mass of the electrons from that of the neutral atom.

$$
\begin{aligned}
\text{nuclear mass prior to reaction} &= Be^9 \text{ nucleus} \quad\quad + \text{ proton} \\
&= (Be^9 \text{ atom} - 4m_e) + ({_1}H^1 \text{ atom} - m_e) \\
&= 9.01504 - 4m_e \quad\quad + 1.00814 - m_e \\
&\quad 10.02318 - 5m_e \quad\quad\quad\; amu \\
\text{nuclear mass after reaction} &= Be^8 \text{ nucleus} \quad\quad + \text{ deuteron} \\
&= (Be^8 \text{ atom} - 4m_e) + ({_1}H^2 \text{ atom} - m_e) \\
&= 8.00785 - 4m_e \quad\quad + 2.01474 - m_e \\
&= 10.02259 - 5m_e \quad\quad\quad amu
\end{aligned}
$$

Thus the combined mass has decreased during the reaction and the difference is released as energy. The reaction is therefore positive Q. The decrease in mass is $10.02318 - 10.02259 = 0.00059$ amu. Since 1 amu corresponds to an energy of 931 Mev, the Q of the reaction is

$$
\begin{aligned}
Q &= 0.00059 \times 931 \\
&= 0.55 \text{ Mev}
\end{aligned}
$$

In this case, although nuclear energy is released, it is unsuited for continuous power production. Since the projectile is a proton, and no protons are produced, a self-sustaining chain reaction is impossible.

11–4. THE FISSION REACTION

A most important feature of the nuclear fission reaction is the production, on the average, of more than two new neutrons at each fission. Under certain conditions these new neutrons can cause further fission, and a chain reaction is initiated. This nuclear fission reaction differs from those already considered in that it provides a self sustaining energy source.

In the case of U-235, the fission reaction may be expressed as follows:

$$_{92}U^{235} + {_0}n^1 \rightarrow {_{92}}U^{236} \rightarrow M_1 + M_2 + \nu\, _0n^1 + Q \quad\quad (11\text{–}3)$$

where the U-235 atom splits into two fission-product atoms represented by M_1 and M_2. ν is the number of neutrons released per fission (usually either 2 or 3) with an average value of 2.47, and Q represents the mass equivalent of the energy released.

Since it is possible for the U-235 nucleus to split in many different ways, it is appropriate to examine just one of the possible fission reactions:

$$
\begin{aligned}
_{92}U^{235} + {_0}n^1 \rightarrow {_{92}}U^{236} &\rightarrow {_{54}}Xe^{139} + {_{38}}Sr^{95} + 2{_0}n^1 \\
&\rightarrow {_{57}}La^{139} + 3e + {_{42}}Mo^{95} + 4e + 2{_0}n^1
\end{aligned}
$$

This reaction indicates that a neutron is absorbed into the U-235 nucleus and forms U-236, which is unstable and fissions into two new atoms, Sr-95 and Xe-139, and two neutrons (prompt neutrons). However, both Sr-95 and Xe-139 are still highly radioactive, and both decay by ejecting beta particles. For example, Sr-95 decays successively into Y-95, Zr-95, Nb-95, and finally into Mo-95, which is stable. Xe-139 similarly decays in a number of steps to a stable La-139 atom.

In the radioactive decay of some fission products an additional neutron may be ejected during the process. Such neutrons are termed *delayed neutrons*, since they are released into the fission cycle considerably later than the prompt neutrons, which are available almost at the time of fission. Although in the U-235 fission cycle the effective percentage of delayed neutrons produced is only about 0.75 percent of the total, their presence is vital in facilitating control of the chain reaction. Prompt neutrons are released about 10^{-17} sec after the collision of the fission-causing neutron with the nucleus, whereas the delayed neutrons may take up to 80 sec to appear after collision. Their delay provides a stabilizing effect and permits a reasonable amount of time for the reactor control devices to check any excursion which may tend to occur.

The average energy released per U-235 fission is about 203 Mev, but in any particular case this energy depends on the isotopes into which the U-235 fissions. The average total kinetic energy of the fission fragments is about 168 Mev. The total energy released can be calculated from the mass defect. For the particular fission process under consideration, the final stable elements are $_{57}La^{139}$ and $_{42}Mo^{95}$ and the overall nuclear reaction may be written as:

$$_{92}U^{235} + {}_0n^1 \rightarrow {}_{57}La^{139} + {}_{42}Mo^{95} + 2{}_0n^1 + 7e$$

where 2 prompt neutrons are ejected, and also 7 beta particles (electrons) during the decay of the fission products.

nuclear mass prior to fission $= U^{235}$ nucleus $+$ neutron

$= 235.1168 - 92m_e + 1.00898$

$= 236.12578 - 92m_e$ amu

nuclear mass after fission

$= La^{139}$ nucleus $+ Mo^{95}$ nucleus $+$ 2 neutrons $+ 7m_e$

$= 138.955 - 57m_e + 94.945 - 42m_e + 2 \times 1.00898 + 7m_e$

$= 235.91796 - 92m_e$ amu

Therefore, the total mass after fission is less than that before fission by $236.12578 - 235.91796 = 0.20782$ amu. This is equivalent to an energy release of $0.20782 \times 931 = 194$ Mev, which in this case is below the average of 203 Mev.

11-5. NEUTRON REACTIONS

Consider a 1-m cube of material containing N nuclei with a uniform beam of ϕ neutrons/m²-sec incident upon one of the faces. A fraction of the neutrons interact with the nuclei of the material after entering the block. In fact, there are four important ways in which the interaction may take place:

1. Elastic scattering.
2. Inelastic scattering.
3. Capture with or without fission.
4. Absorption.

11-5.1. Elastic Scattering. In the case of an elastic collision, or scattering reaction, the neutron and nucleus obey the laws of classical mechanics. Kinetic energy and momentum are conserved and as a result part of the energy of the bombarding neutron is transferred to the nucleus, which is moved. If this movement is large enough the lattice structure of a material may be permanently altered, and prolonged neutron bombardment may result in significant changes in the structural properties of the material.

11-5.2. Inelastic Scattering. Inelastic collisions may also occur. In such a process the quantum state of the target nucleus is raised to an excited state. It subsequently reverts to the ground state by emitting energy in the form of gamma radiation. An inelastic collision will not occur unless the energy of the bombarding neutron is above a certain minimum threshold level, which equals the energy required to raise the nucleus to the next quantum level.

11-5.3. Capture. In the case of capture with fission, a neutron reacts with a fissionable atom and is momentarily absorbed into the nucleus, which then may be unstable and split into two fission fragments and other particles. On occasion, it is possible that the excess neutron may not cause fissioning of the atom and an isotope is produced.

11-5.4. Absorption. The probability of absorption is greatly dependent on the energy of the neutron and the type of atom with which it collides. Cadmium, for example, has a very large probability for absorption of thermal neutrons, whereas U-238 is a strong absorber of higher energy neutrons.

11-6. NEUTRON REACTION RATE

It is evident from the above discussion that when a beam of ϕ neutrons / m²-sec is incident upon a 1-m cube of material the possible reactions occur with a particular probability. The average rate C at which each reaction takes place within the cube depends on the number of atoms N in the cube and also on the neutron flux ϕ. Therefore it may be written that

$$C = \sigma_r N \phi \text{ reactions/m}^3\text{-sec} \qquad (11\text{-}4)$$

where σ_r is the probability that the particular reaction takes place. Since σ_r has the dimensions of length squared, it is called the *cross-section* for the reaction. But it should be kept in mind that it represents the *probability* for a particular reaction. In general σ_r has a magnitude of the order of 10^{-28} m², and so a new unit of 1 barn = 10^{-28} m² is adopted.

The cross-sections for absorption and scattering for some elements are shown in Appendix B. It should be noted that these cross-sections are for neutrons at thermal (293°K) energies and should be corrected for other energies, as discussed later.

Since the number of atoms per unit volume is given by

$$N = \frac{N_0}{A} \rho \qquad (11\text{-}5)$$

where N_0 is Avogadro's number, and A and ρ the atomic weight and density of the material, respectively, Eq. 11-4 may be written as

$$C = \sigma_r \left(\frac{N_0 \rho}{A} \right) \phi \quad \text{reactions/m}^3\text{-sec} \qquad (11\text{-}6)$$

Example 11-2. A 1 cm by 0.5 cm by 0.1 cm sample of nickel is placed in a thermal neutron flux of 10^{15} neutrons/m²-sec. If the absorption cross-section σ_a is 4.6 barns, determine the rate at which neutrons are absorbed.

The number of neutrons absorbed per sec in a volume V is CV.

$$CV = \sigma_a \frac{N_0 \rho \phi}{A} V$$
$$= \frac{4.6 \times 10^{-28} \times 6.02 \times 10^{26} \times 8860 \times 10^{15} \times 0.05 \times 10^{-6}}{58.94}$$
$$= 2.08 \times 10^9 \text{ neutrons/sec}$$

11-7. VARIATIONS OF CROSS-SECTIONS WITH ENERGY

It is found near thermal energies that both the absorption and fission cross-sections vary inversely with the neutron velocity. This could be expected, since the probability of a neutron entering a nucleus should be proportional to the length of time the neutron is within the vicinity of the nucleus. The absorption cross-sections $(\sigma_a)_0$ given in Appendix B are for thermal neutrons with velocities of $v_0 = 2200$ m/sec. At any other velocity v the absorption cross-section σ_a for "1/v absorbers" may be determined from

$$\sigma_a = (\sigma_a)_0 \frac{v_0}{v}$$

or

$$\sigma_a = (\sigma_a)_0 \sqrt{\frac{E_0}{E}} \qquad (11\text{--}7)$$

where $E_0 = kT_0 = 8.6164 \times 10^{-5} \times 293 = 0.0253$ ev.

Some materials (U-238 being the most notable example) have large absorption cross-sections superimposed on the $1/v$ curve, at certain discrete values of E, as shown in Fig. 11–1. Such absorption resonances,

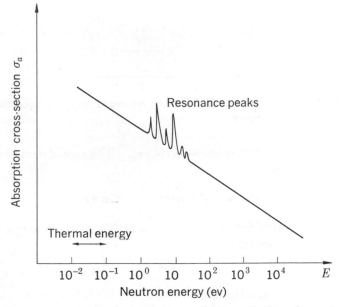

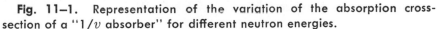

Fig. 11–1. Representation of the variation of the absorption cross-section of a "$1/v$ absorber" for different neutron energies.

or *resonance peaks*, appear at energies corresponding to those required to raise the nucleus to a higher quantum level.

Except at high energies, the scattering cross-section σ_s may be considered independent of E.

11–8. MACROSCOPIC CROSS-SECTION AND MEAN FREE PATH

The macroscopic cross-section Σ is given by $N\sigma$. It is the total cross-section associated with the N nuclei per unit volume, and therefore represents the probability of a neutron undergoing a reaction in passing through a cubic meter of the material.

Consider a uniform beam of neutrons ϕ_0, as in Fig. 11–2, entering a

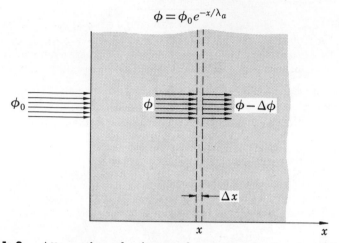

Fig. 11–2. Attenuation of a beam of neutrons due to absorption while passing through a material.

manerial with an absorption cross-section σ_a. The rate of neutron absorption in a distance dx is

$$d\phi = -N\sigma_a\phi\,dx = -\Sigma_a\phi\,dx$$

where ϕ is the neutron flux at x, and the negative sign indicates a decrease in flux. Upon integration

$$\phi = \phi_0 e^{-\Sigma_a x} \tag{11–8}$$

The mean free path λ_a is the distance in which $1/e$ of the incident neutrons remain unabsorbed and so

$$\lambda_a = \frac{1}{\Sigma_a} \tag{11–9}$$

and

$$\phi = \phi_0 e^{-x/\lambda_a} \tag{11–10}$$

The intensity of a beam of monoenergetic neutrons

$$I = \phi E_n \tag{11–11}$$

where E_n is the average neutron kinetic energy. In such a case the beam intensity after penetrating a distance x is

$$I = I_0 e^{-x/\lambda_a} \qquad (11\text{--}12)$$

where I_0 is the intensity of the beam at $x = 0$.

Example 11–3. What thickness of cadmium sheet is required to reduce the intensity of a monoenergetic 500 Mev/m²-sec beam of neutrons to 220 Mev/m²-sec if the incident neutron flux is 10^{10} neutrons/m²-sec and the number of scattering collisions is negligible compared to the number of absorption interactions?

The number of cadmium atoms per cubic meter is

$$N = \rho \frac{N_0}{A} = \frac{8650 \times 6.02 \times 10^{26}}{112} = 4.63 \times 10^{28}$$

The energy of the neutrons

$$E_{n0} = \frac{I_0}{\phi_0} = \frac{500 \times 10^6}{10^{10}} = 0.05 \text{ ev}$$

From Eq. 11–7, the absorption cross-section for the incident neutrons at 0.05 ev is

$$\sigma_a = 2450(0.0253/0.05)^{1/2} = 1740 \text{ barns}$$

The mean free path is

$$\begin{aligned}
\lambda_a &= \frac{1}{\Sigma_a} = \frac{1}{N\sigma_a} \\
&= \frac{1}{4.63 \times 10^{28} \times 1740 \times 10^{-28}} \\
&= 1.24 \times 10^{-4} \text{ m}
\end{aligned}$$

From Eq. 11–12, $I = I_0 e^{-h/\lambda_a}$ where h is the thickness of the cadmium sheet required. Therefore

$$\begin{aligned}
h &= \lambda_a \ln \frac{I_0}{I} \\
&= 1.24 \times 10^{-4} \ln \tfrac{500}{220} = 1.02 \times 10^{-4} \text{ m}
\end{aligned}$$

PROBLEMS

11–1. If P-31 undergoes the following reactions, write the nuclear equation in each case, and give the sign and magnitude of the Q of the reaction in Mev for case (a).

a. (n,p).
b. (n,d).
c. (α,n).
d. (α,2p).
e. (d,p + α).
f. (p,α).

11-2. One of the fission products of a U-235 fission is Y-94. If three prompt neutrons are also emitted, write the equation for the reaction.

11-3. The power requirements of a space craft are to be supplied by a nuclear reactor during a 437-day mission. If the average output power required is estimated to be 10 kw, calculate the mass of U-235 "burned up" during the mission, if 0.1 percent of the U-235 is converted into energy.

11-4. A nuclear reactor has been operating for a time period during which 0.5 percent of the fuel mass* has been fissioned. Initially the fuel consisted of 5680 kg of 2.3 percent enriched uranium. If the nuclear reactor is supplying power to a power station with an output of 250×10^3 kw, a 0.8 plant-utilization factor, and an overall efficiency of 27 percent, calculate the length of time for which the reactor has been operating since being fueled. Assume the average energy per fission is 202 Mev.

11-5. A monoenergetic, 7×10^4 Mev/m²-sec beam of neutrons impinges on a block of indium. If the neutron flux at the face of the block is 10^{11} neutrons/m²-sec, find

    a. The average neutron energy.
    b. The thickness of indium required to reduce the beam intensity to 40 Mev/m²-sec, assuming that the probability of scattering is negligible.
    c. What is the neutron flux after the neutrons have passed through the indium?

11-6. Repeat Prob. 11-5 for thermal neutrons with an incident flux of 10^{11} neutrons/m²-sec.

11-7. The maximum permissible neutron intensity level for the 0.1-ev neutrons, which are assumed emitted as a monoenergetic beam from the shielding around a nuclear reactor, is set at 0.18 Mev/m²-sec. Find the additional thickness of indium which should be placed about the reactor to reduce the radiation intensity to the permitted level if it is found that the existing neutron flux is 30×10^6 neutrons/m²-sec. State what assumptions you make regarding the relative dominance of absorption collisions.

* Fuel consists of both U-235 and U-238.

12

Reactor Theory

12-1. THE MULTIPLICATION FACTOR

The basic objective in the design of a controllable nuclear reactor is the ability to achieve equilibrium in the nuclear chain reaction. In other words, the reactor must be so designed, for steady-state operation, that on the average exactly a single neutron per fission remains available and causes a new fission. Such a desirable situation is expressed by saying the *multiplication factor*, or reproduction factor, k, is equal to unity.

Each fission which takes place within the reactor liberates about 200 Mev of energy, and therefore the more fission reactions which take place per unit time the greater the power produced. Obviously then, in order to increase the power output from a reactor, it is necessary to be able to increase the rate at which fission takes place. This may be done by increasing the existing neutron flux. Therefore it must be possible to make the multiplication factor k slightly greater than unity until the flux builds up to the new level.

When k is greater than unity, the increase of flux during the effective time of one neutron generation $\bar{l}$ is $\phi(k-1)$, and so

$$\frac{d\phi}{dt} = \frac{\phi(k-1)}{\bar{l}} \qquad (12\text{-}1)$$

where ϕ is the flux at time t, and $\bar{l}$ is the average effective lifetime of a generation of neutrons. That is to say in effect $\bar{l}$ is the average time between successive fissions in the chain reaction.

Integration of Eq. 12-1, gives

$$\phi = \phi_0 \exp\left[\frac{t(k-1)}{\bar{l}}\right] \qquad (12\text{-}2)$$

or

$$\boxed{\phi = \phi_0 \exp\left(\frac{tk_{\text{ex}}}{\bar{l}}\right)} \qquad (12\text{-}3)$$

where ϕ_0 is the neutron flux present initially, and the excess multiplication factor

$$k_{ex} \equiv k - 1 \qquad (12\text{--}4)$$

Example 12–1. If the average effective neutron lifetime in a reactor is 0.095 sec, how long must the multiplication factor be held at 1.004 if the center core neutron flux is to be increased from 10^{10} neutrons/m^2-sec to 10^{14} neutrons/m^2-sec?

The neutron flux will increase exponentially during a time t from ϕ_0 to ϕ, so that

$$\phi = \phi_0 \exp\left[\frac{tk_{ex}}{l}\right]$$

Therefore

$$10^{14} = 10^{10} \exp\left[\frac{t(1.004 - 1)}{0.095}\right]$$

which yields

$$t = 220 \text{ sec}$$

Therefore, after 220 sec the neutron flux will have increased to 10^{14} neutrons/m^2-sec; the multiplication factor should then be returned to a value of unity.

If the multiplication factor is less than unity, then the neutron flux decreases exponentially, as does the generated power. It is therefore by regulating the flux density in the reactor that its operation is controlled. Usually a material such as cadmium, with a large neutron absorption cross-section, is partially inserted to maintain the desired multiplication factor and flux density.

12–2. THE THERMAL NEUTRON FISSION CYCLE

There are two basic types of nuclear reactor: fast and thermal. If most of the fuel atoms are caused to undergo fission as a result of interaction with fast neutrons the reactor is called a *fast reactor;* however, if low-energy, or so-called *thermal neutrons*, cause most of the fission reactions then the reactor is said to be a *thermal reactor*. Since most of the reactors in operation and under construction are thermal, the neutron cycle for thermal neutron fission is now considered in some detail.

In both the thermal and fast reactor the neutrons released in fission are high-energy (about 2 Mev) particles. For operation as a thermal reactor the fast neutrons must be slowed until their mean kinetic energy is about 0.03 ev, which is equivalent to that of neutrons at room temperature. During the slowing-down process some of the neutrons may be lost by either leakage from the core, or absorption by materials in the core. Even after the neutrons have reached thermal energies, there is the probability that some will either leak from the reactor or be absorbed by some material before they enter a U-235 nucleus. It is convenient to represent the neutron cycle as in Fig. 12–1.

Assume that n neutrons, which are grouped as generation number 1, enter the uranium fuel together. Now the fuel is composed of both U-235 and U-238 atoms, so only a fraction of the neutrons which enter the fuel

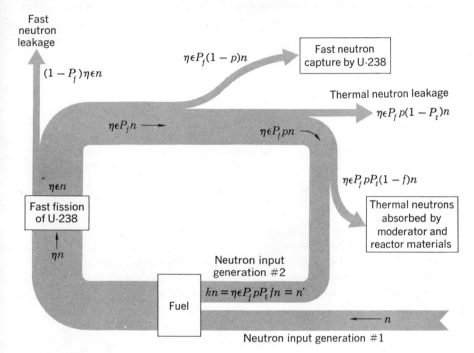

Fig. 12–1. Representation of the neutron cycle associated with the nuclear fission chain reaction.

cause fission of a U-235 nucleus. Some are absorbed by U-238 to form eventually Pu-239, some enter the U-235 nucleus and are captured to form U-236 without fission. The remainder cause fission.

Since the neutron cross-sections indicate the probability of a particular event taking place, the probability that a thermal neutron will cause fission after entering the fuel is given by

$$\frac{N^5 \sigma_f^5}{N^5 \sigma_a^5 + N^8 \sigma_a^8} = \frac{\sigma_f^5}{\sigma_a^5 + R_1 \sigma_a^8}$$

where $R_1 = N^8/N^5$, and superscripts 5 and 8 refer to U-235 and U-238, respectively.

In the case of the neutrons which are absorbed into U-235, some of them cause fission while others do not and are said to be *captured*. Consequently the probability of absorption is equal to the sum of the probability of capture and the probability of fission, so that

$$\sigma_a = \sigma_c + \sigma_f$$

Since ν is the *fast neutron yield per fission* (about 2.47 for U-235) the number of fast neutrons emitted as a result of each thermal neutron captured by the fuel is

$$\eta = \nu \frac{\sigma_f{}^5}{\sigma_a{}^5 + R_1 \sigma_a{}^8} \tag{12-5}$$

As shown in Fig. 12–1 ηn fast neutrons are produced by the n thermal neutrons which initially entered the fuel.

Since it is possible to cause fission of the U-238 nucleus with high-energy neutrons, some of the fast neutrons ejected from the U-235 nucleus cause U-238 fission, and so additional fast neutrons are added to the ηn neutrons produced from the U-235. Correction for this effect is made by the introduction of a *fast fission factor* ϵ. This is usually found to be about 1.03 for natural uranium. Therefore a total of $\eta \epsilon n$ fast neutrons are produced in the fuel. These neutrons must be thermalized, or slowed down, by impact with the atoms of the moderator.

During this process, however, some of the fast neutrons are lost from the cycle. The two loss processes are *leakage* and *absorption*. If the core is large, then the leakage loss is small. However, as the physical dimensions of the core are decreased the leakage loss rapidly rises. It also rises when a neutron must diffuse a considerable distance during the process of slowing down. It will be shown later that the probability of fast neutron loss P_f is given approximately by

$$P_f = \exp\left(-B^2 L_s{}^2\right) \tag{12-6}$$

where B^2 is called the *geometric buckling* and is dependent on the shape and physical dimensions of the core. $L_s{}^2$ (sometimes written as τ) is called the *Fermi age* and is actually one-sixth of the mean-square distance that fast neutrons travel while slowing down.

U-238 is mainly responsible for the capture of fast neutrons while slowing down. Such capture is termed *resonant absorption*. It is found that when the energy of an incident neutron is approximately equal to the energy required to excite the compound nucleus to a higher quantum state, then the probability of capture is greatly increased. As a result, if the capture cross-section for U-238 is plotted as a function of energy, sharp resonant peaks appear on the curve at energies in the ev range, as shown in Fig. 11–1. These peaks are superimposed on the uniform curve, which tends to vary inversely with the speed of the neutrons. A neutron usually undergoes a number of collisions before it is thermalized, and so its energy is decreased in a number of steps. If one of these steps leaves the neutron with an energy within the resonant region there is a high probability that this neutron will be absorbed and so removed from the cycle.

In the cycle under consideration, if p is the probability of avoiding resonant absorption by the U-238 (*resonant escape probability*), then the number of neutrons which reach thermal energy is

$$\eta \epsilon P_f p n$$

Although the neutron is now thermalized, and is ready to cause fission of a U-235 atom, it must still encounter one. Until it does so it is subject to loss either by leakage from the core or absorption by the core materials.

The *thermal utilization coefficient* f gives the ratio of neutrons absorbed in the fuel to the total absorbed, and may be determined from the absorption cross-sections and atom concentration.

$$
\begin{aligned}
f &= \frac{N^5\sigma_a{}^5 + N^8\sigma_a{}^8}{N^5\sigma_a{}^5 + N^8\sigma_a{}^8 + N^m\sigma_a{}^m} \\
&= \frac{\sigma_a{}^5 + R_1\sigma_a{}^8}{\sigma_a{}^5 + R_1\sigma_a{}^8 + R_2\sigma_a{}^m}
\end{aligned}
\tag{12-7}
$$

The $N^m\sigma_a{}^m$ term above is representative of the absorption in the core by materials other than uranium, and $R_2 = N^m/N^5$.

As in the case of fast neutrons, the probability of loss by leakage is dependent on the shape and dimensions of the core and also on the distance which a neutron travels after it becomes thermalized and before it is captured. In this case the probability of thermal neutron leakage P_t is shown later to be

$$P_t = \frac{1}{1 + B^2L^2} \tag{12-8}$$

where L is the *thermal diffusion length* of the neutrons in the core, and L^2 is one-sixth of the mean-square distance that neutrons travel after they have become thermalized and before they are captured.

The actual diffusion length L of neutrons in the presence of the absorbing fuel is considerably less than the diffusion length L_m of neutrons in the pure moderator. When the uranium is uniformly mixed throughout the moderator, the effective thermal diffusion length is determined to a good approximation by

$$L^2 = L_m{}^2(1 - f) \tag{12-9}$$

For example, in a graphite-moderated reactor where $L_m = 0.50$ m and $f = 0.9$, the actual diffusion length is reduced to $L = [0.25(1 - 0.9)]^{1/2} = 0.158$ m.

The number of thermal neutrons n' which avoid the absorption and leakage process and enter the fuel as a new generation of neutrons is therefore

$$n' = \eta \epsilon P_f p P_t f n \qquad (12\text{-}10)$$

The multiplication factor k relates the number of neutrons in one generation to those in the previous generation:

$$n' = kn$$

Therefore

$$\boxed{k = \eta \epsilon p f P_f P_t} \qquad (12\text{-}11)$$

When the reactor is operating at constant power, the numbers of neutrons in successive generations are equal and so

$$k = 1 = \eta \epsilon p f P_f P_t \qquad (12\text{-}12)$$

If the core were infinitely large there could be no leakage and so $P_f P_t = 1$. In such a theoretical situation the *infinite multiplication factor* is expressed as k_∞, and so

$$\boxed{k_\infty = \eta \epsilon p f} \qquad (12\text{-}13)$$

This equation is called the *"four-factor formula."* Since Eq. 12–11 takes leakage into account, k is termed the *effective multiplication factor* and often written as k_{eff}:

$$\begin{aligned} k_{\text{eff}} &= \eta \epsilon p f P_f P_t \\ &= k_\infty P_f P_t \end{aligned} \qquad (12\text{-}14)$$

It is seen that k_∞ is dependent on the type and configuration of materials used to form the reactor core. If this is found to be greater than unity then there exists a reactor of specific size for which

$$k_\infty P_f P_t = 1 \qquad (12\text{-}15)$$

Equation 12–15 permits the determination of the critical size of the core.

Therefore the calculation of the critical size of a reactor may be divided into two parts:

1. Determination of k_∞, which depends on the materials used and the fuel-moderator configuration, but is independent of the size and geometry of the core. k_∞ must be greater than unity.
2. Determination of the non-leakage probability $P_f P_t$, which depends both on the size and shape of the reactor, and on the diffusion lengths of neutrons during slowing down and while thermalized.

12–3. DIFFUSION THEORY

The power density at any point in a reactor core is dependent on the rate at which fission takes place there, which in turn is proportional to the neutron flux at that point. Since we are basically interested in power production, it is important to determine the concentration of neutrons throughout the reactor core. This is no easy task when it is realized that neutron generation, absorption, scattering, and diffusion occur simultaneously in any particular region. The task is further complicated by the fact that the neutrons present have a wide range of energies and the absorption cross-section is energy-dependent. However, a basic neutron-conservation law may be applied to any region:

$$\begin{bmatrix} \text{increase} \\ \text{in} \\ \text{neutrons} \end{bmatrix} = \begin{bmatrix} \text{neutron} \\ \text{generation} \end{bmatrix} - \begin{bmatrix} \text{neutron} \\ \text{leakage} \end{bmatrix} - \begin{bmatrix} \text{neutron} \\ \text{absorption} \end{bmatrix} \quad (12\text{–}16)$$

The Boltzmann transport equation expresses this law of conservation of neutrons and is similar to that developed for the motion of molecules in a gas. Due to the complexity of the reactor problem, the equation can be used satisfactorily only in very simple problems. It is therefore necessary to make some simplifying assumptions.

If it is assumed that the neutron makes a large number of collisions in a region, before being absorbed or escaping, then the transport equation reduces to the simpler diffusion equation as developed for the diffusion of heat in a conductor. The accuracy of diffusion theory may be improved considerably by applying correction factors derived from transport theory. In order to apply diffusion theory with any accuracy, three important requirements must be satisfied:

1. The region considered must be homogeneous.
2. The region considered must be large compared to the scattering mean free path λ_s.
3. The neutron flux must not vary appreciably over a distance λ_s.

The third requirement is satisfied if $\Sigma_a \ll \Sigma_s$, so that many neutrons are not absorbed in a distance equal to one scattering mean free path.

12–4. NEUTRON CURRENT DENSITY

To derive the diffusion equation it is first necessary to evaluate the neutron current density J. This is the number of neutrons which pass each second through a plane of one square meter's area.

Consider a plane of differential area dA located in the y plane as in Fig. 12–2. It is required to find the current density J passing through

dA from above. This may be done by finding the number of neutrons which have a collision in a differential volume dV and are scattered into the area dA, and then integrating over all space above the plane.

The number of neutrons having scattering collisions in volume dV per second is $\Sigma_s \phi \, dV$, where Σ_s is the macroscopic scattering cross-section,

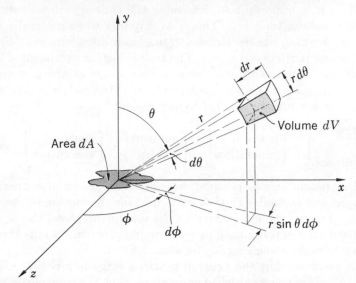

Fig. 12-2. Configuration for neutron diffusion current density calculation.

and $dV = r^2 \sin \theta \, dr \, d\theta \, d\phi$. Assume at present that the scattering is isotropic, that is to say, scattering in all directions is equally probable, then the number of neutrons reaching dA from dV without further collisions is

$$\Sigma_s \phi \, dV \, e^{-\Sigma_s r} \left(\frac{dA \cos \theta}{4\pi r^2} \right)$$

where it is assumed that loss by absorption is negligible over the distance r. Then the total number of neutrons passing through dA from above per second is

$$J_- \, dA = \int_0^\infty \int_0^{\pi/2} \int_0^{2\pi} \Sigma_s \, \phi \, e^{-\Sigma_s r} \left(\frac{dA \cos \theta}{4\pi r^2} \right) r^2 \sin \theta \, dr \, d\theta \, d\phi$$

and the number of neutrons passing through unit area per second from above is therefore

$$J_- = \frac{\Sigma_s}{4\pi} \int_0^\infty \int_0^{\pi/2} \int_0^{2\pi} \phi \, e^{-\Sigma_s r} \sin \theta \cos \theta \, dr \, d\theta \, d\phi \qquad (12\text{-}17)$$

Since the flux is a space variable $\phi(x,y,z)$, it may be approximated by the Taylor expansion, so that

$$\phi(x,y,z) = \phi(0,0,0) + x\left(\frac{\partial\phi}{\partial x}\right)_0 + y\left(\frac{\partial\phi}{\partial x}\right)_0 + z\left(\frac{\partial\phi}{\partial x}\right)_0 + \cdots \quad (12\text{--}18)$$

Upon substituting Eq. 12–18 into Eq. 12–17 and integrating:

$$J_- = \frac{\phi}{4} + \frac{1}{6\Sigma_s}\left(\frac{\partial\phi}{\partial y}\right) \quad (12\text{--}19)$$

Similarly, the neutron current density from below is

$$J_+ = \frac{\phi}{4} - \frac{1}{6\Sigma_s}\left(\frac{\partial\phi}{\partial y}\right) \quad (12\text{--}20)$$

and the net current density J_y in the y direction is

$$J_y = -\frac{1}{3\Sigma_s}\left(\frac{\partial\phi}{\partial y}\right) \quad (12\text{--}21)$$

A similar analysis for differential areas in the x and z planes gives

$$J_x = -\frac{1}{3\Sigma_s}\left(\frac{\partial\phi}{\partial x}\right) \quad (12\text{--}22)$$

$$J_z = -\frac{1}{3\Sigma_s}\left(\frac{\partial\phi}{\partial z}\right) \quad (12\text{--}23)$$

These current densities are based on diffusion theory and on the assumption of isotropic scattering; however, it is obvious that there will be preferential scattering in the direction of previous motion, and so the net current is in fact greater than that given directly by diffusion theory. The *correction factor* derived from transport theory is $1/(1-b)$, where b is the average cosine of the scattering angle and is found to be

$$b = \frac{2}{3A} \quad (12\text{--}24)$$

where A is the mass number of the scattering medium. The current density is

$$J_y = -\frac{1}{3\Sigma_s(1-b)}\left(\frac{\partial\phi}{\partial y}\right) = -\frac{1}{3\Sigma_t}\left(\frac{\partial\phi}{\partial y}\right) \quad (12\text{--}25)$$

Therefore $J_y = -D(\partial\phi/\partial y)$ where

$$\frac{1}{\Sigma_s(1-b)} = 1/\Sigma_t = \lambda_t$$

is the *transport mean free path*, and the *diffusion coefficient* is

$$D = \frac{1}{3\Sigma_t} = \frac{\lambda_t}{3} \quad (12\text{--}26)$$

The total current through any plane may be represented by the vector sum of the three x,y,z components:

$$J_x = -D \frac{\partial \phi}{\partial x} \qquad J_y = -D \frac{\partial \phi}{\partial y} \qquad J_z = -D \frac{\partial \phi}{\partial z}$$

or by

$$\boxed{\mathbf{J} = -D \nabla \phi} \tag{12-27}$$

where

$$\nabla = \mathbf{i} \frac{\partial}{\partial x} + \mathbf{j} \frac{\partial}{\partial y} + \mathbf{k} \frac{\partial}{\partial z}$$

12-5. NEUTRON DIFFUSION RATE

Having developed an expression for the neutron current density it is now possible to derive the neutron diffusion equation. Consider the differential volume $dV = dx\, dy\, dz$ in Fig. 12-3. If the number of neutrons entering the lower face per second is $J_y\, dx\, dz$ and the number leaving the upper face per second is $[J_y + (\partial J_y/\partial y)\, dy]\, dx\, dz$, the net outward flow rate

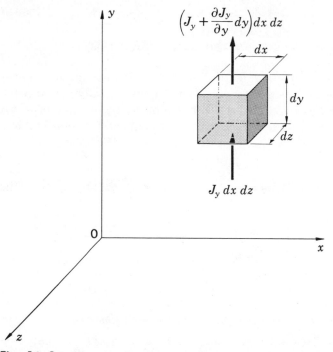

Fig. 12-3. Neutron leakage from an elemental volume.

of neutrons from the faces in the y plane is

$$\left(\frac{\partial J_y}{\partial y}\, dy\right) dx\, dz = -\frac{\partial}{\partial y}\left(D\,\frac{\partial \phi}{\partial y}\right) dx\, dy\, dz$$

$$= -D\,\frac{\partial^2 \phi}{\partial y^2}\, dV \qquad (12\text{--}28)$$

Similarly, the net flow rate of neutrons from the faces in the x and z planes is

$$-D\left(\frac{\partial^2 \phi}{\partial x^2}\right) dV \qquad \text{and} \qquad -D\left(\frac{\partial^2 \phi}{\partial z^2}\right) dV$$

respectively. Therefore the net leakage rate from the differential volume dV is

$$-D\left(\frac{\partial^2 \phi}{\partial x^2} + \frac{\partial^2 \phi}{\partial y^2} + \frac{\partial^2 \phi}{\partial z^2}\right) dV$$

neutron leakage per unit volume per second

$$= -D\left(\frac{\partial^2 \phi}{\partial x^2} + \frac{\partial^2 \phi}{\partial y^2} + \frac{\partial^2 \phi}{\partial z^2}\right) \qquad (12\text{--}29)$$

$$= -D\nabla^2 \phi \qquad (12\text{--}30)$$

where ∇^2 is the Laplacian operator (see Appendix C). Equation 12–30 is called a *diffusion equation*.

12–6. THE REACTOR EQUATION

The neutron conservation equation (Eq. 12–16) may now be applied. The rate of neutron absorption in a differential volume dV is $N\sigma_a\phi\, dV = \Sigma_a\phi\, dV$; and the rate of neutron generation is $S\, dV$, where S is the volumetric neutron source strength. Then, upon substituting for the terms in Eq. 12–16,

$$\left(\frac{dn}{dt}\right) dV = S\, dV - (-D\nabla^2\phi)\, dV - \Sigma_a\phi\, dV$$

or

$$\frac{dn}{dt} = S + D\nabla^2\phi - \Sigma_a\phi \qquad (12\text{--}31)$$

Under steady-state conditions $dn/dt = 0$; so

$$\nabla^2\phi - \frac{\Sigma_a}{D}\,\phi + \frac{S}{D} = 0 \qquad (12\text{--}32)$$

In applying Eq. 12–32 to a nuclear reactor problem, it must be realized that the neutrons within the reactor have a wide range of energies and so the reaction cross-sections are not the same for each neutron reaction. An approximate solution might be obtained by assuming that all the neutrons present in the system are at thermal energy. Such an assumption is made in the so-called "*one-group method*." Obviously, this is a radical assumption.

Improvement may be made by assuming that

$$\frac{D}{\Sigma_a} = M^2 = L_s^2 + L^2 \qquad (12\text{-}33)$$

where M is the *migration length* and is proportional to the distance traveled by a neutron from birth to capture, L_s^2 is called the *Fermi age* and is one-sixth of the mean-square distance traveled by a neutron in becoming thermalized, and L is the *thermal diffusion length*, which is the square root of one-sixth of the mean-square distance traveled by a neutron between becoming thermalized and capture.

For a homogeneous reactor, the fast neutron source term S in Eq. 12-32 may be expressed as

$$S = k_\infty \phi \Sigma_a \qquad (12\text{-}34)$$

Since $\phi \Sigma_a$ expresses the rate of neutron absorption, and k_∞ represents the number of neutrons produced per neutron absorbed, substituting Eq. 12-34 in Eq. 12-32 gives

$$\nabla^2 \phi - \frac{\Sigma_a}{D} \phi + \frac{\Sigma_a}{D} k_\infty \phi = 0$$

or

$$\nabla^2 \phi + \frac{1}{M^2} (k_\infty - 1) \phi = 0$$

or

$$\boxed{\nabla^2 \phi + B^2 \phi = 0} \qquad (12\text{-}35)$$

where B^2 is called the *buckling* of the reactor. (The term "buckling" originates from a similar equation for the buckling of an axially loaded column.) Equation 12-35 is called the *wave* or sometimes the *reactor equation*. Since

$$B^2 = \frac{k_\infty - 1}{M^2} \qquad (12\text{-}36)$$

and is expressed in terms of the nuclear properties of the core materials, B in this case is called the *material buckling*, and is equal to the *geometric buckling* of Eq. 12-6 and Eq. 12-8 when the reactor is critical. From Eq. 12-36

$$\frac{k_\infty}{1 + M^2 B^2} = 1 \qquad (12\text{-}37)$$

Since $M^2 = L_s{}^2 + L^2$, and since the initial assumptions indicate that $B^2 \ll L_s{}^2$ or L^2, Eq. 12–37 may be closely approximated by

$$\frac{k_\infty}{1 + B^2(L_s{}^2 + L^2) + L_s{}^2 L^2 B^4} = \frac{k_\infty}{(1 + B^2 L_s{}^2)(1 + B^2 L^2)} = 1 \quad (12\text{–}38)$$

or approximately by

$$k_\infty(e^{-B^2 L_s{}^2}) \left(\frac{1}{1 + B^2 L^2}\right) = 1 \quad (12\text{–}39)$$

Comparing Eq. 12–39 with Eq. 12–15 and associating the leakage coefficients indicates that under critical conditions

$$\boxed{P_f = e^{-B^2 L_s{}^2}} \quad (12\text{–}40)$$

$$\boxed{P_t = \frac{1}{1 + B^2 L^2}} \quad (12\text{–}41)$$

It is therefore possible to evaluate the fast and thermal leakage probabilities from a knowledge of the slowing-down and thermal diffusion lengths, and the *reactor buckling B*.

The buckling may be determined for reactors of different shapes by solving the reactor equation Eq. 12–35.

12–7. REACTOR BUCKLING

From Eq. 12–35 and Appendix C, the reactor equation for a rectangular core is

$$\frac{\partial^2 \phi}{\partial x^2} + \frac{\partial^2 \phi}{\partial y^2} + \frac{\partial^2 \phi}{\partial z^2} + B^2 \phi = 0 \quad (12\text{–}42)$$

In order to solve Eq. 12–42 it is assumed that the variables x, y, and z are separable, that is to say, that the flux distribution in the x direction is not dependent on the flux distribution in the y or z directions. Then let

$$\phi = X(x) \, Y(y) \, Z(z)$$

or

$$\phi = XYZ \quad (12\text{–}43)$$

Substituting for ϕ in Eq. 12–42 gives

$$YZ \frac{\partial^2 X}{\partial x^2} + XZ \frac{\partial^2 Y}{\partial y^2} + XY \frac{\partial^2 Z}{\partial z^2} + B^2 XYZ = 0 \quad (12\text{–}44)$$

or

$$\frac{1}{X} \frac{\partial^2 X}{\partial x^2} + \frac{1}{Y} \frac{\partial^2 Y}{\partial y^2} + \frac{1}{Z} \frac{\partial^2 Z}{\partial z^2} + B^2 = 0 \quad (12\text{–}45)$$

Since the x, y, and z terms are independent, the only non-trivial solution to Eq. 12–45 is obtained when each term is a constant. Therefore let

$$\frac{1}{X}\frac{d^2X}{dx^2} = -\alpha^2 \qquad (12\text{--}46)$$

$$\frac{1}{Y}\frac{d^2Y}{dy^2} = -\beta^2 \qquad (12\text{--}47)$$

$$\frac{1}{Z}\frac{d^2Z}{dz^2} = -\gamma^2 \qquad (12\text{--}48)$$

where α, β, and γ are constants. Then Eq. 12–45 yields

$$B^2 = \alpha^2 + \beta^2 + \gamma^2 \qquad (12\text{--}49)$$

The next step is to apply boundary conditions and solve Eqs. 12–46, 12–47 and 12–48 for α, β, and γ. Consider Eq. 12–46:

$$\frac{d^2X}{dx^2} + \alpha^2 X = 0 \qquad (12\text{--}50)$$

which has the solution

$$X = C_1 \cos \alpha x + C_2 \sin \alpha x \qquad (12\text{--}51)$$

Assuming a symmetrical flux distribution with the origin at the core center, $C_2 = 0$, so that

$$X = C_1 \cos \alpha x \qquad (12\text{--}52)$$

which indicates a cosinusoidal flux distribution along the x axis.

Since there is neutron leakage from the core, the flux density at the edge must be greater than zero. If the neutron current density leaking from the core in the x direction is J_+, then from Eq. 12–20,

$$J_+ = \frac{\phi}{4} - \frac{\lambda_t}{6}\left(\frac{\partial \phi}{\partial x}\right) \qquad (12\text{--}53)$$

Assuming there is no neutron reflector present, the neutron current density going into the core from outside may be considered zero, so

$$J_- = \frac{\phi}{4} + \frac{\lambda_t}{6}\left(\frac{\partial \phi}{\partial x}\right) = 0 \qquad (12\text{--}54)$$

and hence

$$\frac{d\phi}{dx} = -\frac{3}{2}\frac{\phi}{\lambda_t} \qquad (12\text{--}55)$$

It is convenient to assume that the flux density becomes zero at some distance λ_e outside the edge of the core. This distance is found by linearly extrapolating the flux density distribution of Fig. 12–4. Since the slope is known from Eq. 12–55, the flux density extrapolates to zero

at a distance

$$\lambda_e = \tfrac{2}{3}\lambda_t \qquad (12\text{–}56)$$

from the edge of the core.   A more accurate analysis gives

$$\lambda_e = 0.71\lambda_t \qquad (12\text{–}57)$$

It should be kept in mind that it is only for theoretical convenience that the flux density is assumed to go to zero at a distance λ_e from the edge of

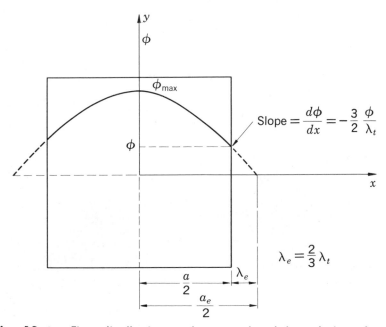

Fig. 12–4. Flux distribution and extrapolated boundaries of a rectangular reactor core.

the core.   When calculations involving core dimensions arise, a length λ_e is added on to the actual physical dimensions, and the simple boundary condition of zero flux density at the extrapolated boundaries is assumed.

In the case of the rectangular core under consideration, the extrapolated distance from the center of the core is

$$\frac{a_e}{2} = \frac{a}{2} + \lambda_e \qquad (12\text{–}58)$$

and so the boundary condition for Eq. 12–45 is that $\phi = 0$, for $x = a_e/2$. Therefore

$$C_1 \cos\left(\frac{\alpha a_e}{2}\right) = 0$$

If the flux is to be finite and positive throughout the core $\alpha a_e/2 = \pi/2$. Therefore,

$$\alpha = \frac{\pi}{a_e} \tag{12-59}$$

Similarly,

$$\beta = \frac{\pi}{b_e} \tag{12-60}$$

and

$$\gamma = \frac{\pi}{c_e} \tag{12-61}$$

where b_e and c_e are the extrapolated lengths in the y and z directions, respectively. Then the buckling from Eq. 12–49 is

$$B^2 = \left(\frac{\pi}{a_e}\right)^2 + \left(\frac{\pi}{b_e}\right)^2 + \left(\frac{\pi}{c_e}\right)^2 \tag{12-62}$$

The buckling may be determined similarly for other geometries. For example, for the spherical core of extrapolated radius R_e,

$$B^2 = \left(\frac{\pi}{R_e}\right)^2 \tag{12-63}$$

and for a cylindrical core of extrapolated height H_e and radius R_e,

$$B^2 = \left(\frac{\pi}{H_e}\right)^2 + \left(\frac{2.405}{R_e}\right)^2 \tag{12-64}$$

Example 12–2. A cubical reactor core is to be constructed from a homogeneous mixture of uranium and a graphite moderator in the ratio of 500 carbon atoms to 1 uranium atom. The uranium is 10 atomic percent enriched. If the fast fission factor $\epsilon = 1.01$ and the resonant escape probability $p = 0.87$, determine if it is possible to construct a critical assembly under these conditions. If it is, calculate the size of such an unreflected cubical critical assembly. What masses of carbon and uranium are required?

It is possible to construct a critical assembly under the above conditions only if the infinite multiplication factor k_∞ is greater than unity. Since $k_\infty = \eta \epsilon p f$, it is necessary to determine the two unspecified parameters η and f.

From Eq. 12–5,

$$\eta = \nu \frac{\sigma_f{}^5}{\sigma_a{}^5 + R_1 \sigma_a{}^8}$$

Since the enrichment of the uranium is 10 atomic percent, there are nine U-238 atoms present for each U-235 atom and so $R_1 = 9$, and $\nu = 2.47$. Therefore

$$\eta = \frac{2.47 \times 582}{683 + 9 \times 2.75} = 2.04$$

From Eq. 12–7,

$$f = \frac{\sigma_a{}^5 + R_1\sigma_a{}^8}{\sigma_a{}^5 + R_1\sigma_a{}^8 + R_2\sigma_a{}^m}$$

Since $N^m = 500(N^5 + N^8)$

$$\frac{N^m}{N^5} = 500\left(1 + \frac{N^8}{N^5}\right)$$

and

$$R_2 = 500(1 + 9) = 5000$$

therefore,

$$f = \frac{683 + (2.75 \times 9)}{683 + (2.75 \times 9) + (5000 \times 0.0045)} = 0.96921$$

Therefore

$$k_\infty = \eta\epsilon pf = 2.04 \times 1.01 \times 0.87 \times 0.969$$
$$= 1.74$$

Since k_∞ is greater than unity, it is possible to assemble a critical mass.

In a thermal homogeneous reactor where the moderator is evenly distributed L_s may be taken to be the same as for the pure moderator, and so from Appendix B, $L_s{}^2 = 0.035$ m². From Eq. 12–9, the effective thermal diffusion length squared is given by

$$L^2 = L_m{}^2(1 - f)$$

where $L_m{}^2 = 0.25$ m² for graphite. Therefore

$$L^2 = 0.25(1 - 0.96921) = 7.7 \times 10^{-3} \text{ m}^2$$

and so from Eq. 12–38

$$\frac{1.74}{1 + B^2(0.035 + 0.0077) + 0.035 \times 7.7 \times 10^{-3}B^4} = 1$$

which gives

$$B^2 = 15.7 \text{ m}^{-2}$$

For a cubical core, Eq. 12–62 gives

$$15.7 = 3\left(\frac{\pi}{a_e}\right)^2$$

and hence $a_e = 1.372$ m, which is the extrapolated length of the cube side.

From Eq. 12–58 the actual length is

$$a = a_e - 2\lambda_e$$

where λ_e is 0.71 times the transport mean free path λ_t. From Eq. 12–25 and

Eq. 12–24,

$$\lambda_t = \frac{1}{\Sigma_s \left(1 - \dfrac{2}{3A}\right)} = \frac{1}{N\sigma_s \left(1 - \dfrac{2}{3A}\right)}$$

$$= \frac{A}{\rho N_0 \sigma_s \left(1 - \dfrac{2}{3A}\right)}$$

So for graphite,

$$\lambda_t = \frac{12}{1650 \times 6.02 \times 10^{26} \times 4.8 \times 10^{-28} \times \left(1 - \dfrac{2}{3 \times 12}\right)}$$

$$= 0.0267 \text{ m}$$

Therefore

$$a = 1.372 - (2 \times 0.0267 \times 0.71) = 1.334 \text{ m} = 4.38 \text{ ft}$$

Therefore a 4.38-ft cube, assembled from the specified materials, is the critical size of the core and a self-sustaining fission cycle is possible.

The number of atoms per cubic meter in the core is

$$N = \frac{N_0 \rho_{av}}{A_{av}}$$

where the average core density is

$$\rho_{av} = \frac{N^5 \rho^5 + N^8 \rho^8 + N^m \rho^m}{N^5 + N^8 + N^m}$$

$$= \frac{\rho^5 + R_1 \rho^8 + R_2 \rho^m}{1 + R_1 + R_2}$$

and similarly the average atomic weight

$$A_{av} = \frac{A^5 + R_1 A^8 + R_2 A^m}{1 + R_1 + R_2}$$

Therefore

$$N = N_0 \left(\frac{\rho^5 + R_1 \rho^8 + R_2 \rho^m}{A^5 + R_1 A^8 + R_2 A^m}\right)$$

$$= 6.02 \times 10^{26} \times 10^3 \left[\frac{18.68 + (9 \times 18.68) + (5000 \times 1.65)}{235.1 + (9 \times 238) + (5000 \times 12)}\right]$$

$$= 0.815 \times 10^{29} \text{ atoms/m}^3$$

Of these a fraction

$$\frac{N^5}{N^5 + N^8 + N^m} = \frac{1}{1 + R_1 + R_2}$$

are U-235 atoms. Therefore

$$N^5 = N \frac{1}{1 + R_1 + R_2}$$

and in the case of a volume V,

$$\text{mass of U-235 present} = \left(\frac{VN^5}{N_0}\right) A^5 = \frac{VNA^5}{N_0(1 + R_1 + R_2)}$$
$$= \frac{(1.334)^3 \times 0.815 \times 10^{29} \times 235}{6.02 \times 10^{26}(1 + 9 + 5000)}$$
$$= 15.03 \text{ kg}$$

Since $N^8/N^5 = 9$,

$$\frac{M^8}{M^5} = \frac{N^8 A^8}{N^5 A^5} = 9 \times \frac{238}{235} = 9.12$$

Therefore mass of U-238 required = $9.12 \times 15.03 = 137.5$ kg. The mass of graphite required is obtained from

$$\frac{M^m}{M^5} = \frac{N^m}{N^5} \cdot \frac{A^m}{A^5} = R_2 \frac{A^m}{A^5} = 5000 \times \frac{12}{235} = 255$$

mass of graphite required = $255 \times 15.03 = 3840$ kg

mass of uranium required = $15.03 + 137.5 = 152.5$ kg

It should be kept in mind that the above calculations are based upon an approximated theory, and provide only a rough estimate of the size of core required, and the amount of material involved. Such a calculation is, however, most important in the initial design of a reactor. When the general dimensions are known, it is then possible to go to more refined techniques and develop a precise and detailed design.

In practice it must be possible to make the system supercritical, while the reactor is being started, or while the power level is being increased. Therefore the core is built slightly larger than that required for criticality and the excess reactivity is compensated by control rods, which absorb the excess neutrons.

The availability of excess reactivity is also important during the operating lifetime of a core of fuel. Since the fissile material is being consumed during operation, the excess reactivity continually decreases, and so the greater the initial excess reactivity, the longer is the lifetime of the core.

Excess reactivity is also important in overcoming transient fission product poisoning, particularly that of xenon, when the reactor must be restarted after shut-down for a period of between 3 to about 30 hours.

The excess reactivity usually provided is about 0.007, so that the actual size of the core required is determined for an effective multiplication factor of $k_{eff} = 1.007$.

While Example 12-2 demonstrates the basic approach to reactor design, a number of assumptions were made, which are not typical in practice. For example, no reflector was considered, which would reduce neutron leakage and so permit a smaller critical mass. Also, most reactors are heterogeneous, in that the fuel is distributed throughout the moderator in the form of lumps or rods of uranium. Such an arrangement increases the resonant escape probability, since neutrons with a resonant energy are captured in the outer layers of the fuel element and the uranium near the center "sees" few resonant neutrons and so is effectively isolated from those neutrons, which it could capture.

12–8. EFFECT OF REFLECTOR

Most cores are surrounded by a material, frequently the same as the moderator material, which is a poor neutron absorber, but a good neutron

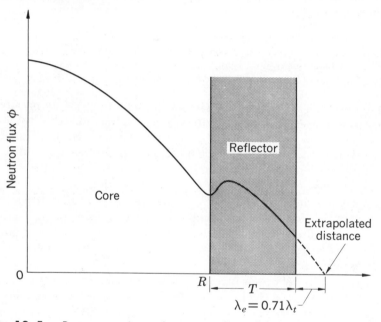

Fig. 12–5. Representation of reactor flux distribution in a reflected core.

reflector.   The neutron leakage from the core is significantly reduced and as a result the critical mass is reduced.   The effectiveness of the reflector is expressed by δ, *the reflector savings*, which is the amount by which the reflector reduces the critical extrapolated dimensions.

To study the effect of the reflector, consider the mathematically simple case of a spherical reflected core of radius R surrounded by a reflector of thickness T, and extrapolated thickness T_e ($= T + 0.71\lambda_t$) as shown in Fig. 12–5.

If subscripts r and c correspond to reflector and core, respectively, then the neutron flux must satisfy the steady-state diffusion equation (Eq.

12–32), and so

$$\nabla^2\phi_c + B^2\phi_c = 0 \qquad \text{for } r \leq R \qquad (12\text{–}65)$$

$$\nabla^2\phi_r - \frac{1}{L_r^2}\phi_r = 0 \qquad \text{for } R \leq r \leq R + T \qquad (12\text{–}66)$$

Since the reflector contains no fuel, Eq. 12–66 is derived from the diffusion equation

$$D_r\nabla^2\phi_r - \Sigma_{ar}\phi_r = 0$$

Both Eq. 12–65 and Eq. 12–66 are subject to the boundary conditions which require

1. ϕ continuous across the boundary, $\phi_c(R) = \phi_r(R)$.
2. The net neutron current density normal to boundary should be continuous.
3. ϕ finite and positive at all points for $r \leq R + T_e$.
4. $\phi = 0$ at extrapolated boundary of reflector, i.e., at $r = R + T_e$.

In the case of the spherical system under consideration, Eq. 12–65 becomes (using the Laplacian of a scalar from Appendix C)

$$\frac{d^2\phi_c}{dr^2} + \frac{2}{r}\left(\frac{d\phi_c}{dr}\right) + B^2\phi_c = 0 \qquad (12\text{–}67)$$

Equation 12–67 may be reduced to a differential equation with constant coefficients if v/r is substituted for ϕ_c. Thus

$$\frac{d^2v}{dr^2} + B^2v = 0 \qquad (12\text{–}68)$$

which has the solution

$$v = A_1\sin Br + A_2\cos Br \qquad (12\text{–}69)$$

or

$$\phi_c = \frac{A_1\sin Br}{r} + \frac{A_2\cos Br}{r} \qquad (12\text{–}70)$$

where A_1 and A_2 are arbitrary constants. If ϕ_c is to be finite at $r = 0$, then $A_2 = 0$, and Eq. 12–70 reduces to

$$\phi_c = \frac{A_1\sin Br}{r} \qquad (12\text{–}71)$$

Equation 12–66 is similarly solved, but due to the difference in sign, hyperbolics are involved, so that

$$\phi_r = \frac{C_1}{r}\sinh\left[\frac{1}{L_r}(C_2 - r)\right] \qquad (12\text{–}72)$$

where C_1 and C_2 are arbitrary constants.

For $\phi_r(R + T_e) = 0$,

$$\sinh\left[\frac{1}{L_r}(C_2 - R - T_e)\right] = 0 \qquad (12\text{-}73)$$

or

$$C_2 = R + T_e$$

Therefore

$$\phi_r = \frac{C_1}{r}\sinh\left(\frac{R + T_e - r}{L_r}\right) \qquad (12\text{-}74)$$

For $\phi_c(R) = \phi_r(R)$, Eq. 12-71 and Eq. 12-74 give

$$A_1\frac{\sin BR}{R} = \frac{C_1}{R}\sinh\left(\frac{T_e}{L_r}\right) \qquad (12\text{-}75)$$

For continuity of current density

$$D_c\frac{d\phi_c}{dr}\bigg|_{r=R} = D_r\frac{d\phi_r}{dr}\bigg|_{r=R}$$

and therefore

$$D_cA_1\left(\frac{B\cos BR}{R} - \frac{\sin BR}{R^2}\right) = D_rC_1\left(-\frac{1}{RL_r}\cosh\frac{T_e}{L_r} - \frac{1}{R^2}\sinh\frac{T_e}{L_r}\right)$$
$$(12\text{-}76)$$

Dividing Eq. 12-76 by Eq. 12-75 gives

$$\boxed{D_c(1 - BR\cot BR) = D_r\left(1 + \frac{R}{L_r}\coth\frac{T_e}{L_r}\right)} \qquad (12\text{-}77)$$

This transcendental equation permits the evaluation of the critical radius for a specified thickness of reflector, since the geometric buckling B, D_c, and D_r may be calculated from the properties of the core materials.

In many cases the reflector is made from the same material as the core moderator and $D_c \approx D_r$, so Eq. 12-77 reduces to

$$-BL_r\cot BR = \coth\frac{T_e}{L_r} \qquad (12\text{-}78)$$

Further simplification may be achieved by noting that the *reflector savings* are

$$\delta \equiv R_e - R$$

where R_e is the extrapolated radius of a bare core spherical reactor. From Eq. 12-63, such a bare reactor becomes critical when $B = \pi/R_e$. Therefore

$$R = \frac{\pi}{B} - \delta \qquad (12\text{-}79)$$

Substituting Eq. 12–79 in Eq. 12–78 gives

$$-BL_r \cot (\pi - B\delta) = \coth \frac{T_e}{L_r}$$

and

$$BL_r \cot B\delta = \coth \frac{T_e}{L_r}$$

or

$$\tan B\delta = BL_r \tanh \frac{T_e}{L_r}$$

Therefore

$$\delta = \frac{1}{B} \tan^{-1} \left(BL_r \tanh \frac{T_e}{L_r} \right) \qquad (12\text{–}80)$$

Under our initial assumptions $R \gg L_r$ and hence both B and L_r are small, so to a close approximation

$$\delta = L_r \tanh \frac{T_e}{L_r} \qquad (12\text{–}81)$$

It is important to note that, for a thick reflector, T_e/L_r is large and $\tanh (T_e/L_r)$ approaches unity. So the reflector savings for a thick reflector is given by

$$\delta \approx L_r \qquad (12\text{–}82)$$

Hence it appears that little is to be gained by making the thickness of the reflector much greater than the thermal diffusion length. More exact calculations indicate that a reflector thickness of about 1.5 times the migration length is effectively equivalent to an infinite reflector.

The equation for reflector savings derived for the spherical core closely approximates that for other geometries, providing the cores are large compared to the migration length. The equations for the critical dimensions of spherical, cubic, and cylindrical cores are therefore as follows:

sphere
$$\boxed{B^2 = \left(\frac{\pi}{R_e} \right)^2 = \left(\frac{\pi}{R + \delta} \right)^2} \qquad (12\text{–}83)$$

cube
$$\boxed{B^2 = 3\left(\frac{\pi}{a_e} \right)^2 = 3\left(\frac{\pi}{a + 2\delta} \right)^2} \qquad (12\text{–}84)$$

cylinder
$$\boxed{B^2 = \left(\frac{\pi}{H_e} \right)^2 + \left(\frac{2.405}{R_e} \right)^2 = \left(\frac{\pi}{H + 2\delta} \right)^2 + \left(\frac{2.405}{R + \delta} \right)^2} \qquad (12\text{–}85)$$

It may also be shown that when the reflector is not made from the same material as the core moderator, the reflector savings may be approximated by

$$\delta = \frac{D_c}{D_r} L_r \tanh \frac{T_e}{L_r} \tag{12-86}$$

A reflector, in addition to reducing the critical size of a reactor, also tends to equalize the flux density throughout the core by reflecting neutrons into the circumferential regions where otherwise the flux density would be low. This is important, since the power density within the core is then more uniform and hence more power may be extracted from a given volume. This effect is termed *flux flattening*, and may be further increased by non-uniform material distribution.

Example 12–3. If a core with the same composition as considered in Example 12–2 is surrounded by a 4.11-cm layer of beryllium, what are the new dimensions of the core and what is the mass of uranium used?

The thermal diffusion length in beryllium is 0.208 m. The transport mean free path is

$$\lambda_{tr} = \frac{1}{\Sigma_{sr}(1 - b)}$$

in which $\Sigma_{sr} = 86.1$ m^{-1} and $(1 - b) = 0.9259$. Therefore

$$\lambda_{tr} = \frac{1}{86.1 \times 0.9259} = 0.0125 \text{ m}$$

and

$$T_e = T + 0.71 \lambda_{tr} = 0.0411 + (0.71 \times 0.0125)$$
$$= 0.05 \text{ m}$$

From Eqs. 12–86 and 12–26,

$$\delta = \frac{D_c}{D_r} L_r \tanh \frac{T_e}{L_r} = \frac{\lambda_{tc}}{\lambda_{tr}} L_r \tanh \frac{T_e}{L_r}$$

Therefore, since $\lambda_{tc} = 0.0267$ m from Example 12–2,

$$\delta = \frac{0.0267}{0.0125} \times 0.208 \tanh \frac{0.05}{0.208} = 0.1047 \text{ m}$$

The extrapolated length a_e of the bare cube side was found to be 1.372 m; and so with the beryllium reflector the actual length, from Eq. 12–84, is

$$a = a_e - 2\delta = 1.372 - (2 \times 0.1047) = 1.163 \text{ m}$$

This gives a core volume reduction of $(1.334)^3 - (1.163)^3 = 0.788$ m^3, which corresponds to a net volume reduction of 33 percent. Therefore the mass of uranium saved is $152.5 \times 0.33 = 50.3$ kg.

This example demonstrates the importance of the reflector. It should be noted that a thin beryllium reflector was used only to demonstrate the computation process, and in practice the more logical choice would be a graphite reflector.

12-9. SLOWING DOWN OF NEUTRONS

The neutrons liberated at fission have energies of the order of 10 Mev and, to be effective in causing additional fission reactions, they must be

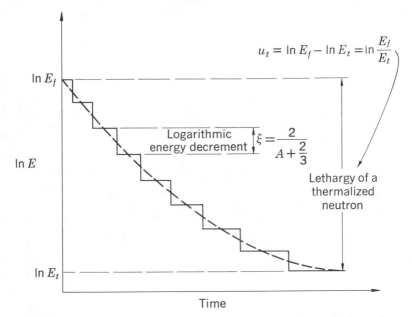

$$u_t = \ln E_f - \ln E_t = \ln \frac{E_f}{E_t}$$

Logarithmic energy decrement $\xi = \dfrac{2}{A + \dfrac{2}{3}}$

Lethargy of a thermalized neutron

Time

Fig. 12-6. Exponential approximation to step-wise variation of energy with time during the slowing down to thermal energies of a group of fast neutrons.

slowed to energies of the order of 10^{-2} ev. During the slowing-down, or thermalization, process, a fraction of the neutrons are lost from the fission process either by absorption or leakage from the core. In order to investigate their loss it is first necessary to examine the slowing-down process itself.

If the average neutron energy at fission is E_f (approximately 10 Mev), this will be dissipated in a number of collisions n_f in slowing down to thermal energies ($E_t \sim 0.025$ ev). Although the neutron loses its energy in a series of steps as shown in Fig. 12-6, it is convenient to consider the energy-loss rate as a continuous process. This is a good approximation for graphite and heavier moderators where n_f is large. Since the energy loss per collision is dependent on the neutron energy before colliding, it is convenient to express the energy in a logarithmic form and to define a quantity u called the *lethargy*, as

$$u = \ln E_f - \ln E = \ln \frac{E_f}{E} \qquad (12\text{-}87)$$

Therefore an average neutron at fission has zero lethargy, since $E = E_f$, whereas a thermal neutron has a lethargy of $u_t = \ln \dfrac{E_f}{E_t}$.

Although the logarithmic decrease in neutron energy per collision varies widely, a mean value ξ, called the *logarithmic energy decrement*, may be determined for a particular moderator; this is approximated by

$$\xi = \frac{2}{A + \frac{2}{3}} \qquad (12\text{-}88)$$

where A (>2) is the atomic weight of the moderator, and, as would be expected, the average loss of energy per collision is low when the atomic weight of the moderator is large.

The total number of collisions n_f, during the slowing-down process may now be calculated. Since the mean logarithmic energy decrement is ξ,

$$n_f = \frac{\ln E_f - \ln E_t}{\xi} \qquad (12\text{-}89)$$

and so

$$n_f = \frac{1}{\xi} \ln \frac{E_f}{E_t} \qquad (12\text{-}90)$$

12-10. RESONANCE ESCAPE PROBABILITY IN THE HOMOGENEOUS REACTOR

The resonance escape probability p was previously defined as the probability that a neutron would avoid resonance absorption by U-238 while slowing down. The accurate theoretical calculation of p is difficult, and so usually a simple theoretical analysis is combined with the use of empirical parameters.

Consider first of all the homogeneous reactor with a mixture of uranium and a moderator. It is assumed that U-238 is accountable for the resonant neutron absorption and that the probability of absorption may be expressed in terms of a cross-section $\sigma^8(u)$, which is dependent on the lethargy of the neutrons. The average value of the cross-section during the slowing-down process is then

$$\bar{\sigma}^8 = \frac{\displaystyle\int_0^{u_t} \sigma^8(u)\, du}{u_t}$$

or in terms of neutron energy

$$\bar{\sigma}^8 = \frac{-\int_{E_f}^{E_t} \sigma^8(E)\, dE/E}{\ln\,(E_f/E_t)} \tag{12-91}$$

since $u = \ln E_f/E$ and $du = -dE/E$.

For a density of N^8 atoms of U-238 per unit volume, the macroscopic cross-section for resonance absorption is

$$\Sigma_a = N^8\bar{\sigma}^8 \tag{12-92}$$

and from Eq. 11–9 the average absorption mean free path is

$$\bar{\lambda}_a = \frac{1}{N^8\bar{\sigma}^8} \tag{12-93}$$

Thus if s is the average distance a neutron travels in slowing down, the resonance escape probability is

$$p = \exp\,(-s/\bar{\lambda}_a) = \exp\,(-N^8\bar{\sigma}^8 s) \tag{12-94}$$

Since a neutron makes n_f collisions on the average while slowing down, and the scattering mean free path $\lambda_s = 1/\Sigma_s$, the total distance traveled is

$$s = \frac{n_f}{\Sigma_s} \tag{12-95}$$

and, substituting for n_f from Eq. 12–90,

$$s = \frac{1}{\Sigma_s \xi} \ln \frac{E_f}{E_t} \tag{12-96}$$

Substituting Eqs. 12–91 and 12–96 in Eq. 12–94 gives

$$p = \exp\left[-N^8 \frac{\int_{E_t}^{E_f} \sigma^8(E)\, dE/E}{\ln\,(E_f/E_t)} \cdot \frac{1}{\Sigma_s \xi} \ln \frac{E_f}{E_t}\right] \tag{12-97}$$

or

$$p = \exp\left[-\frac{N^8 \int_{E_t}^{E_f} \sigma^8(E)\, dE/E}{\Sigma_s \xi}\right] \tag{12-98}$$

This equation does not take into account the fact that due to resonance absorption the flux at the resonance energies is depressed, and so in fact the resonance escape probability is greater than that in Eq. 12–98. Therefore the equation is usually modified to

$$p = \exp\left[-\frac{N^8 \left(\int_{E_t}^{E_f} \sigma^8(E)\, dE/E\right)_{\text{eff}}}{\Sigma_s \xi}\right] \tag{12-99}$$

or

$$p = \exp\left(-\frac{N^8 \sigma_e}{\Sigma_s \xi} \right) \tag{12–100}$$

where

$$\sigma_e = \left(\int_{E_t}^{E_f} \sigma^8(E) \; dE/E \right)_{\text{eff}} \tag{12–101}$$

is the effective resonance integral and is determined empirically.

Experimental results for homogeneous mixtures of UO_2 and moderators such as graphite, D_2O, and water indicate that for $\Sigma_s/\Sigma^8 < 10^3$ the effective resonance integral may be closely approximated by

$$\sigma_e = 180 \left(\frac{\Sigma_s}{N^8} \right)^{0.415} \text{ barns} \tag{12–102}$$

where Σ_s is in per-meter units and N^8 is the number of U-238 atoms per cubic meter, and the limiting value is 240 barns at great dilution.

12–11. RESONANCE ESCAPE PROBABILITY IN THE HETEROGENEOUS REACTOR

It was realized at an early stage that the resonance escape probability could be significantly increased if rods of fuel were distributed throughout the moderator to form a core lattice as shown in Fig. 12–7a. The U-238 at the surface of the rods absorbs the neutrons at resonant energies, so that the flux penetrating the fuel is devoid of resonant neutrons and the resonance capture rate is reduced.

Consider the lattice shown in Fig. 12–7, in which the uranium is in the form of cylindrical rods distributed uniformly throughout the moderator. In heterogeneous lattice calculations it is convenient to isolate one lattice cell and consider it as a cylinder of fuel of volume V^F surrounded by an equivalent cylindrical volume of moderator V^M. Since the average resonance flux in the fuel $\bar{\phi}_R{}^F$ and that in the moderator $\bar{\phi}_R{}^M$ are not the same, the resonance escape probability, as determined for the homogeneous system, must be corrected for both flux and volumetric differences. It is found that a simple ratio correction applied to the effective resonance integral is satisfactory, so that for a heterogeneous system

$$p \approx \exp\left[-\frac{V^F}{V^M} \cdot \frac{\bar{\phi}_R{}^F}{\bar{\phi}_R{}^M} \cdot \frac{N^8 \left(\int_{E_t}^{E_f} \sigma^8(E) \frac{dE}{E} \right)_{\text{eff}}}{\Sigma_s \xi} \right] \tag{12–103}$$

and the effective resonance integral is given by the empirical relationship

$$\left(\int_{E_t}^{E_f} \sigma^8(E) \frac{dE}{E} \right)_{\text{eff}} = 9.25 \left(1 + 26.7 \frac{S}{M} \right) \text{ barns} \tag{12–104}$$

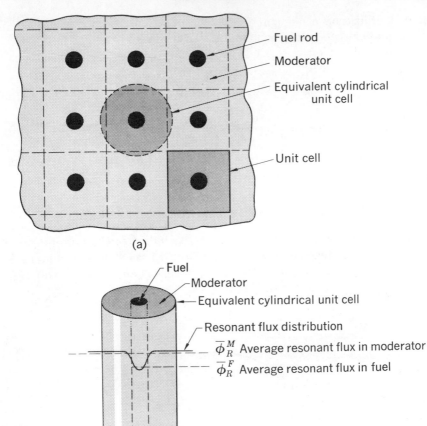

Fig. 12-7. (a) Heterogeneous lattice assembly. (b) Resonant neutron flux distribution in a unit cell.

where S is the "rubber-band" surface area of the fuel element in square meters and M is its mass in kilograms.

The ratio $\bar{\phi}_R{}^M/\bar{\phi}_R{}^F$ in Eq. 12-103 is called the *disadvantage factor* for resonance neutrons.

12-12. THERMAL UTILIZATION IN THE HETEROGENEOUS REACTOR

Due to the difference in average thermal flux between $\bar{\phi}^F$ and $\bar{\phi}^M$, in the fuel and moderator respectively, the expression for the homogeneous thermal utilization coefficient f must be modified. The rate at which absorption takes place is dependent on the flux density and on the moderator-to-fuel volume ratio, so Eq. 12–7 becomes

$$f = \frac{(N^5\sigma_a{}^5 + N^8\sigma_a{}^8)V^F\bar{\phi}^F}{(N^5\sigma_a{}^5 + N^8\sigma_a{}^8)V^F\bar{\phi}^F + N^M\sigma_a{}^M V^M\bar{\phi}^M}$$

or

$$f = \frac{1 + R_1(\sigma_a{}^8/\sigma_a{}^5)}{1 + R_1(\sigma_a{}^8/\sigma_a{}^5) + R_2R(\sigma_a{}^M/\sigma_a{}^5)(\bar{\phi}^M/\bar{\phi}^F)} \tag{12–105}$$

where $R_1 = N^8/N^5$, $R_2 = N^M/N^5$, and $R = V^M/V^F$, and $\bar{\phi}^M/\bar{\phi}^F$ is called the *disadvantage factor* for thermal neutrons.

12–13. OPTIMIZATION OF THE MODERATOR TO FUEL RATIO

Examination of Eqs. 12–103 and 12–105 indicates that lumping the fuel causes an increase in p and a decrease in f, as shown in Fig. 12–8, and therefore for a specified fuel element there is an optimum value for the quantity of moderator in the unit cell.

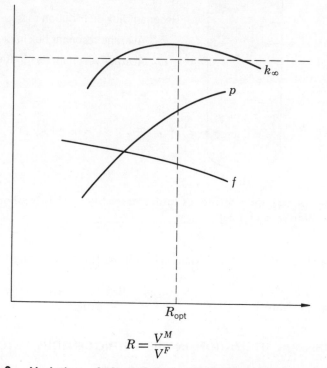

$$R = \frac{V^M}{V^F}$$

Fig. 12–8. Variation of the infinite multiplication factor, the resonant escape probability, and the thermal utilization coefficient with the moderator-fuel volume ratio in a heterogeneous reactor.

In order to optimize the ratio R, Eq. 12–105 is written as

$$f = \frac{A}{A + RC} \qquad (12\text{–}106)$$

where

$$A = 1 + R_1 \frac{\sigma_a{}^8}{\sigma_a{}^5} \qquad (12\text{–}107)$$

and

$$C = R_2 \frac{\sigma_a{}^M}{\sigma_a{}^5} \cdot \frac{\bar{\phi}^M}{\bar{\phi}^F} \qquad (12\text{–}108)$$

Since

$$\Sigma_s = N^M \sigma_s{}^M \qquad \left(\int_{E_t}^{E_f} \sigma^8(E) \frac{dE}{E} \right)_{\text{eff}} = \sigma_e$$

Eq. 12–103 becomes

$$p \approx \exp\left(- \frac{V^F}{V^M} \cdot \frac{\bar{\phi}_R{}^F}{\bar{\phi}_R{}^M} \cdot \frac{N^8}{N^M} \cdot \frac{\sigma_e}{\sigma_s{}^M} \cdot \frac{1}{\xi} \right) \qquad (12\text{–}109)$$

or

$$p \approx e^{-G/R} \qquad (12\text{–}110)$$

where

$$G = \frac{\bar{\phi}_R{}^F}{\bar{\phi}_R{}^M} \frac{R_1}{R_2} \frac{1}{\xi} \frac{\sigma_e}{\sigma_s{}^M} \qquad (12\text{–}111)$$

Substituting Eq. 12–106 and Eq. 12–110 in Eq. 12–13 gives

$$k_\infty = \eta \epsilon e^{-G/R} \left(\frac{A}{A + RC} \right) \qquad (12\text{–}112)$$

Evaluating dk_∞/dR and setting the result equal to zero gives

$$\eta \epsilon e^{-G/R} \left(\frac{G}{R^2} \right) \left(\frac{A}{A + RC} \right) - \eta \epsilon e^{-G/R} \left[\frac{AC}{(A + RC)^2} \right] = 0$$

and therefore

$$R^2 - RG - \frac{GA}{C} = 0 \qquad (12\text{–}113)$$

Solving Eq. 12–113 gives

$$\boxed{ R_{\text{opt}} = \frac{1}{2} \left(G + \sqrt{G^2 + 4\frac{AG}{C}} \right) } \qquad (12\text{–}114)$$

With the aid of Eq. 12–114 it is therefore possible to determine the optimum quantity of moderator required, once the enrichment and configuration of the fuel element have been specified.

12–14. FAST FISSION FACTOR FOR THE HETEROGENEOUS REACTOR

In the heterogeneous system there is little likelihood of a fast neutron causing fast fission of U-238 in a neighboring fuel element, since it would

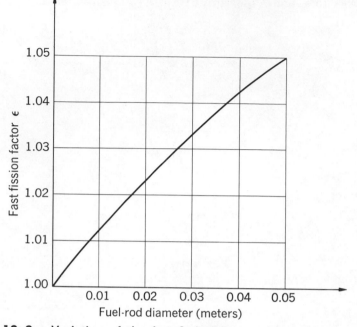

Fig. 12–9. Variation of the fast fission factor with the fuel rod diameter for a uranium-graphite reactor.

be slowed down during migration. Therefore the process of fast fission is independent of lattice pitch, but is found to vary with the diameter of the fuel rod as shown in Fig. 12–9 for a typical uranium-graphite reactor.

Example 12–4. A cubical, heterogeneous, graphite-moderated thermal reactor is to be designed so that the effective multiplication factor at start-up is 1.007. The uranium to be used is in the form of 2.5-cm-diameter rods, enriched 2.3 percent by weight. A 9.11-cm graphite reflector encloses the core. If the average moderator-to-fuel neutron flux ratio is 1.14 and 1.46 for resonance and thermal neutrons, respectively, determine

(a) The optimum moderator-to-fuel volume ratio.
(b) The core size, using the optimum volume ratio determined in (a).
(c) The dimensions of a unit cell.
(d) The number of uranium rods required.
(e) The total mass of uranium and graphite required.

(a) The optimum moderator-to-fuel volume ratio R is given by Eq. 12–114. It is therefore necessary to evaluate the parameters required for the determination of A, C, and G (i.e., R_1, R_2, ξ, σ_e). The enrichment of the fuel is 2.3 percent by weight and so the weight fraction (WF) of U-235 present is

$$WF = 0.023$$

$$R_1 = \frac{N^8}{N^5} = \frac{\text{number of U-238 atoms per m}^3 \text{ of uranium}}{\text{number of U-235 atoms per m}^3 \text{ of uranium}}$$

where

$$N^8 = (1 - WF) \frac{N_0}{A^8} \rho^8$$

and

$$N^5 = WF \frac{N_0}{A^5} \rho^5$$

Therefore

$$R_1 = \frac{N^8}{N^5} = \left(\frac{1 - WF}{WF}\right)\left(\frac{A^5}{A^8}\right)\left(\frac{\rho^8}{\rho^5}\right)$$

$$= \frac{1 - 0.023}{0.023} \times \frac{235}{238} = 42$$

$$R_2 = \frac{N^M}{N^5} = \frac{N_0}{A^M} \rho^M \cdot \frac{A^5}{(WF)N_0\rho^5} = \frac{\rho^M A^5}{(WF)\rho^5 A^M}$$

$$= \frac{1.65 \times 235}{0.023 \times 18.68 \times 12} = 75.2$$

From Eq. 12–88,

$$\xi = \frac{2}{A + \frac{2}{3}} = \frac{2}{12 + 0.67} = 0.158$$

From Eq. 12–104,

$$\sigma_e = 9.25 \left(1 + 26.7 \frac{S}{M}\right) = 9.25 \left(1 + 26.7 \frac{\pi D4}{\pi D^2 \rho^F}\right)$$

$$= 9.25 \left(1 + 26.7 \times \frac{4}{18.68 \times 10^3 \times 2.5 \times 10^{-2}}\right) = 11.4 \text{ barns}$$

From Eq. 12–107,

$$A = 1 + 42 \times \frac{2.75}{683} = 1.169$$

From Eq. 12–108,

$$C = \frac{4.5 \times 10^{-3}}{683} \times 1.46 \times 75.2 = 7.25 \times 10^{-4}$$

From Eq. 12–111,

$$G = \frac{1}{1.14} \times \frac{42}{75.2} \times \frac{1}{0.158} \times \frac{11.4}{4.8} = 7.38$$

The optimum moderator-to-fuel ratio may now be determined from Eq. 12–114:

$$R_{\text{opt}} = \frac{1}{2}\left[7.38 + \sqrt{7.38^2 + \frac{4 \times 1.169 \times 7.38}{7.25 \times 10^{-4}}}\right] = 113$$

(b) Since

$$k_{\text{eff}} = k_\infty P_f P_t = \frac{k_\infty}{1 + M^2 B^2}$$

the buckling, and hence the core size, may be determined once k_∞ and M^2 are evaluated. From Eq. 12–5

$$\eta = \nu \frac{\sigma_f{}^5}{\sigma_a{}^5 + R_1\sigma_a{}^8} = 2.47 \times \frac{582}{683 + (42 \times 2.75)}$$
$$= 1.81$$

From Fig. 12–9, for a fuel rod of diameter 0.025 m,

$$\epsilon = 1.029$$

From Eq. 12–110,

$$p = \exp\,(-G/R) = \exp\,(-7.38/113) = 0.937$$

From Eq. 12–106,

$$f = \frac{A}{A + RC} = \frac{1.169}{1.169 + (113 \times 7.25 \times 10^{-4})} = 0.9347$$

From Eq. 12–13,

$$k_\infty = 1.81 \times 1.029 \times 0.937 \times 0.9347 = 1.63114$$

From Eq. 12–33 and Eq. 12–9,

$$M^2 = L_s{}^2 + L_m{}^2(1 - f)$$
$$= 0.035 + 0.25(1 - 0.9347) = 5.13 \times 10^{-2}\,\text{m}^2$$

Therefore, since

$$k_{\text{eff}} = \frac{k_\infty}{1 + M^2B^2}$$
$$B^2 = \frac{k_\infty - k_{\text{eff}}}{M^2 k_{\text{eff}}} = \frac{1.63114 - 1.007}{5.13 \times 10^{-2} \times 1.007} = 12.03\,\text{m}^{-2}$$

From Eq. 12–84,

$$a + 2\delta = \sqrt{3}\,\pi/B = \sqrt{3}\pi/3.46 = 1.572\,\text{m}$$

From Eq. 12–81,

$$\delta = L_r \tanh \frac{T + 0.71\,\lambda_t}{L_r}$$
$$= 0.5 \tanh \frac{0.0911 + (0.71 \times 0.0267)}{0.5} = 0.1084\,\text{m}$$

and so

$$a = 1.572 - 0.2168 = 1.355\,\text{m}$$

(c) The dimensions of a unit cell may be determined from the ratio R_{opt}. If the fuel rods are the same length as the core, then

$$R_{\text{opt}} = \frac{V^M}{V^F} = \frac{l^2 - \pi D^2/4}{\pi D^2/4} = 113$$

where l is the lattice pitch, or the length of a square unit cell side, and D is the diameter of the fuel rod. This relationship gives $l = 0.236$ m. Therefore a unit cell has a length of 1.355 m and a square cross-section of side 0.236 m. The 2.5-cm-diameter uranium rod is positioned centrally in the cell.

(d) The number of uranium rods required is

$$\frac{V^F}{V^{\text{rod}}} = \frac{a^3}{1 + R_{\text{opt}}} \cdot \frac{4}{\pi a D^2} = \frac{4}{\pi(1 + R_{\text{opt}})} \left(\frac{a}{D}\right)^2$$

$$= \frac{4}{\pi(1 + 113)} \left(\frac{1.355}{0.025}\right)^2 = 32.9$$

(e) The mass of uranium required is

$$M^F = V^F \rho^F = \frac{a^3 \rho^F}{1 + R_{\text{opt}}} = \frac{(1.355)^3 \times 18.68 \times 10^3}{114}$$

$$= 409 \text{ kg}$$

total mass of graphite = mass of graphite in core + mass of reflector

$$= \left[\frac{a^3 R_{\text{opt}}}{1 + R_{\text{opt}}} + (a + 2T)^3 - a^3\right] \rho^M$$

$$= \left\{\frac{2.49 \times 113}{114} + [1.355 + (2 \times 0.0911)]^3 - 1.355^3\right\} 1650$$

$$= 5910 \text{ kg}$$

It must be realized that Example 12–4 illustrates only the procedure involved in a preliminary calculation. However, such a calculation is most important as one of the steps in the design of a nuclear reactor. Subsequent to an analysis similar to that in Example 12–4, it would be appropriate to conduct a thermal analysis of the system. Since the power which a reactor can deliver is governed by the rate at which thermal energy can be removed, it is necessary to ascertain that it is possible to transfer this quantity of heat without exceeding the thermal limits of the materials involved. If such an initial thermal analysis proves satisfactory, then a more detailed nuclear analysis should be conducted, in which account should be taken of the proposed fuel rod configuration and the addition of a coolant circulating through the fuel.

When theoretical calculations have been taken to practical limits, it is usual to construct and test a subcritical assembly composed of the proposed lattice, from which it is possible to predict fairly accurately the size of the critical assembly. If such tests are in agreement with the theoretical calculations of the critical size, then it is assumed that the analysis is accurate and the design of the system may be brought to a conclusion.

PROBLEMS

12–1. Calculate η, the number of fast neutrons produced as a result of each neutron capture, if the fuel is 10 atomic percent enriched uranium.

12–2. Repeat Prob. 12–1 for 99 atomic percent enriched uranium.

12–3. Calculate the thermal utilization factor f in a homogeneous graphite moderated reactor, if the graphite to uranium mass ratio is 200:1, and 10 atomic percent enriched uranium is used.

12–4. Repeat Prob. 12–3 for 99 atomic percent enriched uranium.

12–5. What is the minimum limiting value of the resonant escape probability p for a chain reaction if the fast fission factor is 1.005 and the conditions in Prob. 12–1 and Prob. 12–3 pertain?

12–6. Repeat Prob. 12–5 for 99 atomic percent enriched uranium if the fast fission factor is unity.

12–7. Show for a highly enriched fuel that criticality is achieved when

$$\frac{N^M}{N^5} \approx \left[\frac{\eta \exp{(-B^2 L_s^2)} - 1}{1 + B^2 L_m^2} \right] \left(\frac{\sigma_a^5}{\sigma_a^m} \right)$$

where $\epsilon = p \approx 1$.

12–8. A nuclear reactor for space use is to have a core of cylindrical form with maximum diameter of 0.6 m and height 0.6 m. If the fuel is pure U-235 and the moderator is ZrH_2, as an initial estimate, calculate the maximum permissible atomic moderator to fuel ratio for criticality of a homogeneous unreflected system. Comment on the accuracy of your result in light of the small dimension of the core.

12–9. Repeat Prob. 12–8 for the case of a cylindrical core surrounded with a 5-cm Be reflector, where the external dimensions of the reflector are again limited to a height of 0.6 m and a diameter of 0.6 m. What is the percentage decrease in the mass of uranium required as a result of using a reflector?

12–10. The core of a spherical reactor is to be fabricated from a homogeneous mixture of U-235 and Be in an atomic ratio of 1:10,000 respectively, and surrounded by a 0.1-m-thick Be reflector. Find the radius of the critical core.

12–11. A cubical, heterogeneous, graphite-moderated thermal reactor is to be designed so that the effective multiplication factor is 1.006. The fuel is in the form of 2.0-cm-diameter uranium rods, enriched 3.0 percent by weight, and a 0.15-m graphite reflector surrounds the core. If the average moderator to fuel neutron flux ratio is 1.12 and 1.31 for resonance and thermal neutrons respectively, determine

a. The optimum moderator to fuel ratio.
b. The core size using the optimum volume ratio determined in (a).
c. The dimensions of a unit cell.

12–12. Find the number of fuel rods and the total mass of the uranium and graphite required for the reactor described in Prob. 12–11.

12–13. Repeat Prob. 12–11 and Prob. 12–12 for a Be moderator and reflector.

13

Nuclear Reactors and Their Control

Although nuclear reactors are designed for uses other than the generation of power, consideration in this chapter is given specifically to the nuclear reactor as an energy converter, which converts nuclear energy into thermal energy, and so provides a heat source for either a conventional steam plant or a direct converter which converts the thermal energy into electrical energy.

13–1. NUCLEAR REACTOR SYSTEMS

Numerous reactor system concepts have evolved during recent years, ranging from the small liquid-metal-cooled SNAP 10A reactor system (Fig. 5–9) developed to provide a 300-watt electrical power supply for use in space, to the large gas-cooled reactors the British are building, such as the Hinkley Point power plant shown in Fig. 13–1 which has two gas-cooled reactors producing a net electrical output of 500 Mw.

In fact, there is considerable choice when the three basic thermal reactor components (fuel, moderator, and coolant) are being selected. Three fissile materials of different nuclear species are available. The choice of components is governed by numerous considerations ranging from the reactor application to the economics of power production. Two design proposals for equivalent plants at the same location may differ considerably and it is difficult to conclude that one is better than the other when such vague variables as safety and future fuel reprocessing costs are taken into consideration.

In the United States most of the installed nuclear capacity uses enriched uranium, and ordinary water as both the moderator and coolant. This capacity is subdivided into *pressurized* and *boiling water* reactors.

13–1.1. Pressurized Water Reactors. The design conditions and operating characteristics of all the pressurized water reactors are quite similar. All have a coolant temperature of about 550°K and operating

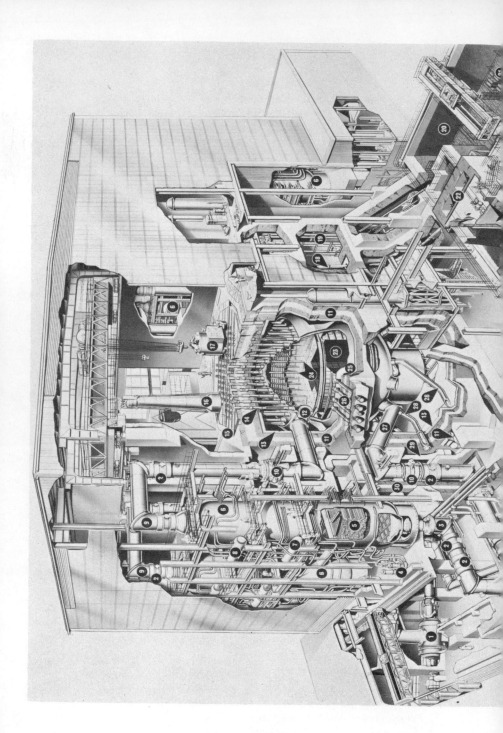

1. Coolant-gas circulating blowers
2. Hinged expansion bellows
3. Coolant-gas outlet from steam-raising unit
4. Steam-raising unit circulating pumps
5. Stud-tube elements
6. Steam-raising units (six per reactor)
7. Low-pressure steam drum
8. High-pressure steam drum
9. Coolant-gas inlet to steam-raising unit
10. Coolant-gas isolating valves
11. Main biological shield
12. Coolant-gas outlet from reactor
13. Thermal shield
14. Charge tubes
15. Charge floor

16. Hole-preparation machine
17. Charge and discharge machine
18. Emergency discharge chute
19. Spent fuel-element skip hoist
20. Cooling pond
21. Storage skips and grid
22. Skip loading bays
23. Graphite-moderator core
24. Control rod
25. Reactor pressure vessel
26. Can-failure detection standpipes
27. Coolant-gas inlet to reactor
28. Debris-removal ducts
29. Shield cooling-air ducting
30. Secondary biological shield

Fig. 13–1. Cutaway diagram of Hinkley Point gas-cooled nuclear power plant, England. (Courtesy of United Kingdom Atomic Energy Authority.)

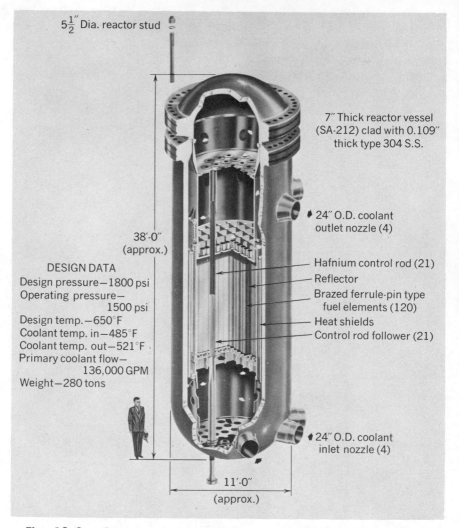

$5\frac{1}{2}''$ Dia. reactor stud

7" Thick reactor vessel
(SA-212) clad with 0.109"
thick type 304 S.S.

24" O.D. coolant
outlet nozzle (4)

38'-0"
(approx.)

Hafnium control rod (21)
Reflector
Brazed ferrule-pin type
fuel elements (120)
Heat shields
Control rod follower (21)

DESIGN DATA
Design pressure—1800 psi
Operating pressure—
1500 psi
Design temp.—650°F
Coolant temp. in—485°F
Coolant temp. out—521°F
Primary coolant flow—
136,000 GPM
Weight—280 tons

24" O.D. coolant
inlet nozzle (4)

11'-0"
(approx.)

Fig. 13–2. Cutaway drawing of the Con Edison thorium pressurized reactor which was designed and manufactured by The Babcock & Wilcox Co. (Courtesy of Con Edison.)

pressures between 1500 and 2000 psi. The enriched uranium fuel is in most cases in the form of uranium oxide pellets clad in stainless steel or zirconium. The only major differences occur in the arrangement of the components and plant layout.

Figure 13–2 shows a cutaway drawing of the Con Edison thorium pressurized reactor. The thermal output of the reactor is 585 Mw and the 120 fuel elements are fabricated from a mixture of 1100 kg of 93 percent enriched uranium oxide and 17,000 kg of thorium oxide. The fuel is clad in 20.5-mill, stainless steel. Fuel composition is varied within the fuel elements and also throughout the reactor in order to provide more uniform power production within the core, and so increase the average-to-peak fuel burn-up ratio. The 21 control rods are cruciform in design and have sections containing hafnium, which acts as the neutron absorber, or *poison*.

The coolant water enters through four 0.61 m-diameter nozzles at the base of the pressure vessel, flows axially through the core and leaves

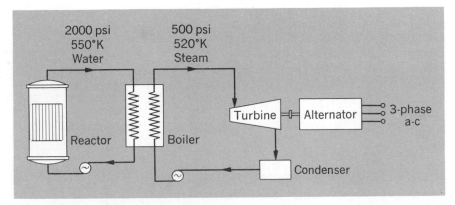

Fig. 13–3. Basic pressurized water reactor system, showing typical temperatures and pressures.

through four similar nozzles near the top of the vessel. Figure 13–3 shows the basic pressurized water reactor system with typical temperatures and pressures.

Many so-called package pressurized water reactors have been developed to provide the U.S. Army with portable power plants to produce both electric power and space heat and meet military base requirements. Such a plant is typified by the PM-24 at Camp Century, east of Thule in Greenland. The power plant is located in tunnels in the icecap, and produces 1.5 Mw of electricity and 10^6 Btu/hour of space heat. The entire plant breaks down into 27 air-transportable packages. The operation of an equivalent conventional plant under similar conditions would require over 15,000 barrels of oil each year.

Both the United States cargo-passenger ship, N.S. *Savannah* and the Russian icebreaker *Lenin* use pressurized water reactors. The N.S. *Savannah* has one reactor producing a thermal power of 69 Mw, while the *Lenin* has three reactors arranged abreast across the beam of the ship, each delivering a thermal output of 90 Mw.

13–1.2. Boiling Water Reactors. Unlike the pressurized water reactors, boiling of the coolant is permitted within the reactor itself. Initially it was felt that the formation of steam voids within the core might create instabilities; however, examination of transient phenomena in the first experimental boiling reactor, the BORAX I, indicated that, although the design of such a reactor is more complicated, stability can be achieved.

The generation of steam within the reactor itself has many advantages.

1. A direct coolant cycle may be used, as in Fig. 13–4, where the steam is produced and even superheated (as in the Pathfinder plant, Sioux Falls,

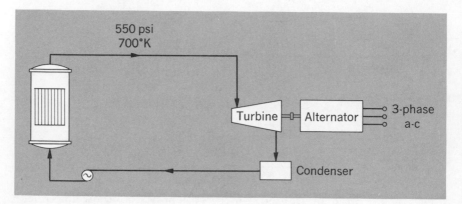

550 psi
700°K

Turbine — Alternator — 3-phase a-c

Condenser

Fig. 13–4. Basic boiling water reactor direct superheat cycle system.

S.D.) within the reactor. The intermediate heat exchange boiler between reactor and turbine is of course eliminated.

2. The pressure required within the reactor vessel is reduced from a typical value of 2000 psi in the pressurized reactor to about 500 psi in the boiling reactor.

3. Due to natural circulation and the direct cycle, pumping power is reduced by about a factor of five.

Boiling water reactors lend themselves to several other different operating cycles from the indirect cycle Elk River plant in Minnesota, to the dual cycle of the Bodega Bay plant in California, in which part of the steam is generated at intermediate pressure in a flash tank through which water from the reactor circulates. This cycle serves to improve the control characteristics of the system.

13–1.3. Other Reactor Concepts. Of the numerous other reactor concepts, perhaps the two most important are the gas-cooled and the liquid-metal-cooled systems.

The gas-cooled reactor concept has been developed extensively by the

British from the first commercial nuclear power plant at Calder Hall, in 1956, to the large 1000-Mw plant at Wylfa Head. Initially the concept was selected because of its potential for development as a power reactor as well as its plutonium production capacity. The fuel for these reactors has been natural uranium, since the British did not have recourse to the enriched uranium initially available only in the United States and the Soviet Union. Due to the large critical size of an unenriched core, the large surface area, required when a gas coolant is used, is easily provided. A total of 11 reactors of the Calder Hall type are in operation or under construction. All are indirect-cycle, cooled by carbon dioxide, and graphite-moderated. The more recently designed reactors operate at exit gas pressures and temperatures of about 350 psi and 700°K, respectively.

Due to the reaction of carbon dioxide with the graphite moderator at temperatures in excess of about 800°K, it has been found necessary to use an inert gas as the coolant in the more advanced *high-temperature gas-cooled reactors*. For example, the 40 Mw Peach Bottom plant in Pennsylvania uses an indirect cycle with helium at an outlet temperature and pressure of 1040°K and 350 psi, respectively. High-temperature, gas-cooled reactors are also being developed for rocket, aircraft, and ship propulsion as well as for mobile power plants.

In contrast to the gas-cooled reactors, liquid metal (Na, NaK, or Li) cooled reactors are being developed which operate at low pressures, and due to the excellent thermal properties of liquid metals, require a minimum of pumping power. The Hallam reactor in Nebraska operates at a coolant pressure and temperature of 20 psi and about 800°K, respectively, while the first fast breeder reactor, the Enrico Fermi, at Lagoona Beach, Mich., operates under 120-psi pressure and a coolant outlet temperature of 710°K.

The liquid-metal-cooled reactor is an appropriate power source for direct conversion devices such as the thermoelectric and MHD generators. Due also to the excellent heat transfer properties of the coolant, operation at a high specific power is possible. Consequently, small, lightweight (~700 kg) reactors for operation in space have been developed in the Systems for Nuclear Auxiliary Power (SNAP) program. The coolant is a eutectic mixture of sodium and potassium (22 wt. % Na and 78 wt. % K). The components of the 114-kg SNAP 10A reactor are shown in Fig. 13–5.

The fuel and moderator (U-235 and zirconium hydride) are in the form of a homogeneous mixture enclosed in thin-walled *Hastelloy* tubes which have beryllium slugs as reflectors at each end. The core measures only 0.3 m high and 0.23 m in diameter, and is surrounded by a 0.05-m radial reflector. Control of the reactor is achieved through angular rotation of

(a) Fuel element

(b) Core

(c) Reflector

(d) Reactor (top view)

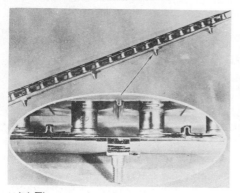

(e) Thermoelectric converter module

(f) Thermoelectric pump

Fig. 13–5. Components of the SNAP 10A nuclear reactor and thermoelectric converter. (Courtesy of Atomics International, a division of
North American Aviation, Inc.)

two semicylindrical beryllium elements in the reflector wall. Emergency shutdown is achieved by complete separation of the reflector from the core, as a result of ground command or re-entry heating.

The conversion of the thermal energy into electrical energy is achieved by conventional means in the SNAP 2 system, and by direct means in the SNAP 10A system. The conventional system employs a secondary mercury loop which drives a turboalternator set. The SNAP 10A system employs a thermoelectric converter (Art. 5–6). The thermoelectric elements are attached to pipes through which the coolant is circulated at a mean temperature of 770°K by an electromagnetic pump. Heat is rejected at the cold junctions by radiation into space.

The SNAP 10A is the first nuclear reactor power system to have operated in space. On April 3, 1965, it was launched into a 700-nautical-mile orbit aboard an Atlas-Agena vehicle from Vandenberg Air Force Base. The reactor was started by ground control and, after operation for 6 days, was turned over to on-board automatic control. During the 6 weeks of operation the electrical output was 500,000 watt-hr. After 45 days malfunction of the voltage regulator caused a spurious command from the on-board decoder to shut down the reactor. The satellite will remain in orbit for 4000 years, permitting the decay of fission products to a safe re-entry level.

Such SNAP-type reactor systems are limited in power to outputs of the order of 10 kw. Higher operating temperatures are required to improve the performance and increase heat rejection rates for unit radiator size. The development of an in-core thermionic converter and the associated reactor system will permit such high power-density operation, and meet the larger power requirements of future space craft.

13–2. POWER DENSITY IN THE REACTOR CORE

Most of the energy liberated when an atom undergoes fission is dissipated by the two main fission fragments in the form of heat within a very short distance of the event. Consequently, the rate at which thermal energy is produced at a point within a reactor core is proportional to the fission rate at that point, i.e., to $N\sigma_f\phi$, where N is the number of fuel atoms per unit volume, σ_f the microscopic fission cross-section, and ϕ is the neutron flux at the point. If N and σ_f are assumed constant throughout the core, then the power-density distribution is directly proportional to the flux-density distribution.

As a simple example, consider the homogeneous unreflected reactor previously examined in Art. 12–7. Based on Eqs. 12–43, 12–52, and

12–59, the spatial flux distribution is

$$\phi(x,y,z) = \phi_m \cos \frac{\pi x}{a_e} \cos \frac{\pi y}{b_e} \cos \frac{\pi z}{c_e} \tag{13-1}$$

where ϕ_m is the flux at $(0,0,0)$.

The power-density distribution is therefore

$$P_0 = E_f N \sigma_f \phi_m \cos \frac{\pi x}{a_e} \cos \frac{\pi y}{b_e} \cos \frac{\pi z}{c_e} \tag{13-2}$$

where the maximum power density

$$P_{0m} = E_f N \sigma_f \phi_m \tag{13-3}$$

occurs at $(0,0,0)$ and E_f is the average energy released per fission. The average power density within the core is

$$\bar{P}_0 = \frac{1}{abc} \int_{-a/2}^{a/2} \int_{-b/2}^{b/2} \int_{-c/2}^{c/2} P_{0m} \cos \frac{\pi x}{a_e} \cos \frac{\pi y}{b_e} \cos \frac{\pi z}{c_e} \, dx \, dy \, dz$$

Therefore

$$\bar{P}_0 = \frac{8}{\pi^3} P_{0m} \left(\sin \frac{\pi a}{2a_e} \sin \frac{\pi b}{2b_e} \sin \frac{\pi c}{2c_e} \right) \tag{13-4}$$

When the core is large and $a \gg \lambda_e$,

$$\bar{P}_0 \approx \frac{8}{\pi^3} P_{0m} \tag{13-5}$$

or the ratio of maximum to average power density is 3.87. For similar unreflected spherical and cylindrical cores this ratio is 3.29 and 3.64, respectively. When a reflector is added the flux density at the surface is increased, so that the power ratio is decreased to about 2.4.

Example 13–1. An unreflected homogeneous 1.50-m cubical reactor core contains 4×10^{24} fissile atoms/m³. If the average thermal energy released per fission is 190 Mev, the microscopic fission cross-section is 582 barns, and the extrapolated length $\lambda_e = 0.0135$ m, find the maximum neutron flux density necessary to sustain a thermal output power of 40 megawatts.

Since $a \gg \lambda_e$, $P_{0m} \approx 3.87 \, \bar{P}_0$ and therefore P_{0m} may be written as

$$P_{0m} = 3.87 \times \frac{40 \times 10^6}{1.5^3} = 46 \times 10^6 \text{ watts/m}^3$$

From Table 11–1,

$$E_f = 190 \times 1.602 \times 10^{-13} = 3.05 \times 10^{-11} \text{ joule}$$

From Eq. 13–3,

$$\phi_m = \frac{P_{0m}}{E_f N^5 \sigma_f} = \frac{46 \times 10^6}{3.05 \times 10^{-11} \times 4 \times 10^{24} \times 582 \times 10^{-28}}$$
$$= 6.5 \times 10^{18} \text{ neutrons/m}^2 - \text{sec}$$

As seen from Ex. 13–1, the power density in the center of the core is 46 watts/cm³, while the average power density is only 11.8 watts/cm³. In general, the power output of a reactor is limited by the maximum permissible temperature of the fuel, i.e., by P_{0m}. Therefore, it is desirable to reduce the P_{0m}/P_0 ratio. Although the use of a reflector does reduce the ratio, further reduction, or *power flattening*, is usually resorted to. P_{0m} may be reduced by placing fuel of lower fissile-atom content in the central region, by preferentially inserting the control rods about the center of the core, or by providing a higher coolant flow rate through the central ducts. When power flattening is used, the power-density distribution is of course no longer given by the simple spatial distribution relationships considered in Art. 12–7 but is considerably more complex and governed by the nuclear and thermal conditions which exist.

13–3. TRANSIENT REACTOR OPERATION

As discussed in Chapter 12, steady-state reactor conditions can exist only when the effective multiplication factor is equal to unity. If k_{eff} is less than or greater than unity, the neutron density n at any point within the core decreases or increases respectively as a function of time.

13–3.1. Stabilizing Effect of Delayed Neutrons. Consider first the simplest case in which it is assumed that all neutrons are emitted at the instant of fission. If the average neutron lifetime is l, and the excess multiplication factor is k_{ex}, then based on Eq. 12–3, the neutron density $n(t)$ at time t is related to the initial density n_0 by

$$n(t) = n_0 \exp\left(\frac{tk_{ex}}{l}\right) \qquad (13\text{–}6)$$

or

$$n(t) = n_0 \exp(t/T) \qquad (13\text{–}7)$$

where $T = l/k_{ex}$, *the reactor period*, may be considered as the periodic time of the reactor.

Example 13–2. The time between successive neutron generations in a particular reactor is $l = 3 \times 10^{-3}$ sec. If a small excess reactivity of 0.001 occurs, find the percentage increase in neutron density after 1 sec, if it is assumed that all neutrons are emitted at the instant of fission.

From Eq. 13–6,

$$\frac{n(1)}{n_0} = \exp\left(\frac{1 \times 0.001}{3 \times 10^{-3}}\right)$$
$$= 1.4$$

Therefore for a 0.1 percent excess multiplication factor, the neutron density, and hence the power density, increases by 40 percent in a time of only 1 sec.

This would indicate that control of the thermal nuclear reactor poses some formidable problems.

However, as discussed in Art. 11–4, all the neutrons are not *"prompt,"* but the appearance of some from the fission fragment process may be delayed by as much as 80 sec. Consideration of the *delayed* neutrons leads to a modification of Eq. 13–6 and a considerable increase in the effective reactor period.

The delayed neutrons from U-235 (<0.75 percent) appear in six major groups, each with a different average delay time. However, the average delay time $\bar{\tau}$ of all the delayed neutrons is 12.74 sec.

The average effective lifetime between successive generations of neutrons may now be calculated if it is assumed that a fraction $1 - \beta$ of prompt neutrons take the usual time l to complete a cycle, whereas a fraction β delayed neutrons take the average delay time $\bar{\tau}$ as well as the usual time l to complete the cycle. The average effective lifetime is therefore

$$\bar{l} = l(1 - \beta) + (l + \bar{\tau})\beta$$
$$\bar{l} = l + \beta\bar{\tau} \tag{13–8}$$

Thus for U-235, $\bar{l} \approx 3 \times 10^{-3} + (0.0075 \times 12.74) = 0.098$ sec, and so the existence of delayed neutrons increases the average lifetime by a factor of about 30. If the value of $\bar{l} = 0.098$ sec is now used in Ex. 13–2, the neutron density is found to increase by only a little more than 1 percent, as compared with the previous 40 percent increase in a time of 1 sec. Consequently, reactor control is not as formidable a problem as was initially assumed. However, the excess reactivity should never be made large, otherwise the multiplication factor for the prompt neutrons alone can be greater than unity, and a rapid excursion can take place without any contribution from the delayed neutrons. Under such conditions a reactor is said to *outrun* the delayed neutrons and to go *prompt critical*. A U-235 thermal reactor goes prompt critical for an excess multiplication factor of 0.0065. Therefore, when increasing the power level of such a reactor, the effective multiplication factor is never permitted to exceed 1.0065, and in many cases sufficient fuel to achieve prompt criticality is not provided.

13–3.2. Temperature Effects. A critical assembly can have a positive or negative temperature coefficient; however, all nuclear reactors are designed so that the coefficient is always negative. As a result, negative feedback is introduced into the system, in that an increase in temperature causes a decrease in the effective multiplication factor and hence a reduction in the power level. The temperature coefficient α_T is defined as the increase in the effective multiplication factor per degree change in temperature.

In general it is not difficult to ensure that α_T is negative. The moderator expands with an increase in temperature, reducing the number of nuclei per unit volume, which causes the neutron mean free path to increase and so more neutrons are able to leak from the reactor. Also, since the neutron temperature increases, the cross-sections of $1/v$ absorbers decrease, which further increases the neutron mean free path and the leakage. Resonance absorption is also increased due to the broadening of the resonance peaks (the *Doppler effect*).

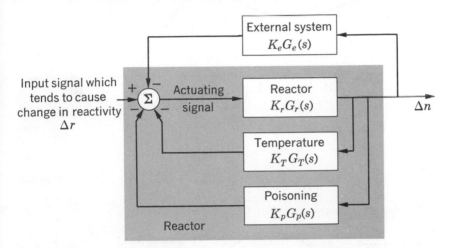

Fig. 13–6.   Control loops of a basic nuclear power plant.

13–3.3. General Stability Considerations.

Certain fission products act as good neutron absorbers, or *poisons*. An increase in fission rate causes an increase in the production of neutron absorbers, tending to reduce the excess multiplication factor.

The temperature and poisoning feedback effects are an inherent part of a reactor. They may be considered as internal feedback loops. When a reactor is part of a power plant the operating conditions of the system as a whole influence the behavior of the reactor. Consequently, the control system of a basic nuclear power plant may be represented by the block diagram in Fig. 13–6, where it is assumed that the external system provides negative feedback.

In general, the input signal Δr is one for movement of a control rod, while the output signal is the resultant change in neutron density Δn. The reactor transfer function $K_r G_r(s)$ relates, in the usual manner, the magnitude and phase of the output signal to the input signal. The temperature, poisoning, and external system transfer functions are $K_T G_T(s)$, $K_p G_p(s)$, and $K_e G_e(s)$, respectively. So that, as discussed in

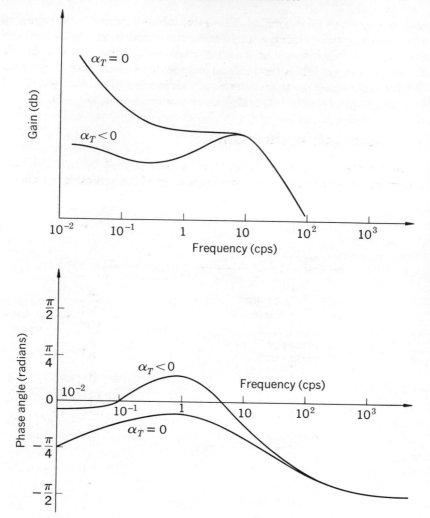

Fig. 13–7. Typical gain and phase-angle plots for a nuclear reactor system.

Art. 2–17, if all feedback is negative,

$$\Delta n = \Delta r \left\{ \frac{K_r G_r(s)}{1 + K_r G_r(s)[K_T G_T(s) + K_p G_p(s) + K_e G_e(s)]} \right\} \quad (13\text{–}9)$$

Under typical conditions, the frequency response of a nuclear reactor system is similar to that in Fig. 13–7. The *gain* is defined as

$$G \equiv 20 \log_{10} \left(\frac{\Delta n}{\Delta r} \right) \quad (13\text{–}10)$$

and is expressed in decibels. The gain falls off rapidly at frequencies above 10 cps; consequently, any oscillation of the input signal at higher frequencies would cause only small variation of the neutron density. However, the system is particularly responsive to low-frequency inputs. With negative temperature feedback, the system remains stable as the frequency goes to zero, while this is not the case when $\alpha_T = 0$.

13–4. AUTOMATIC REACTOR CONTROL

Once a reactor has been brought up to the desired operating level an automatic control circuit is usually employed to maintain a constant

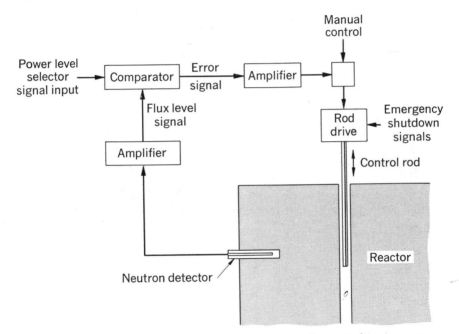

Fig. 13–8. Schematic of a basic automatic control system.

flux level. Figure 13–8 shows a schematic of a basic automatic control system. The amplified output from a neutron detector is compared with a power level selector signal and the difference fed through an amplifier to the rod drive mechanism. Provision is made for direct manual control of the rod drive and emergency "override" by signals from any of the safety devices throughout the system.

13–4.1. **The Comparator.** The comparator may be electrical, hydraulic, pneumatic, or mechanical. A simple electrical comparator circuit is shown in Fig. 13–9. Under non-equilibrium conditions an error signal

V_e is obtained when the voltage drop across kR (where $0 \leq k \leq 1$) is not equal to a fixed voltage E_b. The control rods move until $V_e = 0$, i.e., until $kV_f = E_b$, where V_f is the amplified signal from the neutron detector, applied across the resistor R. The desired power level may be varied by adjusting the rheostat and so the value of k.

13–4.2. The Neutron Detector System. Due to the fact that neutrons have no charge, their presence cannot be detected as easily as can other forms of radiation. However, neutron detection is made possible by observing the fission or other nuclear reactions which neutrons cause.

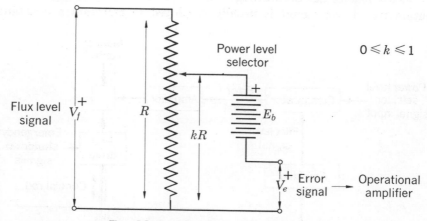

Fig. 13–9. Simple comparator circuit.

The fission counter consists of a gas-filled tube lined with uranium. In the presence of neutrons fission occurs within the chamber, and the resultant high-energy fission fragments ionize the gas. Two electrodes which are maintained at different potential collect the ions. As a result a pulse of current can be detected in the external electrode circuit whenever a fission occurs within the tube. If the tube is lined with U-235, then the pulse rate is proportional to the thermal neutron flux. If a suitable mixture of U-235 and U-238 is used, then the pulse rate can be made proportional to the total neutron flux.

Boron counters are particularly useful when the neutron flux is very low and are used in nuclear reactors during the early stages of startup. The detector tube is filled with the gas boron trifluoride. Slow neutrons are absorbed by the boron and initiate the nuclear reaction

$$_5B^{10} + _0n^1 \rightarrow _3Li^7 + _2He^4 \tag{13–11}$$

The resultant lithium ion and alpha particle ionize the gas and the current pulse is detected by the external electrical circuit. Since B-10 has such a large thermal neutron absorption cross-section, the counter is particularly suitable for detecting slow neutrons at low flux levels.

However, gamma radiation also causes ionization of the detector gas, and at start-up of a nuclear reactor, when the neutron flux is low and the gamma radiation caused by the decay of existing fission products may be

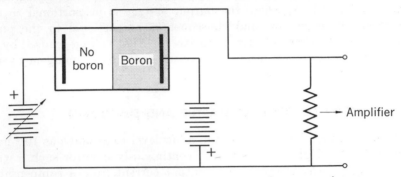

Fig. 13–10. Schematic of compensated neutron detector.

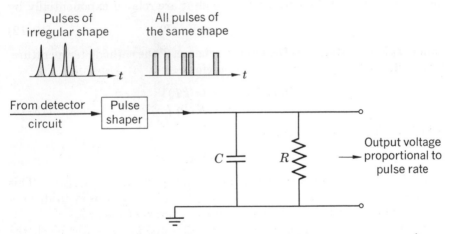

Fig. 13–11. Integrating circuit which provides an output voltage proportional to the incoming pulse rate.

high, reliable neutron detection would not take place. Under such circumstances, compensated detectors are used. The tube is divided into separate regions, as shown schematically in Fig. 13–10. One region contains boron and is sensitive to both neutron and gamma radiation. The other does not contain boron and responds only to gamma radiation. The electrical circuit is such that if the detector is exposed to a source of gamma radiation the outputs from the two regions are in opposition and may be adjusted so that the net output is due only to neutron activity and the detector may be calibrated in terms of neutron flux.

When the pulse rate from the detector is high, it is often desirable to obtain a signal which is proportional to the pulse rate. The pulses of random shape generated within the detector are first shaped into pulses of uniform size. These pulses are passed to the simple RC integrating circuit in Fig. 13–11, where the output voltage is proportional to the charge on the capacitor, and consequently proportional to the pulse arrival rate. In a reactor system an excess output voltage, caused by an excess flux density in the reactor, can be used to trip the emergency shutdown mechanism.

13–5. REACTOR CONTROL AT STARTUP AND SHUTDOWN

During startup the flux rises from a low level to as much as 10^{19} neutrons/m²-sec or higher. In order to continuously monitor such a wide range a *log n meter* is used. The output current from a compensated neutron detector is fed directly to the plate of a diode. The voltage V across a diode and the current I through it are related exponentially by

$$I = I_0 \exp\left(-eV/kT\right) \qquad (13\text{–}12)$$

where I_0 is a constant, e is the electron charge, T the cathode temperature, and k the Boltzmann constant. Therefore

$$\ln\left(I/I_0\right) = -(e/kT)V$$
$$V = -K_1 \ln I \qquad (13\text{–}13)$$

where K_1 is a constant; and so

$$V \propto -\log_{10} I$$

Therefore, the voltage across the diode is proportional to $\log_{10} I$. This voltage may be applied to the grid of an amplifier and used to drive a linear indicator, whose scale is calibrated in terms of $\log_{10} n$.

While a reactor is being brought up to its operating power level, the effective multiplication factor is permitted to exceed unity. During this time careful attention must be given to its control in order to avoid accident. As discussed in Art. 13–3, it is most important that the excess effective multiplication factor should never be greater than 0.0065, so that the system never becomes "prompt critical." A convenient way to ensure that the reactor never "runs away" is to provide a signal which is proportional to the reactor period. The reactor period is the time during which the neutron density increases by a factor of 2.71. Therefore, if the reactor period is always maintained greater than some minimum, say 15 sec, then "run-away" is most improbable.

A signal proportional to the reactor period may be obtained by applying the voltage which appears across the diode of the log n meter circuit, to the differentiating circuit of Fig. 13–12.

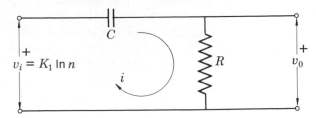

Fig. 13–12. Differentiating circuit which provides a signal proportional to the reactor period.

The current $i = dQ/dt$, and if R is small, then the charge on the capacitor C is close to $Q = Cv_i$, so that

$$i = \frac{d}{dt}(Cv_i)$$

$$= K_1 C \frac{d}{dt}(\ln n)$$

From Eq. 13–7, $n = n_0 \exp(t/T)$, so that

$$i = K_1 C \frac{d}{dt}\left(\ln n_0 + \frac{t}{T}\right)$$

$$= K_1 C \frac{d}{dt}(\ln n_0) + \frac{K_1 C}{T} \tag{13–14}$$

Therefore the current through R is linearly dependent on the inverse of the reactor period, and so the output voltage v_0 may be used to indicate the reactor period. Since v_0 becomes large when the period is small, an output greater than a certain value may be used to trip the emergency shutdown mechanism.

Shutdown of a reactor may be deliberate or enforced. An enforced shutdown (or "*scram*") may be triggered by any of the numerous safety systems of either the reactor or the associated plant. For example, a violent rise in the recorded neutron flux, or loss of coolant, or excessive vibration, etc., would trigger the drop of control rods into the core within 30 to 50 msec. However, most potential emergencies can be anticipated and brought to the attention of the operator by audible and visible signals, whereupon corrective measures can be taken. Accident as a result of error on the part of the operator is also protected against by an *interlock* system, which prevents startup without coolant circulation, for example.

Two important factors should be considered when deliberate shutdown is called for. First, although the system is made subcritical, heat continues to be liberated after shutdown as a result of fission product decay, and adequate cooling must continue to be provided.

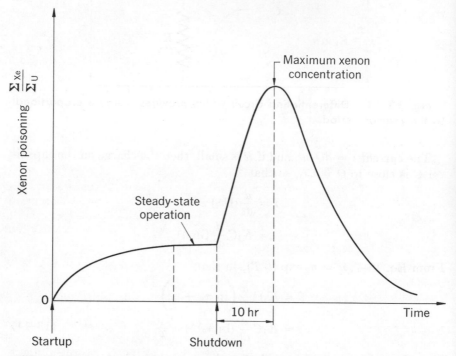

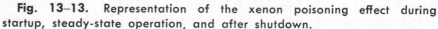

Fig. 13–13. Representation of the xenon poisoning effect during startup, steady-state operation, and after shutdown.

The second factor is concerned with *xenon poisoning* after shutdown. Xe-135 has an exceptionally large absorption cross-section of about 3×10^6 barns, for thermal neutrons. During operation of the reactor, xenon is maintained at a low level by neutron burn-up and only constitutes about 0.2 percent of the fission product. However, after shutdown I-135 continues to decay to Xe-135 and, due to the lack of burn-up, the Xe-135 accumulates and reaches a peak concentration about 10 hr after shutdown, as shown in Fig. 13–13, before finally decaying. As a result the built-in "excess" reactivity of the reactor may be insufficient to counter the poison of the Xe-135 and startup may be impossible within the period of about 2 to 24 hr after shutdown. This is particularly true of reactors which operate at a flux of more than 10^{20} neutrons/m²-sec.

PROBLEMS

13-1. A cylindrical, unreflected, homogeneous, ZrH_2-moderated reactor has a core of radius 2.5 m and height of 4.65 m. The fuel is 5 atomic percent enriched uranium and the atomic moderator to uranium ratio is 200:1. For an extrapolated length of 1.5 cm and an average thermal energy release of 190 Mev per fission find the maximum neutron flux density when the total thermal output power is 500 Mw.

13-2. In order to maintain the xenon poisoning effect at a tolerable level the average neutron flux in a nuclear reactor is not to exceed 2×10^{18} neutrons/m²-sec. For a spherical, reflected, homogeneous reactor with a core radius of 0.4 m and containing 5.1×10^{24} fissile uranium atoms/m³, find the maximum permissible output power. What is the approximate value of the maximum power density?

13-3. If the reactor in Prob. 13-2 is cooled by liquid sodium, find the necessary flow rate in kg/sec if the sodium enters the core at 600°K and leaves at 950°K. (Specific heat of sodium = 1300 joule/kg-°K.)

13-4. The effective lifetime for neutrons in a 2 percent enriched graphite-uranium reactor is 0.095 sec. A small rod of 95 percent enriched uranium is suddenly inserted into the core when the output power is 1.3 Mw and the neutron flux commences to increase with a stable period of 307 sec. After what time does the power level reach 2.0 Mw?

13-5. What is the excess reactivity caused by the introduction of the rod in Prob. 13-4?

13-6. Due to meteorite damage it is found that the automatic control system of the nuclear reactor on board a space craft is inoperable and during a time of 4 min a constant negative excess reactivity of 2×10^{-4} has existed. The astronauts are instructed to manually restore the reactor power level to that prior to the malfunction by introducing an excess reactivity of 0.004. For what duration should the excess reactivity be provided, and what was the percentage drop in power during the 4 min while the excess reactivity was negative? Assume a neutron effective lifetime of 0.095 sec.

13-7. During startup of the reactor in a nuclear rocket the power level must increase by a factor of 10^6 in 40 sec. Find the period required.

13-8. Due to conditions external to a power reactor the core temperature commences to increase linearly at a rate β from θ_0 at time $t = 0$, so that $\theta(t) = \theta_0 + \beta t$ at time t. If the reactor has a temperature coefficient α_T and is producing a constant power P_0 at $t = 0$, determine the power production rate as a function of time.

13-9. Using the result from Prob. 13-8, find the reactor power level after 3 min when

$$\beta = 0.3°K/sec$$
$$\alpha_T = -3 \times 10^{-5}/°K$$
$$l = 0.095 \text{ sec}$$

and the initial power level is 150 Mw.

13–10. A homogeneous, spherical, nuclear reactor for use as a lunar power supply is to be constructed using a fuel of pure U-235 and a beryllium moderator. A 1-cm-thick beryllium reflector surrounds the core. If the moderator to fuel atomic ratio is 10,000:1, find the outer diameter of the reflector. If the neutron flux at the center of the core is not to exceed 10^{18} neutrons/m²-sec find the maximum possible power output. Assume the ratio of maximum to average power density in the reflected core is 2.8, $\nu = 2.47$, and $E_f = 190$ Mev.

Bibliography: Part III

ASH, M. *Nuclear Reactor Kinetics.* New York: McGraw-Hill Book Co., Inc. 1965.

EL-WAKIL, M. M. *Nuclear Power Engineering.* New York: McGraw-Hill Book Co., Inc. 1962.

ETHERINGTON, H. *Nuclear Engineering Handbook.* New York: McGraw-Hill Book Co., Inc. 1958.

GLASSTONE, S., and EDLUND, M. C. *Elements of Nuclear Reactor Theory.* Princeton, N.J.: D. Van Nostrand Co., Inc. 1952.

GLASSTONE, S., and SESONSKE, A. *Nuclear Reactor Engineering.* Princeton, N.J.: D. Van Nostrand Co., Inc. 1963.

HALLIDAY, D. *Introductory Nuclear Physics,* 2d ed. New York: John Wiley & Sons, Inc. 1955.

JACOBS, A. M., *et al. Basic Principles of Nuclear Science and Reactors.* Princeton, N.J.: D. Van Nostrand Co., Inc. 1960.

KAPLAN, I. *Nuclear Physics.* Reading, Mass.: Addison-Wesley International Division. 1955.

LOFTNESS, R. L. *Nuclear Power Plants.* Princeton, N.J.: D. Van Nostrand Co., Inc. 1964.

MAWSON, C. A. *Management of Radioactive Wastes.* Princeton, N.J.: D. Van Nostrand Co., Inc. 1960.

MURPHY, G. *Elements of Nuclear Engineering.* New York: John Wiley & Sons, Inc. 1961.

MURRAY, R. L. *Nuclear Reactor Physics.* Englewood Cliffs, N.J.: Prentice-Hall, Inc. 1957.

SCHULTZ, M. A. *Control of Nuclear Reactors and Power Plants,* 2d ed. New York: McGraw-Hill Book Co., Inc. 1961.

SPROULL, R. L. *Modern Physics,* 2d ed. New York: John Wiley & Sons, Inc. 1963.

WEINBERG, A. M., and WIGNER, P. E. *Physical Theory of Neutron Chain Reactors.* University of Chicago Press. 1958.

Appendix

A

Atomic Weights of Selected Isotopes, with Atomic Numbers and Mass Numbers

Element	Atomic Number	Mass Number	Atomic Weight (amu)
H	1	1	1.00814
H	1	2	2.01474
H	1	3	3.01700
He	2	4	4.00387
Li	3	6	6.01702
Li	3	7	7.01822
Be	4	8	8.00785
Be	4	9	9.01504
B	5	10	10.01611
B	5	11	11.01278
C	6	12	12.00380
C	6	13	13.00747
C	6	14	14.00768
N	7	14	14.00752
N	7	15	15.00486
O	8	16	16.00000
O	8	17	17.00453
O	8	18	18.00487
Ne	10	20	19.99886
Ne	10	22	21.99827
Na	11	23	22.99714
Mg	12	24	23.99270
Mg	12	25	24.99462
Al	13	27	26.99014

Element	Atomic Number	Mass Number	Atomic Weight (amu)
Al	13	28	27.99076
Si	14	28	27.98584
Si	14	29	28.98651
Si	14	30	29.97880
Si	14	31	30.98620
P	15	31	30.98430
P	15	32	31.98402
P	15	33	32.97660
Cl	17	34	33.97280
Ni	28	59	58.938
Mo	42	95	94.94500
Mo	42	96	95.9356
Cd	48	112	111.908
In	49	115	114.909
Sn	50	118	117.940
Sn	50	120	119.939
La	57	139	138.955
Th	90	232	232.110
U	92	235	235.1168
U	92	238	238.125

B

Properties of Reactor Materials

FUELS

Material	Atomic Weight (amu)	Specific Gravity (kg/m³)	Microscopic Cross-section* σ_f	σ_c (barns)	σ_a	σ_s	Fast Neutron Yield/Fission ν
U-233	233.0	18,680	525	53	578		2.51
U-235	235.1	18,680	582	101	683	10	2.47
U-238	238.1	18,680	4×10^{-4}	2.75	2.75	8.3	
Pu-239	239.1	19,600	742	286	1028	9.6	2.89

MODERATORS

Material	Atomic Weight (amu)	Specific Gravity (kg/m³)	Thermal Diffusion Length L_m (m)	Fermi Age L_s^2 (m²)	Microscopic Cross-section* σ_s	σ_a (barns)	Macroscopic Cross-section* Σ_s	Σ_a (m⁻¹)
Deuterium	20.029	1100	1.00	0.012	10.4	0.0026	35.5	0.0086
Graphite	12.01	1650	0.5	0.035	4.8	0.0045	39.5	0.0375
Beryllium	9.013	1850	0.208	0.0098	7.0	0.01	86.1	0.123
Water	18.016	1000	0.0288	0.0033	103	0.66	345	2.21
ZrH₂	93.2	5610	0.03	0.0027	48.6	0.84	176	3

*For thermal, 2200 m/sec, 0.0253 ev neutrons.

OTHER MATERIALS

Material	Specific Gravity (kg/m³)	Microscopic Cross-section* σ_a (barns)	σ_s	Macroscopic Cross-section* Σ_a (m⁻¹)	Σ_s
Li	534	71	1.4	329	6.5
Ni	8860	4.6	17.5	42	160
Cd	8650	2450	7	11.4×10^3	32.5
In	7280	191	2.2	730	8.4
Xe	5.9	35	4.3	0.095	0.012
Cs	1873	28	20	23.8	17
Sm	7700	5600	5	17.3×10^3	15.5
Gd	7950	46×10^3		140.3×10^3	
Au	19320	98.8	9.3	579	55

* For thermal, 2200 m/sec, 0.0253 ev neutrons.

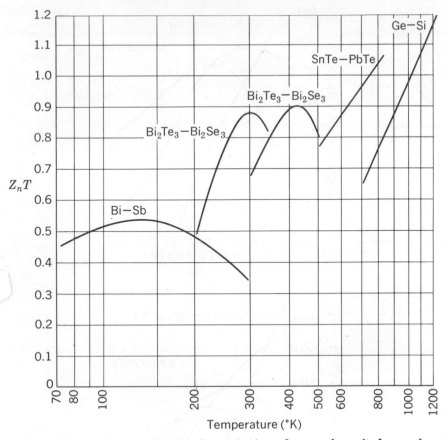

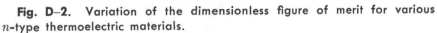

Fig. D–2. Variation of the dimensionless figure of merit for various n-type thermoelectric materials.

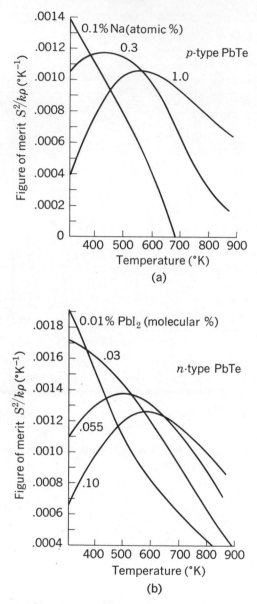

Fig. D–3. Variation of the figure of merit with temperature for (a) p-type PbTe alloys; (b) n-type PbTe alloys. (By permission, from R. W. Fritts.)

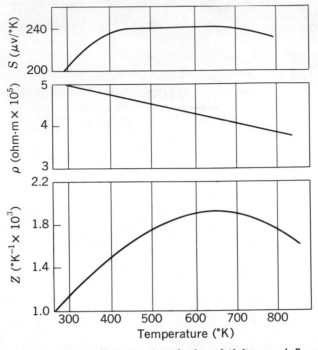

Fig. D–4.   Seebeck coefficient, electrical resistivity, and figure of merit for the p-type alloy $AgSbTe_2$.   (By permission, from F. D. Rosi, E. F. Hockings, and N. E. Lindenblad, "Semiconducting Power Generation," *RCA Review,* **22**: 103, 1961.)

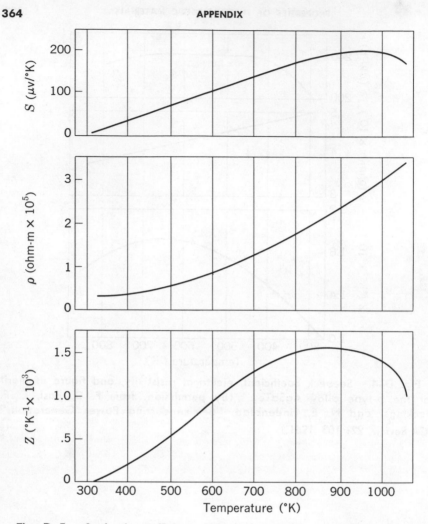

Fig. D–5. Seebeck coefficient, electrical resistivity, and figure of merit for the n-type alloy 75% PbTe, 25% SnTe. (By permission, from F. D. Rosi, E. F. Hockings, and N. E. Lindenblad, "Semiconducting Power Generation," *RCA Review,* 22: 111, 1961.)

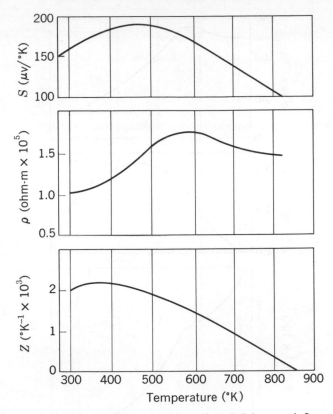

Fig. D–6. Seebeck coefficient, electrical resistivity, and figure of merit for the n-type alloy 75% Bi_2Te_3, 25% Bi_2Se_3. (By permission, from F. D. Rosi, E. F. Hockings, and N. E. Lindenblad, "Semiconducting Power Generation," *RCA Review*, 22: 96, 1961.)

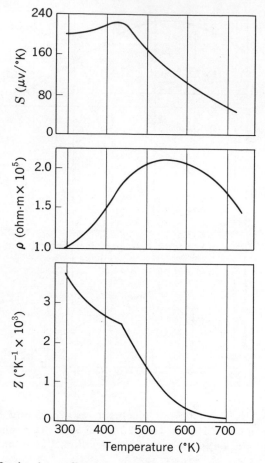

Fig. D–7. Seebeck coefficient, electrical resistivity, and figure of merit for the p-type alloy 75% Sb_2Te_3, 25% Bi_2Te_3 (1.75% Se). (By permission from F. D. Rosi, E. F. Hockings, and N. E. Lindenblad, "Semiconducting Power Generation," *RCA Review*, **22**: 99, 1961.)

E

Constants

$$c = 2.998 \times 10^8 \quad \text{m/sec}$$
$$\sigma = 5.67 \times 10^{-8} \quad \text{watts/m}^2\text{-}{}^\circ\text{K}^4$$
$$e = 1.602 \times 10^{-19} \text{ coulomb}$$
$$\epsilon_0 = 8.854 \times 10^{-12} \text{ coulomb/newton-m}^2$$
$$\mathfrak{F} = 96.5 \times 10^6 \quad \text{coulomb/kg mole}$$
$$h = 6.625 \times 10^{-34} \text{ joule-sec}$$
$$k = 8.617 \times 10^{-5} \text{ ev/}{}^\circ\text{K}$$
$$= 1.380 \times 10^{-23} \text{ joule/}{}^\circ\text{K}$$
$$m_e = 9.109 \times 10^{-31} \text{ kg}$$
$$N_0 = 6.023 \times 10^{26} \text{ /kg mole}$$
$$\mu_0 = 4\pi \times 10^{-7} \text{ weber/amp-turn-m}$$
$$\mathfrak{R} = 8314 \qquad \text{joule/kg mole-}{}^\circ\text{K}$$
$$e/k = 11{,}600 \qquad {}^\circ\text{K/volt}$$

F

Conversion Factors

1 amu	$= 1.66 \times 10^{-27}$	kg
	$= 3.66 \times 10^{-27}$	lb (*mass*)
1 ev	$= 1.602 \times 10^{-19}$	joule
	$= 4.45 \times 10^{-26}$	kw-hr
1 joule	$= 1$	watt-sec
	$= 1$	newton-m
	$= 0.738$	ft-lb
	$= 10^7$	erg
1 m	$= 10^{10}$	Å
	$= 3.281$	ft
	$= 39.37$	in.
1 newton	$= 0.225$	lb (*force*)
	$= 10^5$	dyne
1 watt	$= 1.341 \times 10^{-3}$	hp
	$= 10^7$	erg/sec
1 weber	$= 10^8$	lines
1 weber/m²	$= 64.5$	kilolines/in.²
	$= 10^4$	gauss

G

Dynamic Electromechanical System Analysis Using Lagrange's Equations

Frequently it is required to develop a mathematical model of an electromechanical system or develop an electrical analog of the system. Although this task is relatively easy for static conditions, it is considerably more difficult for transient or dynamic conditions where there is interplay between the electrical and mechanical parameters. The Lagrange equations provide a means for developing the differential equations which mathematically represent the system. With these equations it is often possible to proceed with a purely mathematical analysis of the system under the desired dynamic conditions. However, it may be more expedient to use an analog computer to solve the differential equations, in which case the circuit developed from the differential equations is the electrical analog of the electromechanical system.

G-1. ANALOGS AND DUALS

Analogous systems are defined as those which may be represented by the same set of integrodifferential equations. We are interested in analogous electrical and mechanical systems. For example, consider the mechanical system of Fig. G-1a. The governing force equation is

$$f = f_m + f_D + f_k \qquad (G-1)$$

where f is the driving force and f_m, f_D, and f_k are: the force due to the acceleration of the mass, the damping force, and the spring force, respectively. Substituting expressions for the forces in terms of velocity in

Eq. G–1 gives

$$f = M \frac{dv}{dt} + Dv + k \int_0^t v \, dt \tag{G–2}$$

where M is the mass, v the velocity of displacement, D the system damping coefficient, and k the spring constant.

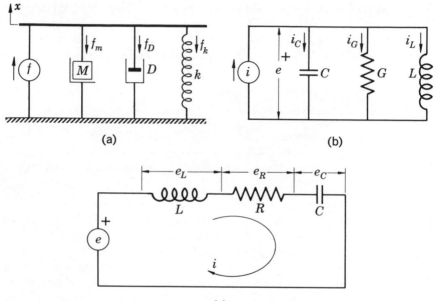

(a)   (b)

(c)

Fig. G–1. (a) Simple mechanical system. (b) Direct analog of the mechanical system. (c) Inverse analog of the mechanical system.

The differential equation governing the electrical circuit of Fig. G–1b is

$$i = C \frac{de}{dt} + Ge + \frac{1}{L} \int_0^t e \, dt \tag{G–3}$$

where i is the source current, e the potential across the parallel elements, C the capacitance, G the conductance, and L the inductance. Comparing Eq. G–2 and Eq. G–3, it is seen that the form of both is the same and that there is a direct correspondence between force and current, mass and capacitance, velocity and voltage, etc. Therefore the mechanical system of Fig. G–1a and the electrical system of Fig. G–1b are analogous systems. However, these are not unique, because it is possible to draw at least two electrical analogs of any given mechanical system. For example, the differential equation governing the series electrical circuit of Fig. G–1c is

$$e = L \frac{di}{dt} + Ri + \frac{1}{C} \int_0^t i \, dt \qquad (G–4)$$

which has the same form as Eq. G–2, and so the mechanical system of Fig. G–1a and the electrical system of Fig. G–1c are analogous. The electrical circuits of Fig. G–1b and Fig. G–1c are said to be *dual* circuits since they are both analogs of the same system. They are distinguished by calling the parallel circuit the *direct analog*, since the elements of the mechanical system are also in parallel, and the series circuit the *inverse analog*. Table G–1 lists the corresponding system elements for the

TABLE G–1

Electrical Analogs of Rotational and Translational Mechanical Systems

Mechanical Systems		Electrical Analogs		
Rotational	Translational	Direct Analog	Inverse Analog	Displacement Analog
T	f	i	e	$\dfrac{de}{dt}$
J	M	C	L	L
D	D	G	R	R
k	k	$1/L$	$1/C$	$1/C$
θ	x	$\displaystyle\int_0^t e \, dt$	q	i
ω	v	e	i	$\dfrac{di}{dt}$

various analogs. In practice, when representing a mechanical system by an electrical analog the choice of direct, inverse, or some other analog is governed mainly by the convenience of measurement. For example, if the velocity of displacement is of primary interest and it is more convenient to measure voltages in the analogous circuit, then the direct analog would be selected, but if it is more convenient to measure current, then the inverse analog would be selected.

A problem arises if the displacement of the mechanical system is of primary interest. Although displacement is represented by charge in the inverse analog system, electrical measurements of this quantity are unsatisfactory in practice. For this reason a new analog, called the *displacement analog*, is developed in which displacement is represented by current.   Equation G–2 may be expressed in terms of displacement x by

$$f = M \frac{d^2x}{dt^2} + D \frac{dx}{dt} + kx \qquad (G–5)$$

and upon differentiating Eq. G–4 with respect to time

$$\frac{de}{dt} = L \frac{d^2i}{dt^2} + R \frac{di}{dt} + \frac{1}{C} i \qquad (G–6)$$

Equation G–5 and Eq. G–6 are similar in form if the force is represented by the time rate of change of voltage, displacement by current, etc., as shown in Table G–1.

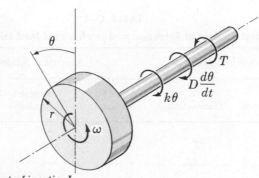

Moment of inertia J

Fig. G–2.   Basic rotational mechanical system.

Rotational mechanical systems (Fig. G–2) are similarly represented by electrical analogs.   In the case of the basic system consisting of a mass with moment of inertia J, driven by a torque T through a shaft with rotational spring constant k and damping coefficient D, the governing differential equation is

$$T = J \frac{d\omega}{dt} + D\omega + k \int_0^t \omega \, dt \qquad (G–7)$$

Equation G–7 is analogous to Eq. G–3 and so Fig. G–1b is the direct analog; and similarly, Fig. G–1c is the inverse analog.

In practice, it is frequently necessary to draw the direct analog from the inverse analog circuit and vice versa.   A convenient way is the "dot method."   Consider the inverse analog circuit in Fig. G–3a and suppose that it is required to find its dual; the procedure is then as follows:

1. Enclose the network with a continuous line called the *datum junction*.
2. Place a numbered dot (loop dot) in each independent loop.

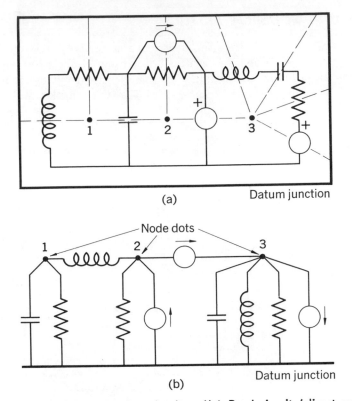

(a)   Datum junction

(b)   Datum junction

Fig. G–3. (a) Inverse analog circuit. (b) Dual circuit (direct analog).

3. For the dual circuit, draw numbered node dots to correspond to those in the loops as in Fig. G–3b.
4. Draw lines from each loop dot to the next.
5. Draw lines from each loop dot to the datum so that a line passes through each circuit element and source.
6. Draw a datum junction under the node dots as in Fig. G–3b.
7. Draw dual circuit elements from node dot 1 to the datum to correspond to the elements cut by the lines from the loop dot 1 to the datum. Repeat for the other nodes.
8. Draw dual circuit elements in parallel between adjacent node dots to correspond to those cut by the lines joining adjacent loop dots.
9. Mark the polarity of current sources. This is done by applying the arbitrary rule: if a potential source in a loop is a voltage rise in the clockwise direction, its dual is a current source directed towards the corresponding node dot.

Conversely, based on the rules outlined above, the dual of a direct analog circuit may be drawn.

G–2. ELECTROMECHANICAL ANALOGS

When it is required to draw the electrical analog of a purely mechanical system, it may be done by writing the integrodifferential equations governing the system and looking for the electrical system which also satisfies the equations. In practice this is often lengthy and unsatisfactory. The following example illustrates this and demonstrates the use of a simpler method.

Example G–1. Find the direct and inverse analogs of the mechanical system represented in Fig. G–4a.

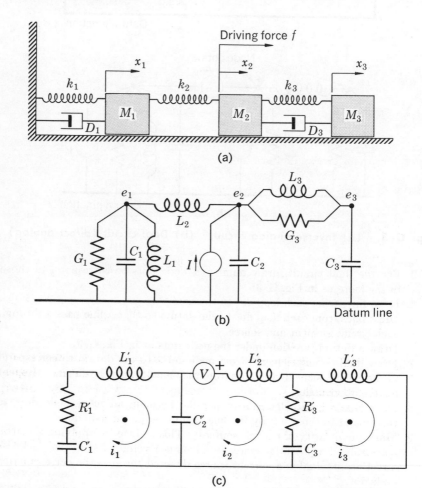

(a)

(b)

Datum line

(c)

Fig. G–4. (a) Mechanical system. (b) Direct electrical analog. (c) Inverse electrical analog.

The integrodifferential equations governing the mechanical system of Fig. G–4a are

$$0 = M_1 \frac{dv_1}{dt} + D_1 v_1 + k_1 \int_0^t v_1 \, dt + k_2 \int_0^t (v_1 - v_2) \, dt \tag{G-8}$$

$$f = M_2 \frac{dv_2}{dt} + D_3(v_2 - v_3) + k_2 \int_0^t (v_2 - v_1) \, dt + k_3 \int_0^t (v_2 - v_3) \, dt \tag{G-9}$$

$$0 = M_3 \frac{dv_3}{dt} + D_3(v_3 - v_2) + k_3 \int_0^t (v_3 - v_2) \, dt \tag{G-10}$$

Referring to Table G–1, the electrical direct analogs of Eqs. G–8, G–9, G–10 are

$$0 = C_1 \frac{de_1}{dt} + G_1 e_1 + \frac{1}{L_1} \int_0^t e_1 \, dt + \frac{1}{L_2} \int_0^t (e_1 - e_2) \, dt \tag{G-11}$$

$$I = C_2 \frac{de_2}{dt} + G_3(e_2 - e_3) + \frac{1}{L_2} \int_0^t (e_2 - e_1) \, dt + \frac{1}{L_3} \int_0^t (e_2 - e_3) \, dt \tag{G-12}$$

$$0 = C_3 \frac{de_3}{dt} + G_3(e_3 - e_2) + \frac{1}{L_3} \int_0^t (e_3 - e_2) \, dt \tag{G-13}$$

Since Eq. G–11, Eq. G–12, and Eq. G–13 are the node equations of the direct analog the circuit of Fig. G–4b results.

In a similar manner the inverse analog equations may be written with the aid of Table G–1; and the resulting loop equations

$$0 = L'_1 \frac{di_1}{dt} + R'_1 i_1 + \frac{1}{C'_1} \int_0^t i_1 \, dt + \frac{1}{C'_2} \int_0^t (i_1 - i_2) \, dt \tag{G-14}$$

$$V = L'_2 \frac{di_2}{dt} + R'_3(i_2 - i_3) + \frac{1}{C'_2} \int_0^t (i_2 - i_1) \, dt + \frac{1}{C'_3} \int_0^t (i_2 - i_3) \, dt \tag{G-15}$$

$$0 = L'_3 \frac{di_3}{dt} + R'_3(i_3 - i_2) + \frac{1}{C'_3} \int_0^t (i_3 - i_2) \, dt \tag{G-16}$$

permit the synthesis of the circuit in Fig. G–4c.

For more complex systems the above is a lengthy process, and in many cases the electrical analog circuit is not readily apparent from the integro-differential equations. A simpler procedure for drawing the direct analog, where the masses have one degree of freedom, follows.

1. Draw a datum line, as in Fig. G–4b.
2. Represent each independent mass by a capacitance between separate node points and the datum line.
3. Represent each spring by an inductance. If the spring is between mass and ground, then the corresponding inductance should be between a node point and the datum. If the spring is between two masses, then the inductance should be between the two corresponding node points.

4. In a similar manner, replace damping elements by conductances.
5. Replace driving forces by current sources between the datum and the corresponding node point. If the driving force is positive in the positive x direction, then the current source should be directed towards the node.

By following the above steps, the direct analog in Fig. G–4b may be drawn. When the inverse analog is required, the dual may be found from the direct analog using the procedure presented in Art. G–1.

G–3. LAGRANGE'S EQUATIONS

The analysis of an electromechanical system is complicated by the fact that, by its very nature, it must obey the laws of both mechanics and of electromagnetics. In practice, the most convenient approach to the problem is to base the analysis on a consideration of the energy associated with the system. However, rather than dividing this energy into electrical and mechanical, it is divided into potential energy, kinetic energy, and Rayleigh dissipation energy. In this way the energy stored in an extended spring and the energy stored in a charged capacitor are grouped under the heading of *potential energy* $\mathfrak{U}$, while the energy associated with a moving mass and the field energy of a conducting inductor are grouped under the heading of *kinetic energy* $\mathfrak{K}$. Rayleigh dissipation $\mathfrak{D}$ accounts for the loss of energy from the system by mechanical friction and electrical resistive loss.

Rather than developing the Lagrange equations in general, it is convenient to develop them for a purely electrical system and then apply a slight modification for the general case. A simple RLC circuit is shown in Fig. G–5. The applied voltage P is equal to the sum of the individual voltages across the three circuit elements

$$e_R + e_C + e_L = P \tag{G–17}$$

or

$$R\dot{q} + \frac{q}{C} + L\frac{d\dot{q}}{dt} = P \tag{G–18}$$

where q is the charge stored in the capacitor and $\dot{q} = dq/dt$ and is the current flowing in the loop. The Lagrange equation for the circuit of Fig. G–5 is simply Eq. G–18 modified so that it is expressed in terms of the energy parameters.

The Rayleigh dissipation is given by $\mathfrak{D} = \frac{1}{2}R(\dot{q})^2$ and therefore $\partial\mathfrak{D}/\partial\dot{q} = R\dot{q}$, which is the voltage drop across the resistor, so

$$e_R = \frac{\partial\mathfrak{D}}{\partial\dot{q}} \tag{G–19}$$

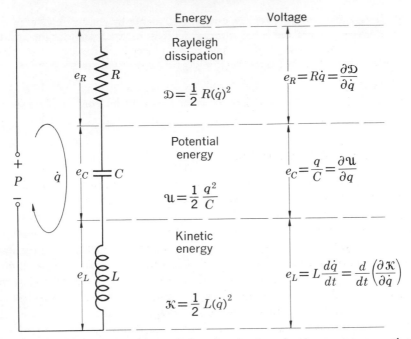

Fig. G–5. Electrical circuit used for developing the Lagrange equations.

Similarly, since the potential energy $\mathcal{U} = \dfrac{1}{2}\dfrac{q^2}{C}$, and the voltage drop across the capacitance is $e_C = \dfrac{q}{C}$,

$$e_C = \frac{\partial \mathcal{U}}{\partial q} \tag{G–20}$$

The kinetic energy stored in the inductor $\mathcal{K} = \frac{1}{2}L(\dot{q})^2$ and since $e_L = L\dfrac{d\dot{q}}{dt}$,

$$e_L = \frac{d}{dt}\left(\frac{\partial \mathcal{K}}{\partial \dot{q}}\right) \tag{G–21}$$

Substituting Eq. G–19, Eq. G–20, and Eq. G–21 in Eq. G–18 gives

$$\frac{d}{dt}\left(\frac{\partial \mathcal{K}}{\partial \dot{q}}\right) + \frac{\partial \mathcal{U}}{\partial q} + \frac{\partial \mathcal{D}}{\partial \dot{q}} = P \tag{G–22}$$

Equation G–22 must be modified so that it is completely general. Upon examination it is found that account must be taken of the possible dependence of the kinetic energy function $\mathcal{K}$ on q. Then it may be shown that

$$\frac{d}{dt}\left(\frac{\partial \mathcal{K}}{\partial \dot{q}}\right) - \frac{\partial \mathcal{K}}{\partial q} + \frac{\partial \mathcal{U}}{\partial q} + \frac{\partial \mathcal{D}}{\partial \dot{q}} = P \qquad (G\text{--}23)$$

Equation G–23 may be put in a simpler form by letting

$$\mathcal{L} = \mathcal{K} - \mathcal{U} \qquad (G\text{--}24)$$

where $\mathcal{L}$ is called the *Lagrangian*. Then Eq. G–23 becomes

$$\boxed{\frac{d}{dt}\left(\frac{\partial \mathcal{L}}{\partial \dot{q}}\right) - \frac{\partial \mathcal{L}}{\partial q} + \frac{\partial \mathcal{D}}{\partial \dot{q}} = P} \qquad (G\text{--}25)$$

A similar equation may be expressed in terms of the mechanical displacement variable x, so that

$$\boxed{\frac{d}{dt}\left(\frac{\partial \mathcal{L}}{\partial \dot{x}}\right) - \frac{\partial \mathcal{L}}{\partial x} + \frac{\partial \mathcal{D}}{\partial \dot{x}} = P} \qquad (G\text{--}26)$$

where P in Eq. G–26 is the mechanical driving function.

Equations G–25 and G–26 are called *Lagrange equations*, and are the corresponding differential equations for a system with one electrical variable and one mechanical variable, respectively. When there are multiple electrical variables $(q_1, q_2, \ldots, q_m)$ and mechanical variables $(x_1, x_2, \ldots, x_n, \theta_1, \theta_2, \theta_3, \ldots, \theta_p)$ a Lagrange equation may be written for each variable.

The procedure for writing the differential equations is as follows.

1. Write the three energy equations for $\mathcal{D}$, $\mathcal{U}$, and $\mathcal{K}$.
2. Write the Lagrangian $\mathcal{L} = \mathcal{K} - \mathcal{U}$.
3. Write a Lagrange equation for each electrical variable.
4. Write a Lagrange equation for each mechanical variable.

The purely mechanical system of Fig. G–4a is considered initially to demonstrate the procedure. There are three mechanical variables, x_1, x_2, and x_3. Therefore, three Lagrange equations may be written. First of all, the energy equations are

$$\mathcal{D} = \tfrac{1}{2}D_1\dot{x}_1{}^2 + \tfrac{1}{2}D_3(\dot{x}_3 - \dot{x}_2)^2 \qquad (G\text{--}27)$$

$$\mathcal{U} = \tfrac{1}{2}k_1x_1{}^2 + \tfrac{1}{2}k_2(x_2 - x_1)^2 + \tfrac{1}{2}k_3(x_3 - x_2)^2 \qquad (G\text{--}28)$$

$$\mathcal{K} = \tfrac{1}{2}M_1\dot{x}_1{}^2 + \tfrac{1}{2}M_2\dot{x}_2{}^2 + \tfrac{1}{2}M_3\dot{x}_3{}^2 \qquad (G\text{--}29)$$

The Lagrangian is

$$\mathcal{L} = \mathcal{K} - \mathcal{U} = \tfrac{1}{2}M_1\dot{x}_1^2 + \tfrac{1}{2}M_2\dot{x}_2^2 + \tfrac{1}{2}M_3\dot{x}_3^2$$
$$- \tfrac{1}{2}k_1x_1^2 - \tfrac{1}{2}k_2(x_2 - x_1)^2 - \tfrac{1}{2}k_3(x_3 - x_2)^2 \quad \text{(G-30)}$$

Applying Eq. G–26 with x_1 as the displacement variable gives

$$\frac{d}{dt}(M_1\dot{x}_1) + k_1x_1 - k_2(x_2 - x_1) + D_1\dot{x}_1 = 0$$

or

$$M_1\ddot{x}_1 + D_1\dot{x}_1 + k_1x_1 - k_2(x_2 - x_1) = 0 \quad \text{(G-31)}$$

Note that the driving force term P of Eq. G–26 is set equal to zero in Eq. G–31, since no external driving force acts on mass M_1.

Applying Eq. G–26, with x_2 and x_3 as the displacement variables, gives respectively

$$M_2\ddot{x}_2 + k_2(x_2 - x_1) - k_3(x_3 - x_2) - D_3(\dot{x}_3 - \dot{x}_2) = f \quad \text{(G-32)}$$

$$M_3\ddot{x}_3 + k_3(x_3 - x_2) + D_3(\dot{x}_3 - \dot{x}_2) = 0 \quad \text{(G-33)}$$

Equations G–31, G–32, and G–33 are seen to be the same as Eqs. G–8, G–9, and G–10, which were derived from the force-balance equation in the classical manner. Although in this particular instance the use of the Lagrange equations does not appear of particular help, there are two important beneficial points to note:

1. Due to the fact that the displacement and velocity terms, which appear in the Lagrangian and in $\mathfrak{D}$, are all squared, their assigned polarity is insignificant. That is to say, it does not matter whether a displacement or velocity is taken as positive or negative when computing the energy terms. When the Lagrange equation is subsequently applied, the correct sign appears. This is most significant in complicated electromechanical systems where it may not be immediately apparent whether a positive displacement, or current change, causes a positive or a negative force.
2. The procedure for deriving the governing system equations is the same for a small system or for a large system and in fact the Lagrange equations approach is most suited to the large and complex electromechanical system.

G–4. USE OF LAGRANGE'S EQUATIONS IN ELECTROMECHANICAL SYSTEM ANALYSIS

The basic procedure involved in analyzing an electromechanical system may be demonstrated by the simple system in Fig. G–6a. The system consists of a solenoid and spring-loaded plunger. The coil, which has an inductance L, is excited by a source which is assumed to be equivalent to a time-dependent potential e superimposed on the constant potential E_0.

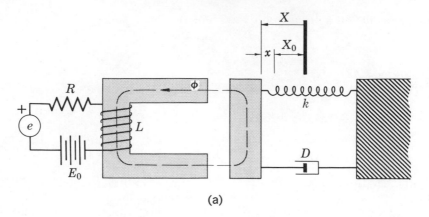

(a)

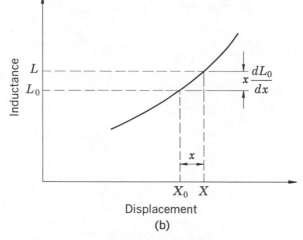

Displacement

(b)

Fig. G–6. (a) Elementary electromechanical system. (b) Variation of inductance with the displacement of the plunger.

The total resistance of the electrical circuit is R. The plunger is restrained by a spring of constant k, and the associated damping constant is D. It is assumed that the constant potential E_0 alone causes a constant current $I_0 = \dot{Q}_0$ and a constant displacement X_0; with addition of the time-dependent source e, the deflection changes by x, giving a total deflection $X = x + X_0$. In this case the reluctance of the air gap decreases as X increases, and therefore the inductance of the coil also increases, as shown in Fig. G–6b. Hence the fact that the inductance L is a function of X must be taken into consideration. When x is small compared to X_0, a linear approximation,

$$L = L_0 + x \frac{dL_0}{dx} \tag{G-34}$$

is acceptable.

The energy equations for the system are as follows:

$$\mathcal{D} = \tfrac{1}{2}D\dot{X}^2 + \tfrac{1}{2}R\dot{Q}^2 \tag{G-35}$$

$$\mathcal{U} = \tfrac{1}{2}kX^2 \tag{G-36}$$

$$\mathcal{K} = \tfrac{1}{2}M\dot{X}^2 + \tfrac{1}{2}L\dot{Q}^2 \tag{G-37}$$

and therefore the Lagrangian is

$$\mathcal{L} = \tfrac{1}{2}M\dot{X}^2 + \tfrac{1}{2}L\dot{Q}^2 - \tfrac{1}{2}kX^2 \tag{G-38}$$

The two system variables are the displacement X and the charge Q. Applying the Lagrange equation in X gives

$$\frac{d}{dt}(M\dot{X}) + kX + D\dot{X} - \frac{1}{2}\frac{dL}{dX}\dot{Q}^2 = 0$$

or

$$M\ddot{X} + D\dot{X} + kX - \frac{1}{2}\frac{dL}{dX}I^2 = 0 \tag{G-39}$$

Similarly, the Lagrange equation in Q is

$$\frac{d}{dt}(L\dot{Q}) + R\dot{Q} = e + E_0 \tag{G-40}$$

Since L is a function of X, which in turn is in general a function of time, Eq. G-40 becomes, upon replacing $\dfrac{d}{dt}$ by $\dfrac{dX}{dt}\dfrac{d}{dX}$,

$$L\ddot{Q} + \dot{X}\frac{dL}{dX}\dot{Q} + R\dot{Q} = e + E_0$$

or

$$L\dot{I} + \frac{dL}{dX}\dot{X}I + RI = e + E_0 \tag{G-41}$$

Equations G-39 and G-41 are the differential equations governing the system. It is important to recognize the significance of the I^2 term in Eq. G-39. The system under consideration is a simple transducer which may represent devices such as a loudspeaker, microphone, or seismograph. In each case it is desirable that the relationship between the displacement and the electrical signal be linear. However, this is apparently impossible, due to the presence of the I^2 term in Eq. G-39. For example, suppose that a sinusoidal electrical input is applied; then the solution of Eq. G-39 and Eq. G-41 yields an expression for x containing multiple sine and cosine terms, and so the displacement of the plunger is not a true reproduction of the electrical signal, but is distorted by harmonics. This distortion may, however, be reduced to an insignificant level if the applied signal e is small in comparison to the constant voltage E_0, and the time-dependent displacement x is small in comparison to the constant deflection X_0. This is demonstrated in the following analysis.

Substitute $X = x + X_0$, $I = i + I_0$, and $L = L_0 + x\dfrac{dL_0}{dx}$ in Eqs. G–39 and G–41. Then

$$M\ddot{x} + D\dot{x} + k(X_0 + x) - \frac{1}{2}\frac{dL_0}{dx}(i + I_0)^2 = 0$$

Upon rearranging and neglecting the product of small terms, Eq. G–42 becomes

$$M\ddot{x} + D\dot{x} + kx - \frac{dL_0}{dx}I_0 i = \frac{1}{2}\frac{dL_0}{dx}I_0^2 - kX_0 \qquad (G\text{–}42)$$

The right-hand side of Eq. G–42 is equal to zero, since the first term is equal to the field force on the plunger under steady-state conditions (by Eq. 1–33), and the second term is the equal and opposite mechanical force under steady-state conditions. Hence Eq. G–42 becomes

$$M\ddot{x} + D\dot{x} + kx - \frac{dL_0}{dx}I_0 i = 0 \qquad (G\text{–}43)$$

Upon substitution, Eq. G–41 becomes

$$L\dot{i} + \frac{dL_0}{dx}\dot{x}(I_0 + i) + R(I_0 + i) = e + E_0$$

or

$$L\dot{i} + Ri + \frac{dL_0}{dx}\dot{x}i + \frac{dL_0}{dx}I_0\dot{x} = e + E_0 - RI_0$$

But $E_0 = RI_0$; therefore

$$L_0\dot{i} + Ri + \frac{dL_0}{dx}I_0\dot{x} + \frac{dL_0}{dx}\dot{i}x + \frac{dL_0}{dx}\dot{x}i = e \qquad (G\text{–}44)$$

If the acceleration and rate of change of current are small, then the governing equations are

$$M\ddot{x} + D\dot{x} + kx - \frac{dL_0}{dx}I_0 i = 0 \qquad (G\text{–}45)$$

and

$$L_0\dot{i} + Ri + \frac{dL_0}{dx}I_0\dot{x} = e \qquad (G\text{–}46)$$

Having obtained the differential equations governing the system, the procedure at this point depends on the desired method of solution. Suppose that the response of the system is required for a simple electrical input, e.g., a sine wave; then a purely mathematical approach may be found most convenient in solving for $\dot{x}$. If an extensive analysis is required, with perhaps unconventional driving functions, then the development of an electrical analog for the complete system is desirable.

For a particular steady-state condition, let $\dfrac{dL_0}{dx} I_0 = K$; then Eq. G–46 becomes

$$e = L_0 \frac{di}{dt} + Ri + K\dot{x} \tag{G-47}$$

Equation G–47 may obviously be represented by a loop containing the driving source e, inductance L_0, and resistance R, with an output voltage

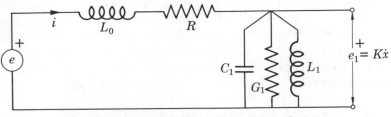

Fig. G–7.   Electrical analog of Fig. G–6a.

$e_1 = K\dot{x}$ which is proportional to the velocity of the plunger, as shown in Fig. G–7.   Since

$$\dot{x} = \frac{e_1}{K}$$

then

$$x = \frac{1}{K} \int_0^t e_1 \, dt \qquad \ddot{x} = \frac{1}{K} \frac{de_1}{dt}$$

Substituting for $\ddot{x}$, $\dot{x}$, and x in Eq. G–45 gives

$$\frac{M}{K} \frac{de_1}{dt} + \frac{D}{K} e_1 + \frac{k}{K} \int_0^t e_1 \, dt - Ki = 0 \tag{G-48}$$

or

$$\frac{M}{K^2} \frac{de_1}{dt} + \frac{D}{K^2} e_1 + \frac{k}{K^2} \int_0^t e_1 \, dt = i \tag{G-49}$$

Equation G–49 is in the form of a node current equation in which the potential across the components is e_1, and the total current flowing is i. The three parallel circuit elements $C_1 = \dfrac{M}{K^2}$, $G_1 = \dfrac{D}{K^2}$ and $L_1 = \dfrac{K^2}{k}$ correspond to the mass and to the damping and spring constants, respectively. With the complete electrical analog obtained, the response of the system may be studied. For example, if the mechanical response to a square-wave driving function is required, then a square-wave signal generator is introduced at e, and by observing the output voltage e_1 the variation of plunger velocity with time is obtained. The effect of changes in the mechanical or electrical parameters may be readily observed by changing the values of the appropriate circuit elements.

Having studied analogous and dual circuits in Arts. G–1 and G–2, it is apparent that the analog derived in Fig. G–7 is the direct analog, since the parallel mechanical elements are represented by the three parallel elements C_1, G_1, and L_1. An inverse analog is also possible, but in this particular case is rather impractical, since it requires the use of an element called a *gyrator*. This unit effects an apparent reversal of current direction between two adjacent loops, which is called for by the difference in sign of the current in the two governing differential equations. While such a reversal may be obtained with microwave components, it is much more convenient to use the direct analog and conventional components.

Rotary systems are perhaps the most important of electromechanical devices. While motors and generators are included in this category, there are other rotary devices which may require analysis.

Example G–2. The integrodifferential equations which govern the rotary electromechanical system in Fig. G–8 are required. The system consists of a rotor and a stator. The rotor, with moment of inertia J, is attached to a spring of constant k by means of a lever arm of radius r. The spring in turn is connected to a frictionless slider of negligible mass, which is free to move in a horizontal direction. The spring exerts no force when $\theta = \pi/2$.

The stator and rotor windings, which have self-inductances of L_1 and L_2, are connected to sources of potential e_1 and e_2, respectively. The mutual inductance between the two windings is $M \cos \theta$. It is assumed that the effective resistances of the stator and rotor circuits are R_1 and R_2 and a capacitor C_2 is in series with the rotor circuit.

Since the system has two electrical inputs and has one degree of mechanical freedom, there are three governing equations. These may be found from the Lagrange equation in θ, q_1, and q_2.

The three energy equations are

$$\mathfrak{D} = \tfrac{1}{2}R_1(\dot{q}_1)^2 + \tfrac{1}{2}R_2(\dot{q}_2)^2$$

$$\mathfrak{U} = \frac{1}{2}\,kr^2(1 - \sin\,\theta)^2 + \frac{1}{2}\frac{q_2^2}{C_2}$$

$$\mathfrak{K} = \tfrac{1}{2}J(\dot{\theta})^2 + \tfrac{1}{2}L_1(\dot{q}_1)^2 + \tfrac{1}{2}L_2(\dot{q}_2)^2 + \dot{q}_1\dot{q}_2M\,\cos\,\theta$$

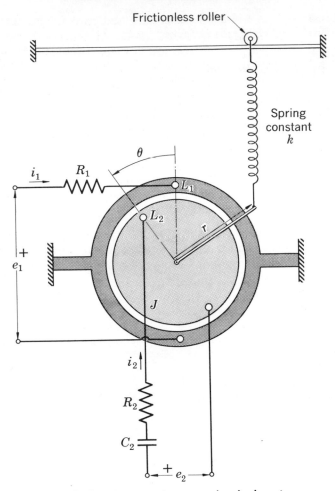

Fig. G–8. Rotary electromechanical system.

and therefore the Lagrangian is

$$\mathcal{L} = \frac{1}{2} J(\dot{\theta})^2 + \frac{1}{2} L_1(\dot{q}_1)^2 + \frac{1}{2} L_2(\dot{q}_2)^2 + \dot{q}_1\dot{q}_2 M \cos \theta - \frac{1}{2} kr^2 (1 - \sin \theta)^2 - \frac{1}{2} \frac{q_2{}^2}{C_2}$$

The Lagrange equations in θ, q_1, and q_2 are respectively

$$\frac{d}{dt}(J\dot{\theta}) - \{- \dot{q}_1\dot{q}_2 M \sin \theta + kr^2(1 - \sin \theta) \cos \theta\} = 0$$

$$\frac{d}{dt}(L_1\dot{q}_1 + \dot{q}_2 M \cos \theta) + R_1\dot{q}_1 = e_1$$

$$\frac{d}{dt}(L_2\dot{q}_2 + \dot{q}_1 M \cos \theta) + \frac{q_2}{C_2} + R_2\dot{q}_2 = e_2$$

which become

$$J \frac{d^2\theta}{dt^2} - kr^2(1 - \sin \theta) \cos \theta + i_1 i_2 M \sin \theta = 0$$

$$L_1 \frac{di_1}{dt} + \frac{di_2}{dt} M \cos \theta - i_2 \frac{d\theta}{dt} M \sin \theta + R_1 i_1 = e_1$$

$$L_2 \frac{di_2}{dt} + \frac{di_1}{dt} M \cos \theta - i_1 \frac{d\theta}{dt} M \sin \theta + R_2 i_2 + \frac{1}{C_2} \int_0^t i_2 dt = e_2$$

The first of these three governing equations is a torque-balance equation, in which the first two terms are the inertial and spring torques, while the third term is the torque produced by the interaction of the stator and rotor fields. The remaining two equations are potential-loop equations in which the third term accounts for the potential induced in one winding due to its relative motion with respect to the field of the other.

The importance of the Lagrange equation for developing the governing equations of complex electromechanical systems should now be apparent. Once the three energy equations have been formulated, the remaining work should follow without difficulty. Again, the fact that the signs of the various terms in the governing equations are automatically accounted for is most helpful in practice.

Index

DATE